Contents

OPEN 2017 CELEBRATES a terrific year's work at the Department of Architecture; an inspiring record of the possibilities of architecture, and its importance, when opened to a rooted imagination and creative commitment. The Department promotes design practice that balances experimentation with rigour as a creative route to a better future. The inventiveness that suffuses the catalogue illustrates our students' capability as designers of beautiful places and spaces, and their ability to shape and make a project itself.

The Department continues to uphold its Polytechnic tradition that an ambitious, transformative higher education should be accessible to all, and draws students from the most diverse of backgrounds. Profoundly committed to our immediate hinterland of London and the UK, we also maintain a welcome to overseas students from the EU and further afield: a mix of perspectives that is a major factor in the character and quality of our students' work – and, I believe, a prerequisite for any school that wishes to contribute to contemporary culture.

Our students won major international and national awards during the last year, including in the RIBA Presidents' Medals for the third year in a row, and Best Student at the Interior Educators Awards 2016. We continue to add to our staff, with Matt Haycocks joining the Interior Architecture team, Benson Lau taking up a Readership in Architecture & Environmental Design, François Girardin returning as Making Tutor, Scott Batty joining Technical Studies, and Corinna Dean, Kate Jordan, Maria Kramer and John Zhang taking up research and teaching roles in Cultural Context and Design Practice. Alongside them, we continue to draw on an extraordinary number of part-time Visiting Lecturers who engage students with live practice issues. Without being complacent, perhaps it is no surprise that practices continue to value our graduate students as, alongside the visiting practitioner-lecturers and -experts, we offer work placements and mentoring as part of our courses, and the Department's RIBA Part 3 course educates some 40% of all architects in this country.

As part of the Faculty of Architecture & the Built Environment under the leadership of the Dean, Professor David Dernie, the Department continues to benefit from the wider horizons of a cross-disciplinary environment. These include research initiatives such as the Latitudes programme and the expanding physical resources of the Digital Fabrication Laboratory. Over this coming summer, we will invest £3 million in upgrading and expanding our wood-, metal- and casting workshops, along with a new environmental laboratory and photographic studio, print room and materials shop. Through the generosity of the Quintin Hogg Trust, we are funding field trips for all students – from downtown Tokyo to the Finnish forests – and building new exchanges with schools from Paris to Hong Kong. September 2016 saw the successful launch of the new BA Designing Cities planning degree, and September 2017 will see the start of our new BSc. in Architecture and Environmental Design.

Please enjoy the show.

Harry Charrington
Head of the Department of Architecture

Welcome to OPEN 2017

INTERIOR ARCHITECTURE IS a distinct context-based practice concerned with re-reading, re-using and altering an architectural shell. Whether at the scale of the city, a building, or a room, the 'interiorist' always starts with something and within something. By altering host structures, Interior Architecture allows a building to have many different lives. London is our campus and projects this year included study spaces in the Victoria and Albert Museum, installations at Wilton's Music Hall, live-work dwellings on Columbia Road and a broadcasting facility in Unity House, Woolwich.

Extra curricular activities are encouraged and this year we have looked outward. With generous support from the Quintin Hogg Trust, in November 47 BAIA students visited the 2016 Venice Biennale, a field trip that linked with the studio theme Home Acts. Following Westminster OPEN, the same group of students will be exhibiting their final project work at the Interior Educators Free Range Art and Design Show at Truman Brewery, Brick Lane, where last year graduating student Laura Metcalfe won the national prize for the Best Student Studio Degree Project. Students and staff have been on exchange visits to Oslo National Academy of the Arts and RMIT in Melbourne and in June a group will travel to New York to take part in the Parallel Cities workshop with Pratt Institute. Back in London as part of the Architects for Health Student Design competition, students worked with Great Ormond Street Children's Hospital and Guys and St Thomas' Charity while others participated in the Disabled Artists Making Dis/Ordinary Spaces project.

The course has been set up to have strong links to practice and this year we were delighted when Sadie Morgan joined us as Professor of Interior Architecture, whose role includes being an industry mentor for students. A wide range of international design companies including Thomas Heatherwick Studio, Perkins + Will, and Wood Bagot London, contribute to the course through inviting students to in-office design crits, presenting their approach to careers at our Employers Events, and judging student awards. In addition to this, a weekly series of guest speakers has included: George Bradley and Ewald Van Der Straeten (Bradley Van Der Straeten), Professor Stephen Brookhouse, Chee-Kit-Lai (Mobile Studio), William Hardie + Hamish Boden (Studio Hardie), Rob Garvey, Michele Haniotis (Wandle HA), Professor Sadie Morgan (de Rijke Marsh Morgan Architects), Paul Smyth (Something and Son), James Stroud (Loyn & Co Architects), Francis Bradshaw (Anne Thorne Architects), and Amaya Eastman (VOLA). Special thanks to Dr Eva Branscome for History and Theory delivery and Dr Jane Madsen for the third year film project.

Ro Spankie
Course Leader

BA INTERIOR ARCHITECTURE

Images of some of the extra curricula activities from top left:

Staff and students on a site visit to Long Island City, Queens, as part of the Parallel Cities Workshop with the New School, Parsons, New York; First Year students building a collaborative structure during the Fabrication Workshop; Second Year students occupying a 1:1 sectional drawing of Wilton's Music Hall constructed in masking tape on the studio floor; Third Year students photographing details in Carlo Scarpa's Olivetti Showroom in Venice; and exercises from the Tilted Horizons workshop – part of the Disabled Artists Making Dis/Ordinary Spaces project.

Lara Rettondini (Module Leader), Sue Phillips, Yota Adilenidou, Allan Sylvester, Matt Haycocks

Lara Rettondini *is a Senior Lecturer, architect, and co-director Studio X Design Group, a London-based practice specialised in architecture and interior design projects. She is a Senior Fellow of the Higher Education Academy and the recipient of the Westminster Teaching Excellence Award 2017.* **Sue Phillips** *is an Architect and Visiting Lecturer at two Universities in London. She has been teaching for over 20 years and aims to empower students to understand their own learning processes.* **Allan Sylvester** *is Visiting Lecturer, practicing architect, and founding partner of Ullmayer Sylvester Architects a design-led, and multidisciplinary collaborative practice.* **Yota Adilenidou** *is an architect, an MSc AAD graduate from GSAPP, Columbia University, and currently a PhD Researcher at the Bartlett, UCL. She is the Director of Arch-hives Ltd, a practice that focuses on the research of computational methodologies and digital fabrication for the activation of matter and form.*

YEAR 1: Design Fundamentals & Strategies

Students: Oreoluwa Adebayo, Nafeesa Banaras, Fatine Bengelloun, Sara Bint Faisal, Laura Breggia, Nora Brudevold, Andreea Caplea, Karolina Chwiluk, Sinead Cooke-Lindo, Ekaterina Dellos, Caroline Dew, Aleksandra Dreczkowska, Zehra Duven, Ffion Ellis, Alendita Fanaj, Emilija Fedorovic, Kristine Florian, Gabija Gliaudelyte, Jessica Gower, Vanda Hajizadeh, Dominic Hogg, Jade Hopkinson, Anyun Jiang, Stine Kaastad, Amir Kamali, Golnaz Keihani, Ashpreet Khurll, Kamil Koszela, Karolina Lapinska, Jeremie Lapuz, Suthida Liuwatanachotinan, Monique Lucas, Sandy Mitchell, Syeda Monsur, Jade Papadimitriou, Angel Parada, Anna Perfileva, Anca Petrescu, Soma Rahem, Jovana Rasic, Abigail Reynolds, Maria Sabrekova, Fatimatou Said Anatt, Luanne Santana, Hira Shafique, Orkidea Shala, Nawal Shaw, Karen Tipan Romero, Teodora Todorova, Koto Uchida, Maria Zlatareva

IN FIRST YEAR, students on the BA Interior Architecture course are introduced to underlying concepts and principles associated with the discipline and learn fundamental processes, skills and techniques relevant to conceive, develop, resolve, and communicate spatial design proposals. They are also introduced to the use of graphic design, CAD and 3D modelling software as well as the Faculty's Fabrication Lab.

In the first term, students are set a range of activities and short tasks, from designing modular structures and making them, a light box study involving understanding different qualities of light together with photography and scale, through to group research on existing built projects to understand intent and representation. Building on these skills, students are then asked to design a study space for a researcher-in-residence at the Victoria and Albert Museum, in London. They work in teams to survey allocated rooms and their individual proposals have to facilitate interaction between the researcher and the public. Students are encouraged to design transformable constructs that could be considered as a large piece of furniture and a piece of micro-architecture.

In the second term, students are required to design the interior of a small building by inserting a new hypothetical programme specialised in craftsmanship along Columbia Road, a street in East London well-known for its flower market. The development of each individual project is dictated by the particular craft person's practice, which students define based on their individual site investigation and research. The students are asked to consider how the use of space might change over varying time periods and are introduced to the use of time-based media to investigate and record change. The project's vision is to create a synergy between different types of makers that would allow for trade and a weekly market. This brief gives students the opportunity to speculate and imagine a 'Makers' Row' where crafts people would collectively coexist, forming an imagined 'makers' utopia'.

Guest Critics:
Abdi Ali (Ruimte Design), Marcela Araquez (Lobby), Iliana Capsali (SNAS Design & Development), Clarissa Evans, Inan Gokcek, Thomas Gorringe, Nahed Jawad, Jeong Hye Kim, Samantha Li (Canburg), Lela Listiyani O Sujani, Shneel Malik, Simon Nicholls, Kristel Nurmsalu, Paresh Parmar, Dragan Pavlovic, Eva Sopeoglou, Quynh Vantu, Dylan Warren, Charles Weston Smith, Becky White (Universal Design Studio), Oscar Wilson, Daniel Wu

Special Thanks:
Clarissa Evans, Thomas Gorringe

(top) ***Victoria & Albert Museum 1:20 model;*** *(centre left)* **Stine Kastaad:** ***1:20 Model;*** *(centre right)* **Soma Rahem:** ***1:20 Model;*** *(bottom left)* **Dominic Hogg:** ***1:20 Model;*** *(bottom right)* **Anna Perfileva:** ***1:20 Model***

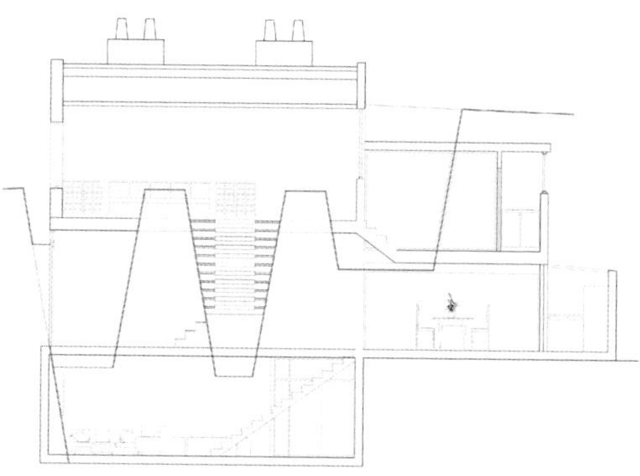

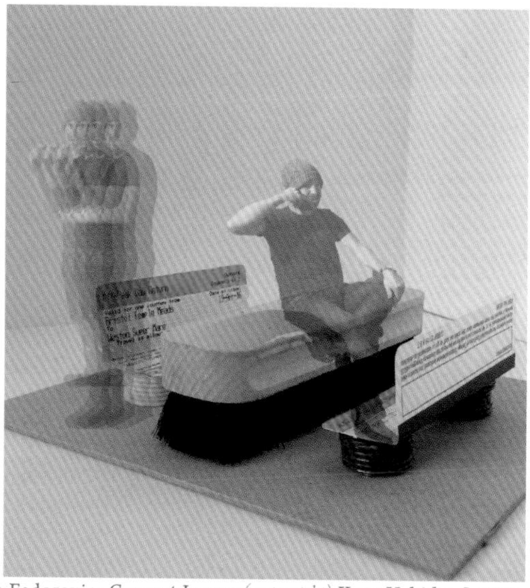

(top left) Anyun Jiang: *1:20 Model;* *(top right)* Emilija Fedorovic: *Concept Image;* *(centre right)* Koto Uchida: *Section;* *(bottom)* Dominic Hogg: *1:20 Model and Concept Model*

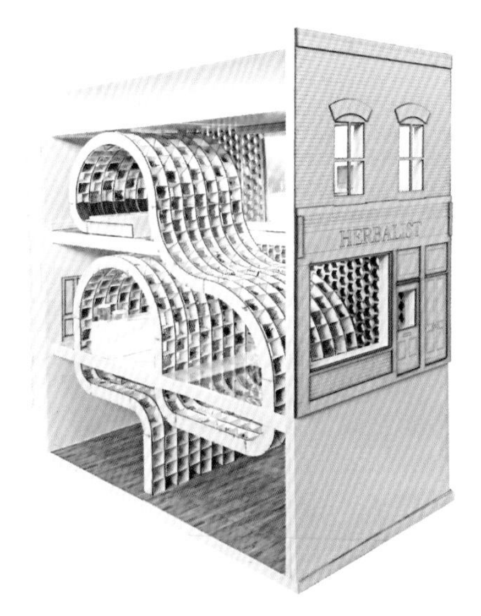

(top left) Andrea Caplea: *Concept Diagram; (top right)* Maria Zlatareva: *Perspective View; (centre left)* Maria Zlatareva: *1:20 Model; (bottom left)* Ashpreet Khrull: *1:20 Model; (bottom centre)* Caroline Dew: *1:20 Model; (bottom right)* Stine Kastaad: *1:20 Model*

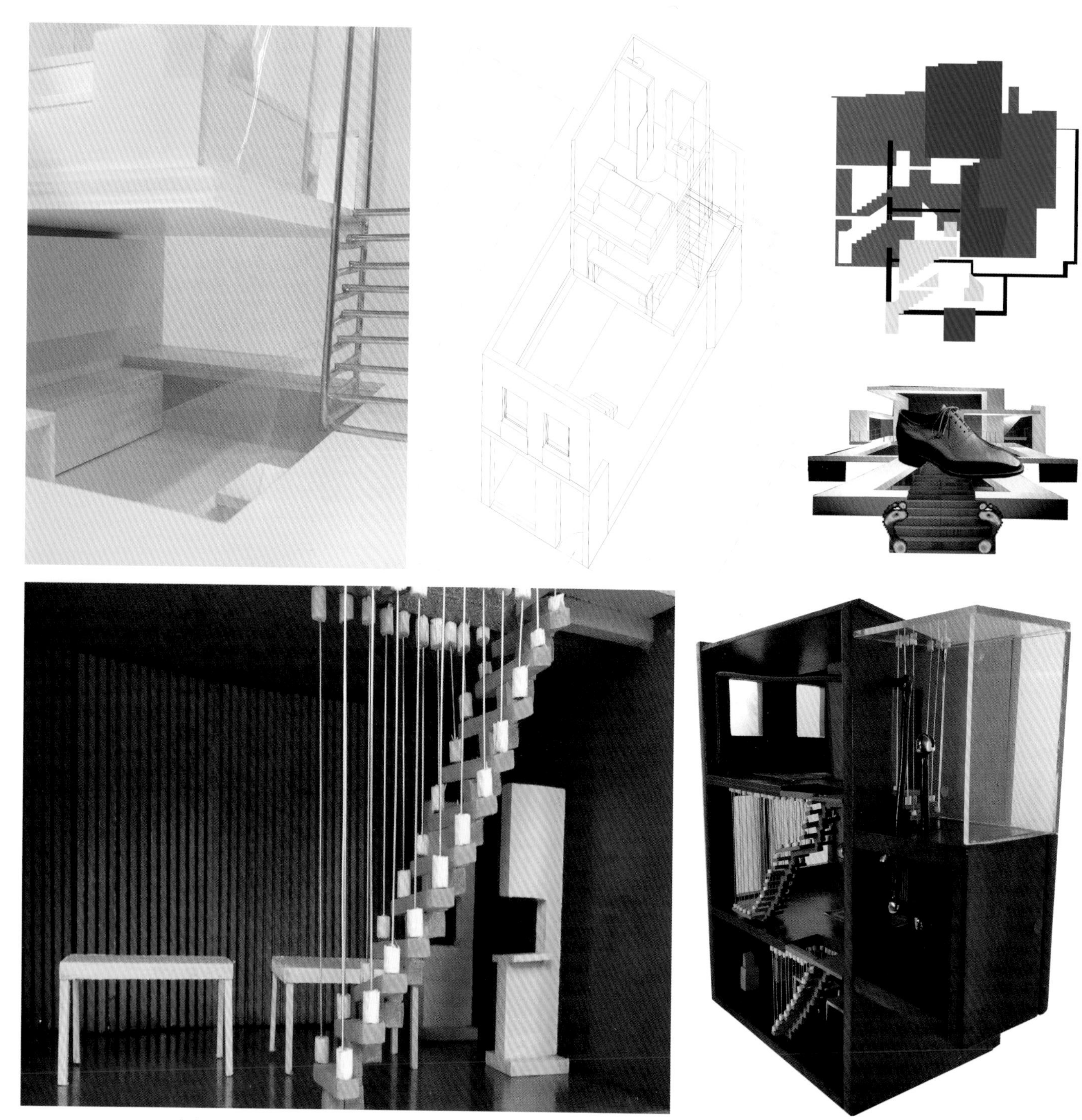

(top) Anna Perfileva: *1:20 Model, Axo and Concept Diagram;* *(centre right)* Sinead Cooke-Lindo: *Concept Image;* *(bottom)* Amir Kamali: *1:20 Model*

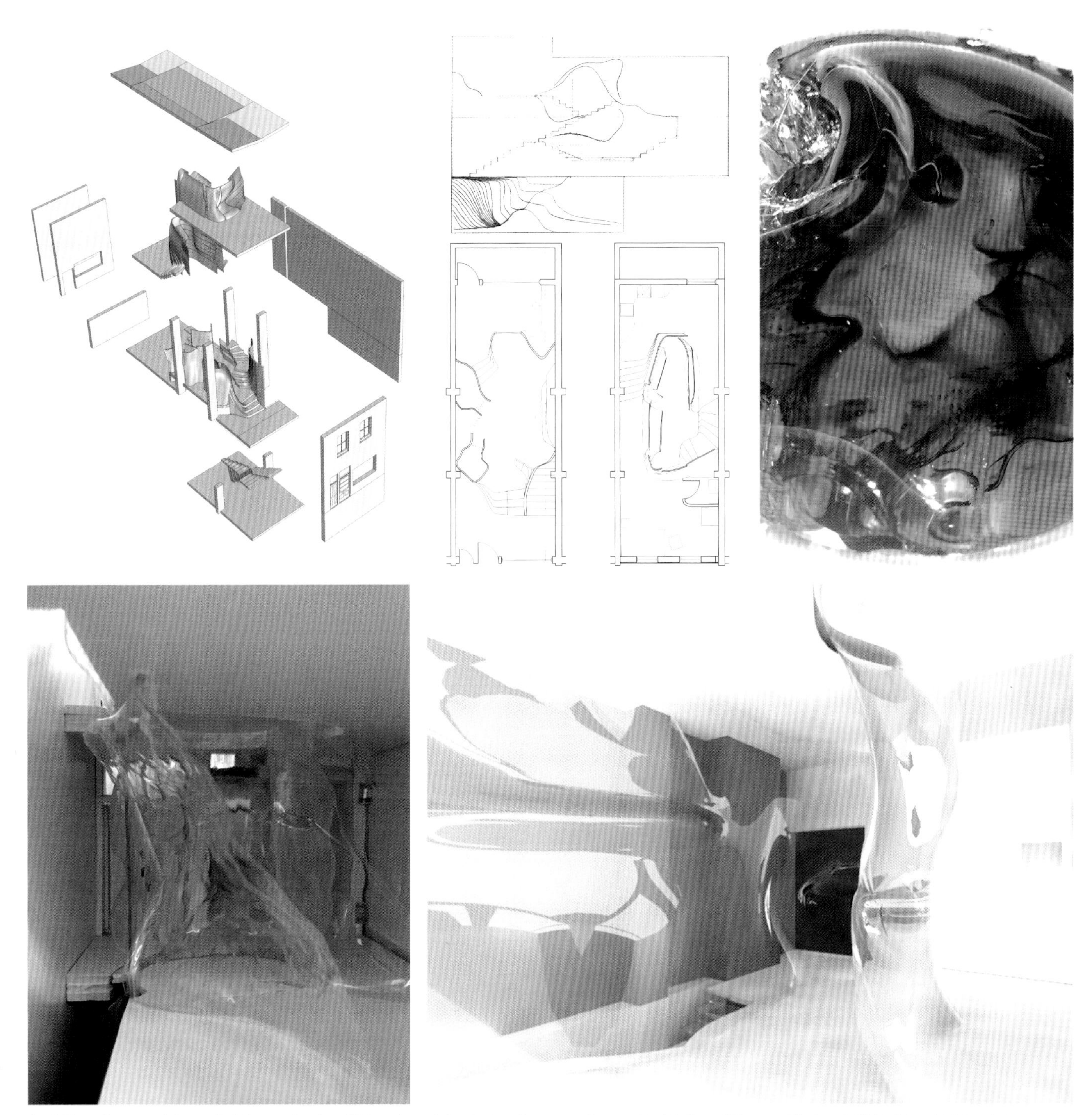

(top left) Vanda Hajizadeh: *Exploded Axo, Sketch and Plans;* *(top right)* Jade Papadimitriou: *Concept Model;* *(bottom)* Kristine Florian: *1:20 Model and 3D Rendering*

Matt Haycocks, Mike Guy, Mohamad Hafeda, Tania Lopez Winkler, Alessandro Ayuso (Semester 1 includes: Julia Dwyer, Diony Kypraiou, Ro Spankie)

Mike Guy *is a registered architect who has combined teaching and practice for over 35 years. Mike's teaching interests include interior architecture and urban agriculture and he is currently engaged in some radical DIY - for the sheer delight of it.* **Mohamad Hafeda** *is an artist, designer and writer. His work focuses on the use of art processes and participatory approaches to negotiate urban sites of conflict. His research addresses issues of displacement, refuge, borders and spatial rights.* **Matt Haycocks** *is Senior Lecturer, designer and maker whose research concerns domestic and family photography, the historicisation of public space and the politics of place-making and branding.* **Dr. Tania Lopez-Winkler** *is an award-winning artist and architect based in London. Her work explores the alter-ego as a means to enquire into different aspects of modernity. She encourages students to be curious, to follow intuitions, and to challenge habits of thought.*

YEAR 2: Home Acts, Woolwich Fabric

Students: Sule Acar, Hatice Akbal, Sandra Appiah Koomson, Weronika Babij, Piyula Balachandran, Nisaanthi Balasingam, Tahmina Begum, Syeda Bokhari, Christine Bowora, Costanza Cerioni, Dulari Chheda, Nina Chrostowska, Seda Eldek, Alyssa Elevare, Salar Ghamari, Florence Goater, Frida Good, Heather Gurarslan, Danielle Harrington, Jack Hoe, Eleanor Hurley, Sukaina Hussain, Stella Idomenea, Stella Idomenea, Silvia Ion, Nida Karafakioglu, Jennifer Kemp, Danial Khan, Mine Kizilkaya, Mahsin Mahbub, Basma Mahgoub, Anne-Mari Maibach, Hristina Manova, Emma McGill, Andra Nemet, Maria Nieto Navas, King Wing Or, Yuliya Pisna, Oliver Pollard, Marija Raletic, Rita Ramanauskaite, Julija Razvadovskaja, Naomi Rimmer, Gabrielle Sarmiento, Celine Singh, Olga Tihhomirova, Ana Toanchina, Lilli Tretter, Beiza Tzampaz Tachir, Ghazal Vaisibiameh

THIS YEAR, SECOND YEAR interior architecture students examined two very different buildings: Wilton's – a Victorian music hall in London's East End; and Unity House – a marine engineering workshop on the banks of the Thames in Woolwich. Both studio projects considered the role of the existing building fabric in regeneration, as well as the place and politics of heritage in interpreting the present, and anticipating and mediating future changes. In the first semester, students joined third year students to research and question ideas of domesticity and the home.

Beginning with a series of short personal studies, students went on to explore aspects of performance and privacy. These explorations became the basis for their own detailed design proposition for the temporary inhabitation of Wilton's Music Hall. In the final semester, students devised their own proposal for the adaption and re-use of Unity House. This project demanded hands-on experimentation with fabrication processes and materials – workshop-based making using an iterative series of fabrication maquettes, followed by drawings, models and moving images to elaborate and translate their material findings into designed elements.

The investigation into Woolwich's manufacturing and industrial past used traditional research strategies including archival investigation, surveying and mapping, combined with more experimental methods such as the fabrication of fictive scenarios and characters: story-telling to understand the existing, interpret recent changes and to speculate on the future of the area and its communities.

Guest Critics:
Dr Nerma Cridge, Cerise Day, Naomi French, Sue Ginsburg, Kitty Heston, Georgia Jacob, Mehdi Jelokhani, Luke Jones, Jake Powley-Baker, Eva Sopeoglou, Linda Tentori, Clay Thompson

Special Thanks:
To David Scott and the Fabrication Lab; Tim Ronalds and Jade Yianni of Tim Ronalds Architects for a lecture on Wilton's Music Hall;
to Holly Kendrick and David Graham for giving 105 students a taste of Wilton's magic.
Jim Denby and Daniel Marsh, Port of London Authority

(top) **Sule Acar, Piyula Balachandran, Christine Bowora, Alyssa Elevare:** ***Barco House Fabrication Maquette;*** *(middle)* **Alyssa Elevare:** ***The Forest Narrative;*** *(bottom)* **Seda Nur Eldek:** ***Fabrication Maquette***

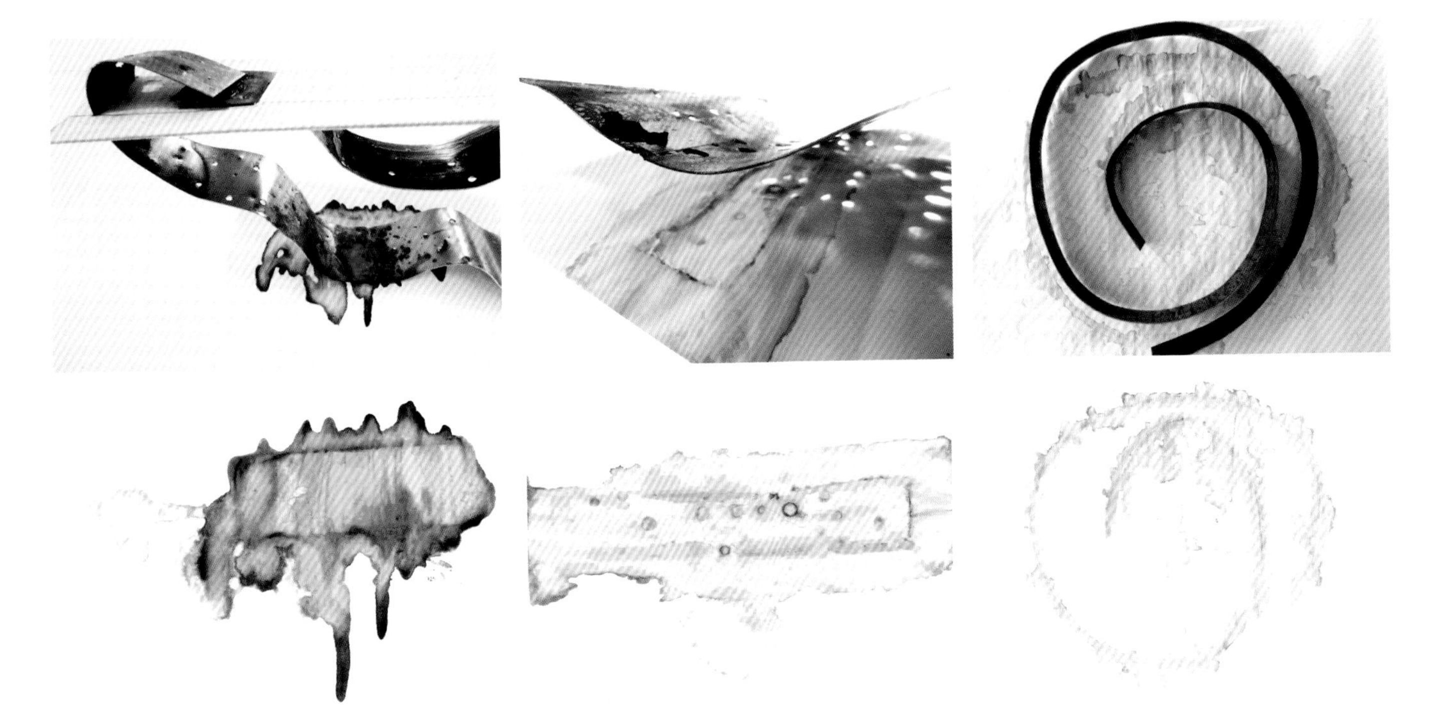

(top) Emma McGill: *House for a Mudlark;* *(bottom)* Gabrielle Sarmiento: *Museum of Archaeology*

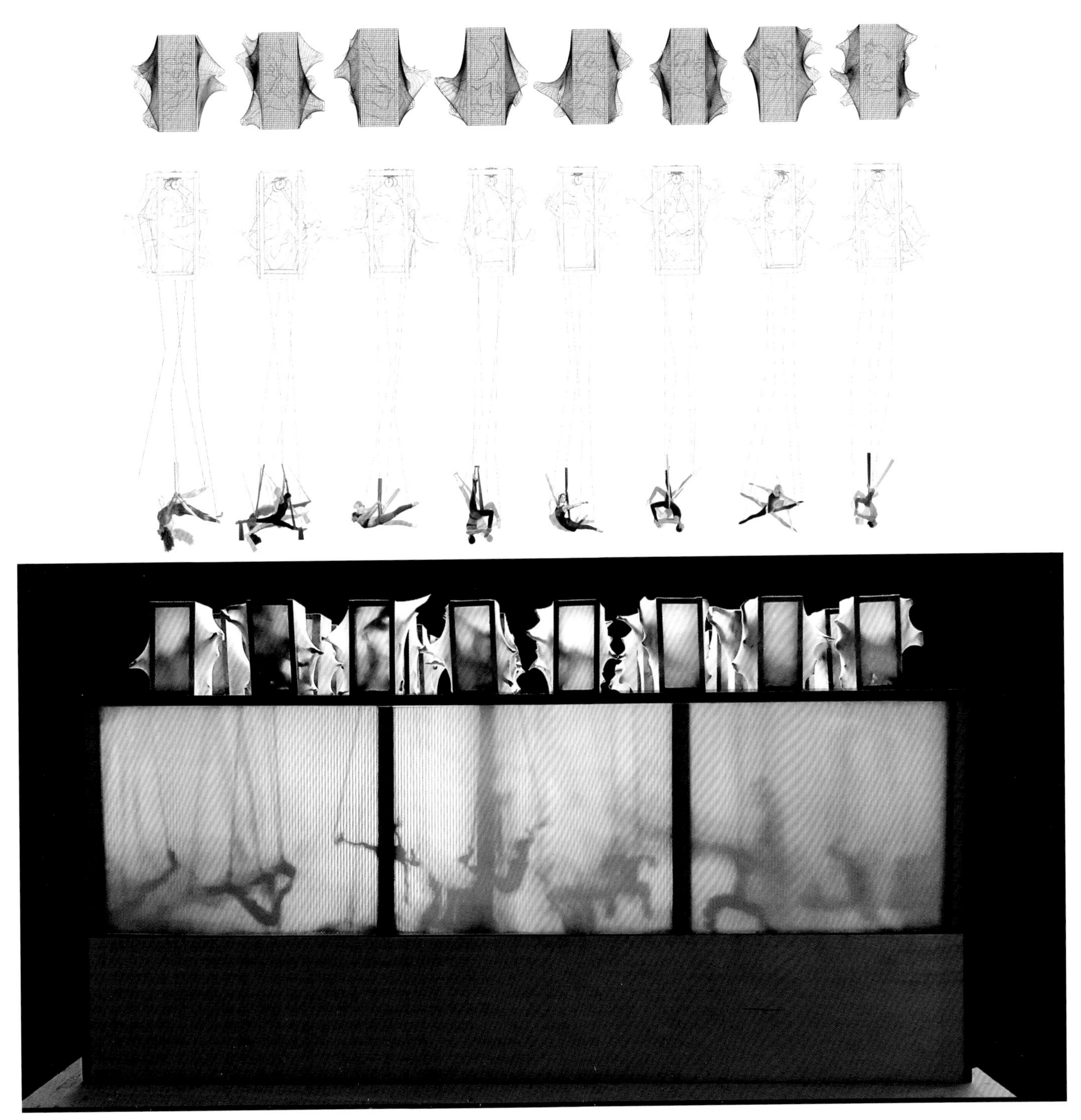

(top) Yuliya Pisna: *Dancing Silhouettes;* *(bottom)* Yuliya Pisna: *Final Model 1:20*

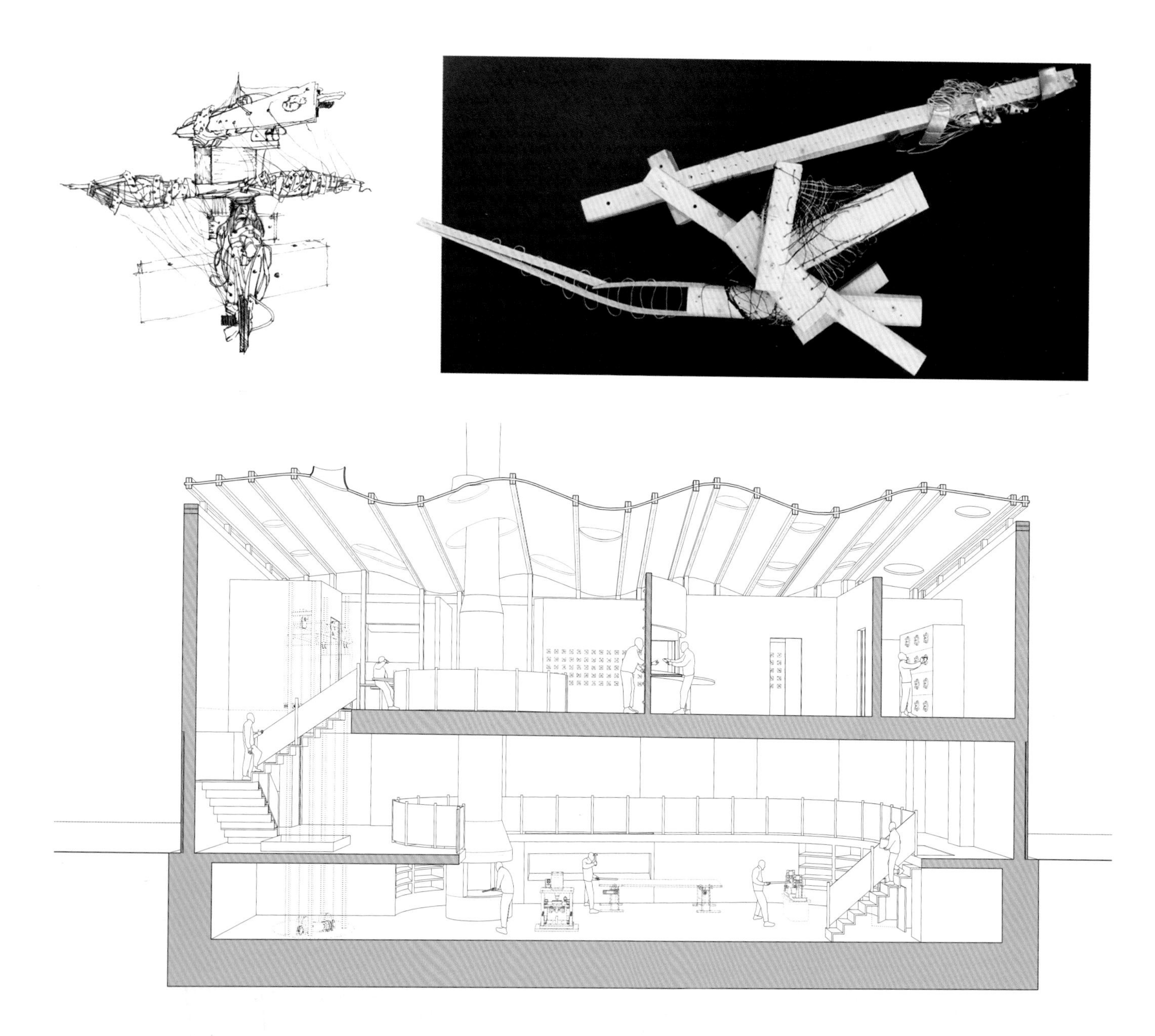

(top) Danial Khan, Salar Ghamari: *Fabrication Maquette;* (bottom) Danial Khan: *Woolwich Mint*

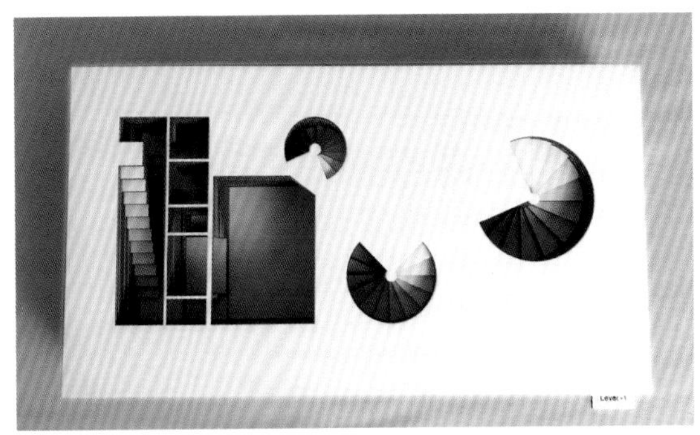

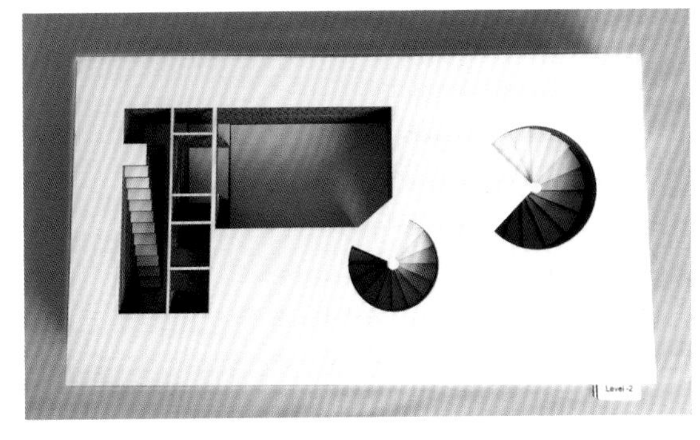

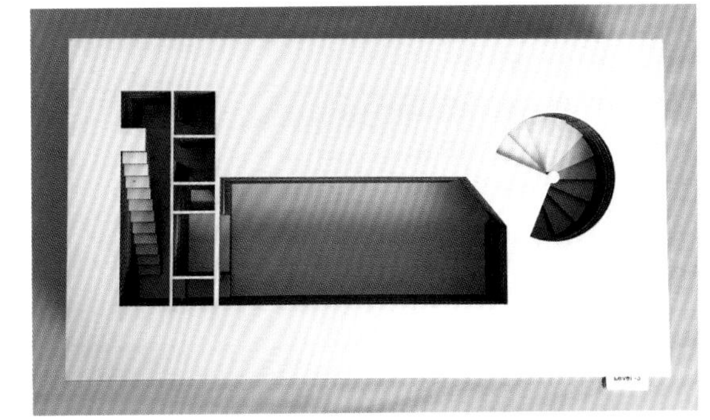

(left) Esther Nieto: *Neverwhere, Collage;* *(right)* Esther Nieto: *Model 1:50*

Ro Spankie, Alessandro Ayuso, Diony Kypraiou, Matt Haycocks
(Semester 1 includes: Julia Dwyer, Mike Guy, Mohamad Hafeda, Tania Lopez Winkler)

Alessandro Ayuso's *research explores the intersection of bodies and architecture. His work on 'Body Agents' was pursued through his PhD by Design. This year he is leading the Parallel Cities workshop: a collaboration between Westminster University and Pratt Institute in New York.* **Julia Dwyer**'s *work addresses feminist spatial practices. She has written on collaborative practice, feminist architectural histories, place and identity, and architectural education. She teaches interior architecture and design, collaborates on public art/design projects, and is a practicing architect.* **Diony Kypraiou** *is an architect and researcher. Her work deploys practices of drawing, writing, and installation design as investigatory tools to explore analogies between architecture, dramaturgy, psychoanalysis, and storytelling.* **Ro Spankie** *is Principle Lecturer and Course Leader of the BA Interior Architecture. Fascinated by the role of the drawing in the design process, she has exhibited and published work internationally related to the interior. She is Associate Editor of the journal,* Interiors: Design/Architecture/Culture.

YEAR 3: Home Acts, Major Project

Students: Saeed Agboke, Anisah Ahmad, Nurcan Altun, Aseil Amgheib, Cecilia Aubouy, Jasmine Bagaria, Kinga Bajor, Lina Benaissa, Nabil Benelabed, Shona Brannan, Urszula Celi, April De Alwis, Carla Dela Pena, Paraskevi Demetriou, Ezgi Dirik, Lelizaveta Drobot, Aine Duffy, Berfin Erdogan, Seem Hajjar, Han He, Louise Heard, Abigail Hinchley, Abigail Horbury, Lewis Huff, See Ip, Alycia Ivory, Pamela Jankowska, Zhea Kapadia, Daria Kaverzina, Aliaksandra Kharlan, Napattararat Komnatchanan, Carlotta Lazzerini, Yinqi Liu, Giorgio Lo Porto, Christina Matay, Katie Northage, Jumoke Oladunni, Freya Osborne, Ning Pang, Rehan Parikh, Viktorija Prusakovaite, Yossra Sbaiti, Edona Selmani, Dilini Senaratne, Rubina Tihanyi, Andre Visinho, Helen Wind

WE STARTED THE year with a joint project with Second Year called Home Acts. The students were asked to explore the idea of a home constructed through acts and rituals rather than bricks and mortar, looking first at their own experience of home then rehousing a selected act or action in the public realm. This housing was then developed into an installation and/or performance at Wilton's Music Hall.

The final Major Project in BA Interior Architecture is self-derived with students selecting their site and setting their own programme. This year the only criteria was that the project should involve the reuse and alteration of an existing building and the students looked at what the user actually does, rather than what they should do, as they developed their programme.

The resulting 47 projects appropriated very different buildings and offered a wide variety of programmes. From the ephemeral and scenographic – a floating stage for Wilton's Music Hall on a barge in the Thames, a production studio for Jamie Oliver or a temporary stage for the Half Moon Youth Theatre – to the more sited and material based – an aeroplane recycling centre in Millennium Mills or a social condenser in an old Martello Tower out in the Thames Estuary. Others are driven more by their specific user, such as an animal prosthetic centre, a research lab for plant-grown meat substitutes, a private club for hungover city workers, or an unofficial residency in a foreign embassy.

All of them are united by a focus on the performative nature of design as well as a thoughtful response to both their host building and London as a city.

Guest Critics:
Sam Aitkenhead (Heatherwick Studio), Marcela Araguez, Helen Brewer, Rafaella Christodoulidi, Owaine Davies, Cerise Day, Lucy Dunn, James Engel (Spaced Out Architecture), Alexander Fell, Francis Field (David Chipperfield Architects), Naomi French, Kitty Heston, Mehdi Jelokhani, Professor Sadie Morgan and Jonas Lencer (de Rijke Marsh Morgan Architects), Ed Harty (Pritchard Themis), Clare Hawes, Jessica In, Juan Oyarbide (Heatherwick Studio), Professor Toni Kauppila, Chee Kit Lai (Mobile Studio), Constance Lau, Martyna Marciniak, Anne Munly, Dragan Pavlovic, Nathaniel Reading, Luis Reis (SimpsonHaugh and Partners), Elena Sorokina (MATT Architecture), Linda Tentori, Clay Thompson, Costas Xenophontos, Manos Zaroukas and Fiona Zisch

Special Thanks:
To David Scott and the Fabrication Lab, to Judit Ferencz for her talk on illustrated guides, to Jane Madsen for the films, to Tim Ronalds and Jade Yianni of Tim Ronalds Architects for a lecture on Wilton's Music Hall, to Holly Kendrick and David Graham for giving 105 students a taste of Wilton's magic.

Lina Benaissa: *Overhead View of a Pontoon for an Arts Workshop on The Thames*

(top) Aseil Amgheib: *Film Still Showing the Interior of the Aviation Mills;* *(bottom)* Aseil Amgheib: *Longitudinal Section of the Aviation Mills*

Urszula Celi: *Deployment of 'Home Acts' Installation on ite*

(top) **Freya Osbourne:** ***Visitor's Equipment for Wiltons on the Water;*** *(bottom)* **Freya Osbourne:** ***Cross Section of Floating Theatre for Wiltons on the Water***

(left) Anisah Ahmad: *1:20 Model of the 'Tick-Tock' Horologist's Studio; (right)* Anisah Ahmad: *Sections showing the Movement of the 'Tick-Tock' Horologist's Studio*

Abigail Hinchley: *1:100, 1:50 & 1:1 Model of the 'Sitopia' Food Research Facility*

Helen Wind: *1:50 Model of the Animal Prosthetic Centre*

ARCHITECTURAL TECHNOLOGY OFFERS specialism in the technological, environmental, material and detailing decisions necessary to solve design problems. It requires sound understanding of design processes, design and architectural composition, construction technology, and management tools for the effective communication of design information.

In the Architectural Technology Studio this year, our 2nd year students were asked to design a nursery school for 85 children, and our 3rd year students a new building for the White Cube Galleries.

Both groups were asked to undertake a design process which spans the development of a design concept, to the production of construction drawings and details. Our intention is that the student project progresses in stages that are as relevant and similar to architectural practice as possible.

Both 2nd and 3rd year projects are divided into two parts – part one / semester one mirrors the process through which Planning Approval is gained. Part two / semester two concerns the technical, i.e. structure, construction technology, building performance, building regulation, and the production of construction drawings and details.

Research

Initial research is key in both semester one and two, in order to understand any and all constraints that might follow from various issues including the site, building use, and the client's desires. And in semester two, construction materials and structures are studied. Architectural and technical precedents are also gathered, as an analysis of existing buildings and technologies relevant to the design project is a vital part of the design process for our students.

Development

With a clear understanding of the design task following the research phase, students then go on to develop an individual design. Sketches, models and 3D visualisations are produced in order to progress their own ideas and as an aid to weekly discussion with other students, lecturers, and visiting Architectural Technologists/Architects.

Realisation

Architectural design and construction is increasingly a collaborative endeavour as new technologies continue to be introduced and as building performance requirements and the need for energy efficiency result in greater complexity. Communication, particularly visual communication, is then of the utmost importance and students must graduate with the ability to sketch ideas and concepts, construct physical and digital models, and produce technical drawings and specifications.

Virginia Rammou
Course Leader

BSc ARCHITECTURAL TECHNOLOGY

Copenhagen School of Design and Technology (KEA) and University of Westminster Charrette

THE CHARRETTE WAS A highly successful two-week long collaboration between KEA, Copenhagen, and University of Westminster BSc Hons Architectural Technology students. The students attended interdisciplinary talks and events run by staff from Construction, Planning, Fabrication Lab and Tourism. We teamed up with Ross Lambie from the architectural Practice RALA, who provided us with a live project for our students to work on.

Mixed teams of students worked on the specification and fabrication of 1:5 scale detailed models of the live project culminating in an end of project 'show and tell' and exhibition.

The event was instrumental for immediate dialogue with KEA for further collaborations between the courses.

Adam Thwaites, Paul Kalkhoven, Tabatha Harris Mills, Virginia Rammou

Virginia Rammou *is a chartered architect and the Course Leader for BSc Architectural Technology at the University of Westminster. She has extensive experience in practice and is interested in the relationship and cross fertilisation between architecture and technology. Her research focuses on the relationship between architecture, health and palliative care.*

Adam Thwaites's *primary areas of interest revolve around design within constraints and the importance of the 'detail', in terms of both function and aesthetic.*

Tabatha Harris Mills *is Senior Lecturer at Westminster where she has taught for 9 years, and previously at Leeds Met and Sheffield Hallam. With 16 years industry experience, she is a practicing Architectural Technologist and has had her own studio since 2005. Her keen interest is in technological solutions and skills for self-building and residential community housing.*

The Ark Nursery School

Students: Muse Abdi, Sara Berakach, Isar Chaudry, Hicham Choutri, Danilo Di Lorenzo, Nicola Gambetta, Julyan Gomez, Kiren Jhinger, Dainis Kaniava, Roland Kassak, Mihriban Kinik, Stefan Kloos, Zoltan Kun, Che Lalgie-Dubois, Zymon Lewandowskis, Usmaan Malik, Shahran Mirdha, Sebastian Mussi, Ye Oo, Helin Saricinar, Francesco Scotto, Bless Sison, Dilara Sonmez, Fintan Sumners, Elis Troake, Scott Wells, Vincent Yoell

THE ARK NURSERY MARYLEBONE is a new collaborative enterprise by the existing Marylebone schools, The St. Marylebone CE School and The St. Vincent's RC Primary School. It is envisioned that this facility will provide space for approximately 85 children from 3 months to 5 years within a safe, secure and stimulating new building or buildings with significant outdoor space and all associated ancillary functions. It is to be located on the southern most third of the vacant lot bordered by Moxon, Aybrook, Cramer and St Vincent Streets, adjacent to The St. Marylebone CE School and St. Vincent's RC Primary Schools.

The client requires an initial 'feasibility study' to be undertaken and proposals to be developed in order to provide accommodation and associated spaces for this new nursery school. The students were expected to carefully examine other successful existing precedents and designs to inform their proposed schemes, and incorporate the various requirements specified by the client. The client's need for the building to be 'super-insulated' and for provision to be made for the inclusion of renewable technologies and/or passive strategies resulted in a range of schemes for low or 'zero' energy consumption buildings.

Guest Critics:
Walter Lismore, Ross Lambie (RALA), John Gray (HTA), Mary Davies (HTA), Anne Marie Murdoch (Veretec), Allan Haines, Maja Jovic, Eliana Voutsadakis, David Scott

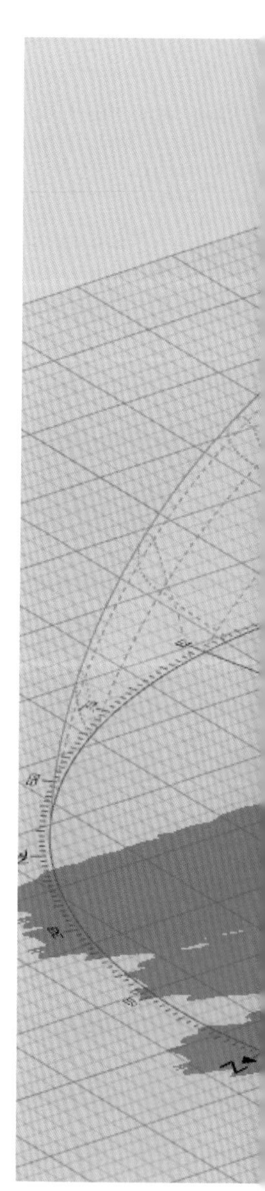

Vincent Yoell

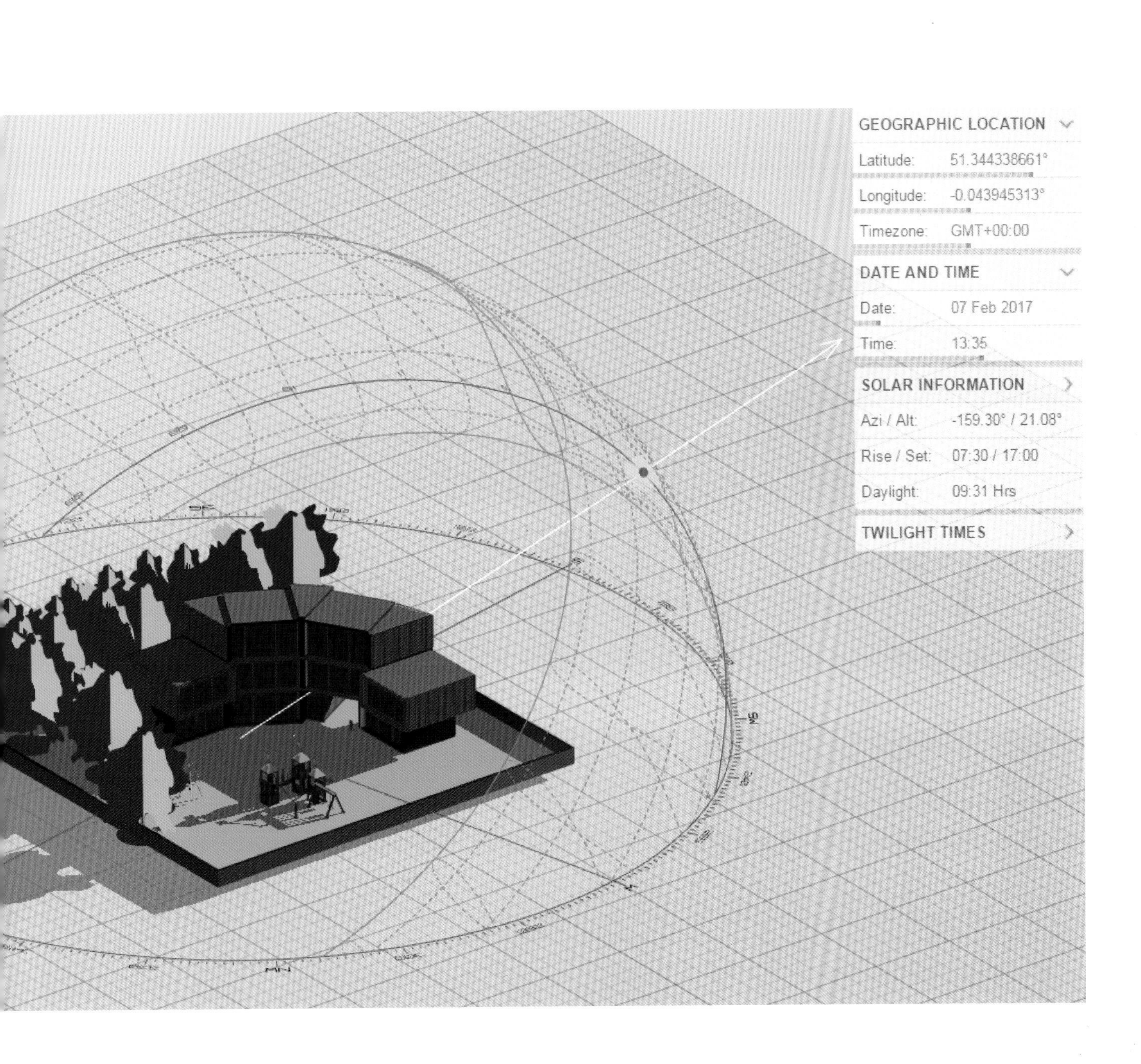
GEOGRAPHIC LOCATION
Latitude: 51.344338661°
Longitude: -0.043945313°
Timezone: GMT+00:00
DATE AND TIME
Date: 07 Feb 2017
Time: 13:35
SOLAR INFORMATION
Azi / Alt: -159.30° / 21.08°
Rise / Set: 07:30 / 17:00
Daylight: 09:31 Hrs
TWILIGHT TIMES

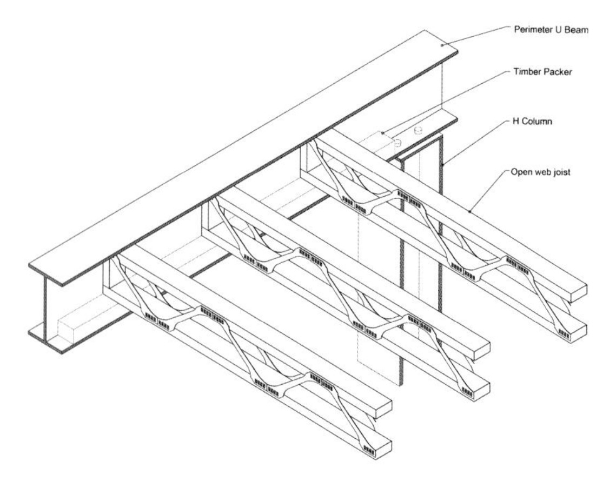

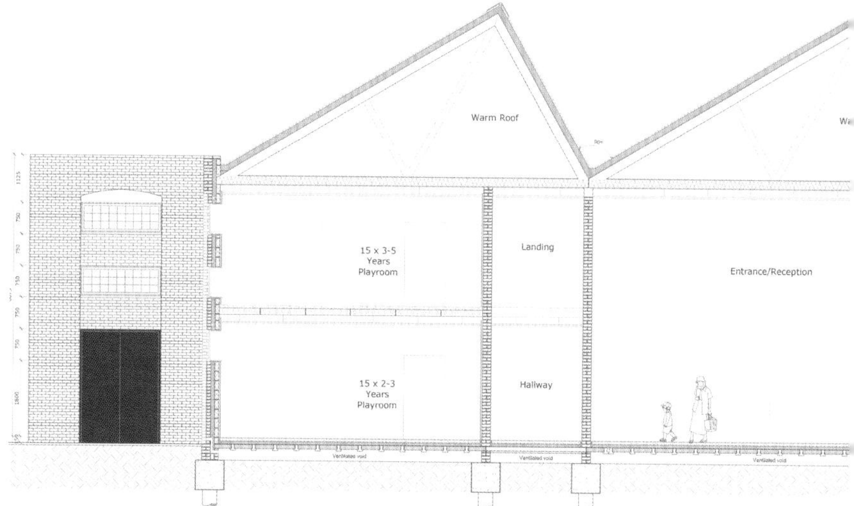

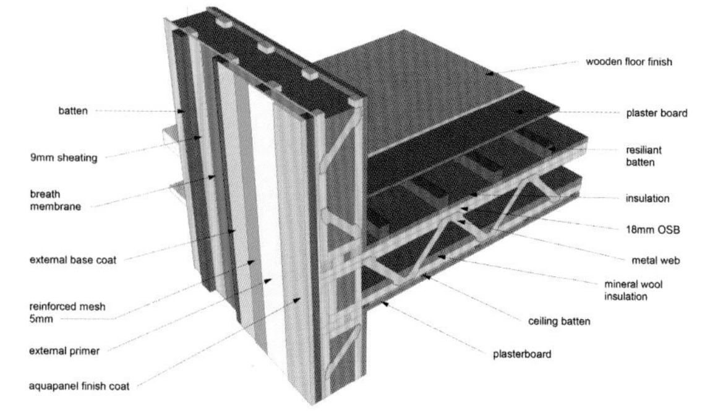

(top left) **Vincent Yoell;** *(centre left)* **Francesco Scotto;** *(bottom left)* **Terry Webster;** *(bottom right)* **Nicola Gambetta**

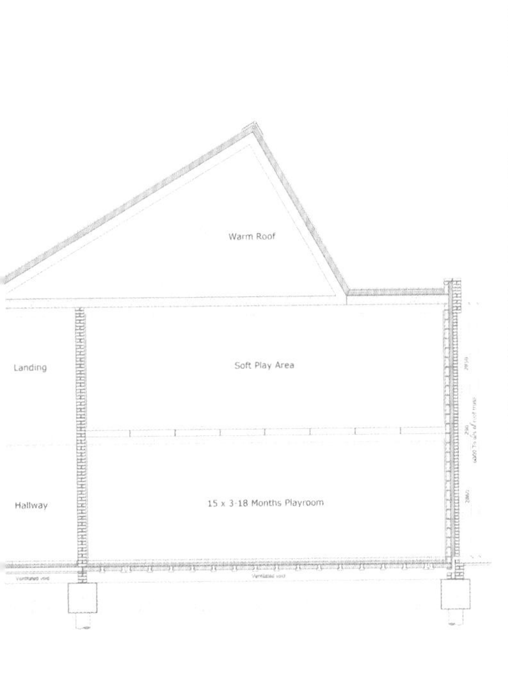

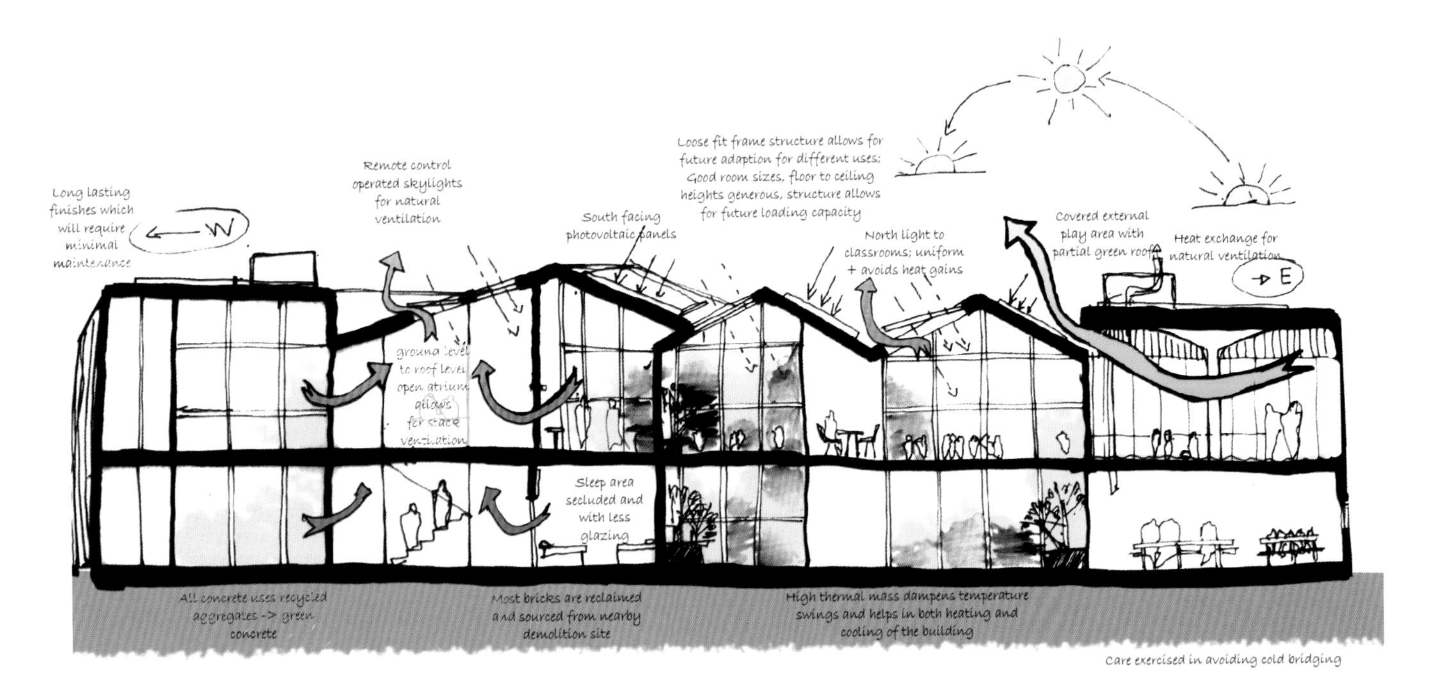

(top centre) Fintan Sumners; *(top right)* Edmund Burkinshaw; *(bottom)* Edmund Burkinshaw

Adam Thwaites, Paul Smith, Tabatha Harris Mills, Virginia Rammou

Virginia Rammou *is a chartered architect and the Course Leader for BSc Architectural Technology at the University of Westminster. She has extensive experience in practice and is interested in the relationship and cross fertilisation between architecture and technology. Her research focuses on the relationship between architecture, health and palliative care.*

Adam Thwaites's *primary areas of interest revolve around design within constraints and the importance of the 'detail', in terms of both function and aesthetic.*

Tabatha Harris Mills *is Senior Lecturer at Westminster where she has taught for 9 years, and previously at Leeds Met and Sheffield Hallam. With 16 years industry experience, she is a practicing Architectural Technologist and has had her own studio since 2005. Her keen interest is in technological solutions and skills for self-building and residential community housing.*

White Cube Gallery Marylebone

Students: Sakariya Abdi, Bushra Ahmed, Anisha Bhanderi, Edward Britton, Issac Brown, Jakob Hald, Rezaul Korim, Darren Mckane, Dennis Meneses Rodriguez, Anna Nilsson, Mauro Preziosa, Diana Soots, Varsika Udhayakumar, Cieran Wilkinson, Aleksandr Zacharov

THE THIRD YEAR students were asked to create schemes for the latest White Cube gallery, having acquired a plot of land in Marylebone. The client seeks proposals for the creation of a significant new arts exhibition space. The land acquired comprises the northern most, two thirds of the vacant lot bordered by Moxon, Aybrook, Cramer and St Vincent Streets. The remaining one third will be sold on.

The students were asked to address the client's brief for a largely column-free exhibition space or spaces, provision for all associated ancillary spaces, and extensive outside space or spaces to comprise a 'sculpture garden'.

An initial 'feasibility study' was undertaken, including the analysis of the site. Proposals were made regarding massing/volumes which were expected to be feasible given the site constraints and area. Once the initial feasibility study was completed, the students developed schemes in order to provide the required accommodation and associated spaces for this new arts complex. The students were expected to carefully examine White Cube Galleries existing facilities, Bermondsey and Mason's Yard, in order to make proposals which complement and expand the existing provision at these locations. Of importance at White Cube Marylebone will be the 'sculpture garden' space or spaces, differentiating it from the other sites. The students had to make provision for the inclusion of a café/ restaurant, shop, ancillary spaces and additional amenities, such as storage spaces, utility-room, plant room, and exterior landscaping.

Each student was expected to make relevant provision for all public access in the proposed design, as well as the client's requirement for the building to be 'super-insulated', and that provision be made for the inclusion of renewable technologies and/or passive strategies resulting in a low or 'zero' energy consumption building.

Guest Critics:
Franek Ryczer (Grimshaw Architects), Ross Lambie (RALA), John Gray (HTA), Mary Davies (HTA), Anne Marie Murdoch (Veretec), Allan Haines, Zhenzhou Weng, Maja Jovic, Eliana Voutsadakis, David Scott

Darren McKane

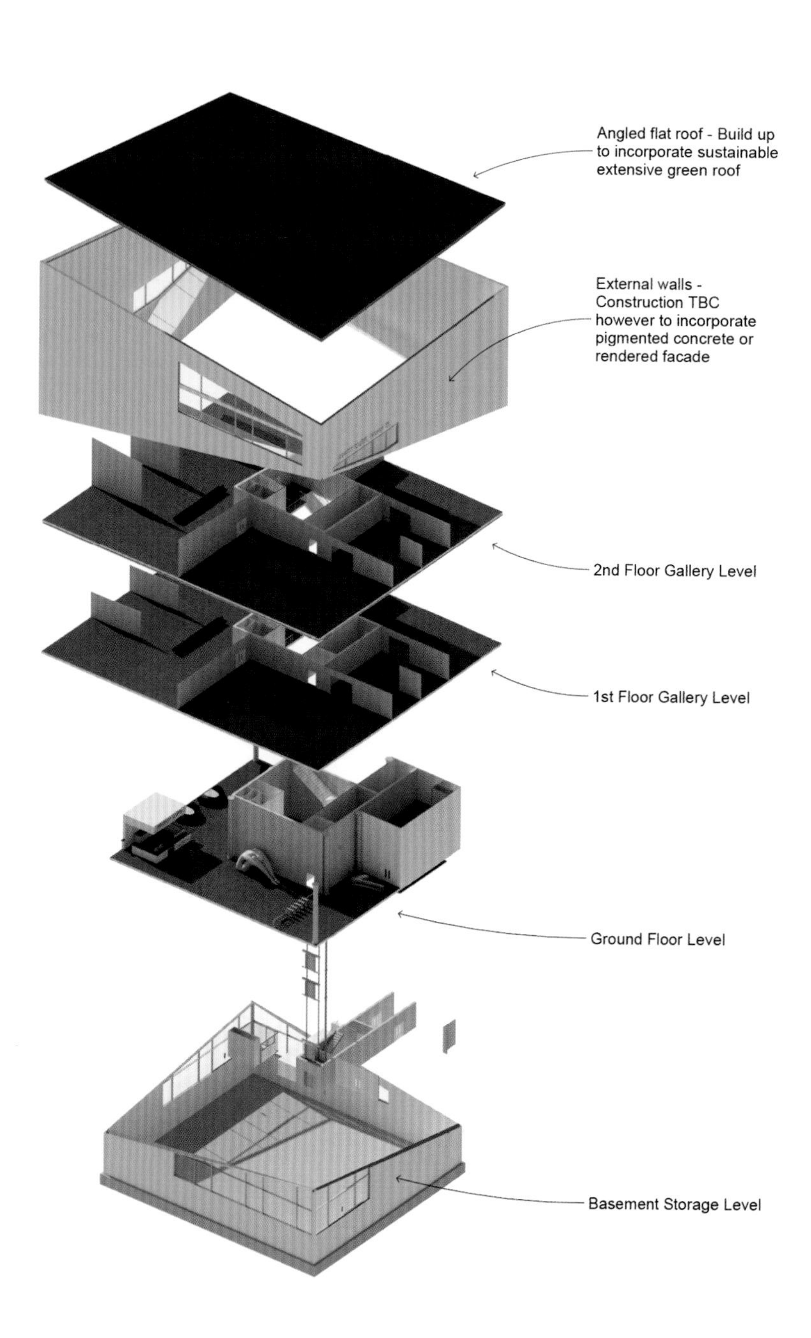

(left) Darren McKane

(top) Isaac Brown; *(bottom)* Isaac Brown

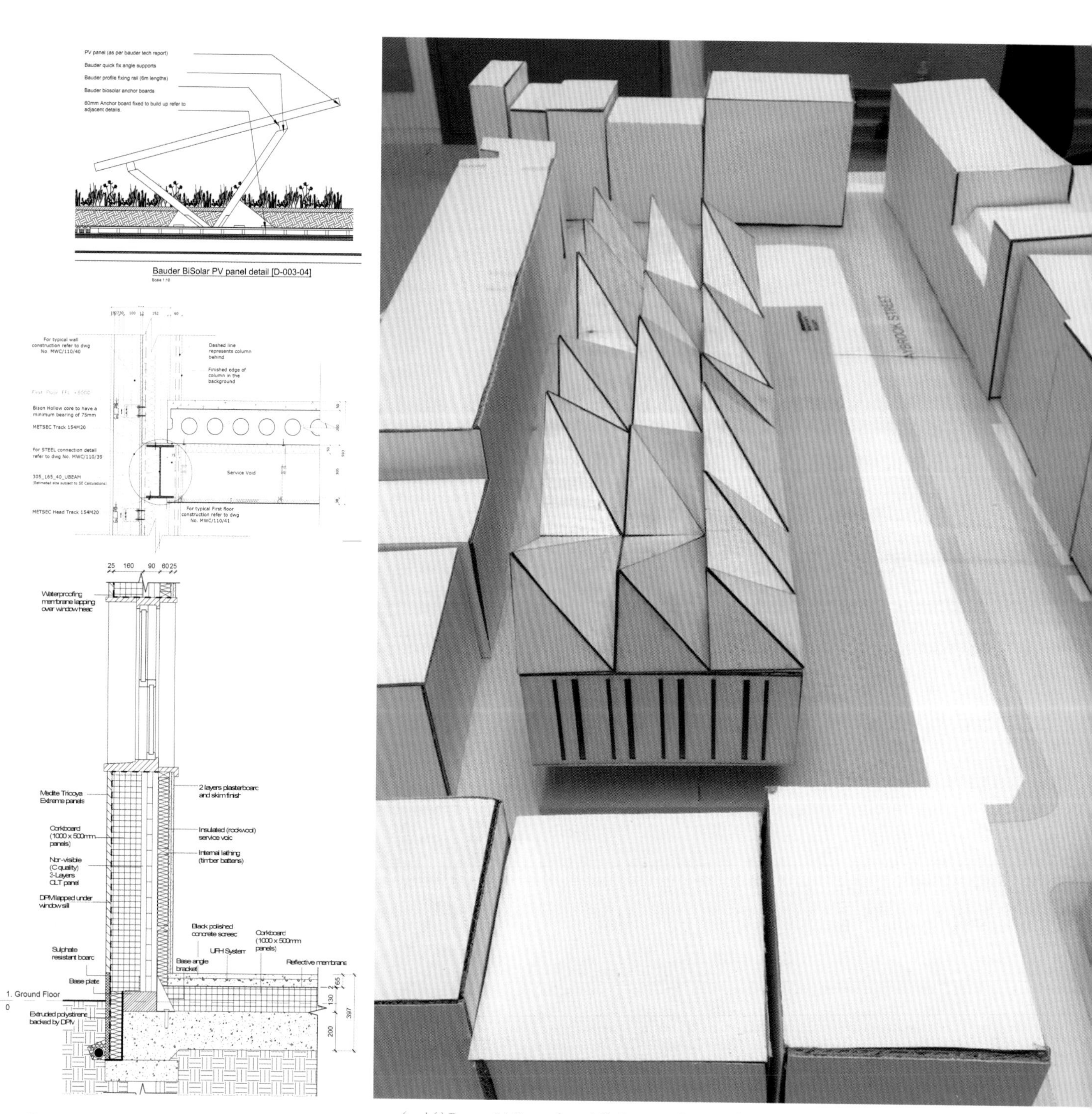

(top left) Darren McKane; *(centre left)* Cieran Wilkinson; *(bottom right)* Mauro Preziosa; *(right)* Anisha Bhanderi

(top) Anisha Bhanderi; *(bottom)* Anisha Bhanderi

DESIGNING CITIES IS a new innovative and interdisciplinary course between the departments of planning and architecture which has been set up to respond to the great urban and environmental challenges of contemporary society. It aims to train a new generation of city experts capable of facing the complexity of cities, to understand the forces that shape them and to provide innovative and creative solutions for their urgent problems.

Issues such as the threats of climate change, the challenges of dealing with increasing cultural and social diversities, and discussions on the 'right to the city' for all are at the base of our studios and London provides a unique learning environment.

The course, which started in September 2016, is accredited by the Royal Town Planning Institute (RTPI) as meeting the requirements for the spatial planning element of initial planning education.

Designing Cities is highly international in nature and extra-curricular activities are encouraged. This year we have signed an agreement with a Chinese research Institute based in Shanghai (WHITRAP) that will facilitate exchanges with China and joint international studios. We have also set up a semester-long student exchange with the Queensland University of Technology in Australia, starting in semester two, next year. Moreover, this coming summer four students will join a participatory design workshop organised in the south of Italy, together with other students from the London School of Economics, the University of Newcastle and the University of Calabria.

The involvement with practice is a priority for us. Full-time teaching staff have normally an experience both in academia and practice and several part-time visiting lecturers from practice teach here. This year, we invited guest lectures from London-based practitioners including Max Farrells, partner at Farrells, a firm of architect-planners with offices in London, Hong Kong and China, and Alistair Macdonald, a director of the London-based architectural and planning practice Allies and Morrison. An event called 'Intrepid Urban Futures' was also organised in March 2017, funded by the EU COST ACTION, involving many UK and EU-based practitioners in a discussion on the future of university and the curriculum in urban studies.

Our students are also engaged in the Designing Cities blog where most of our activities, including field trips, guest lectures, and workshops are regularly posted.

blog.westminster.ac.uk/designingcities

Giulio Verdini
Course Leader

BA DESIGNING CITIES

UNIVERSITY OF
HEART
OF LONDON
WESTMINSTER

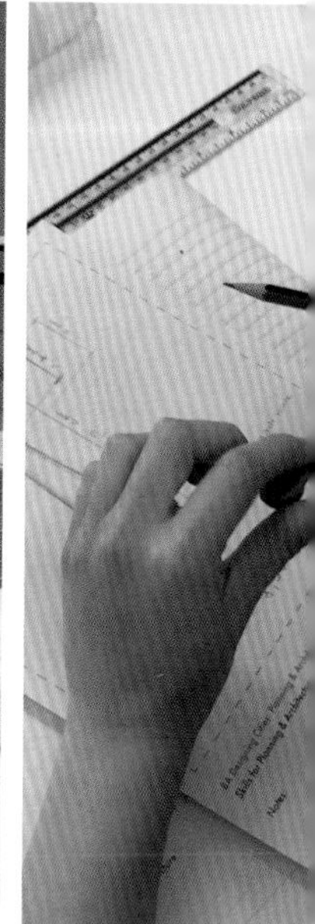

ACROSS YEAR ONE, students are involved in improving their design skills. We started with a project called 'From the Spoon to the City', the famous slogan created by Ernesto Nathan Rogers in the 1950s, to understand notions of space and scale in the design process.

Students develop a portfolio of sketches using both hand drawing and softwares, moving later to practicing additional skills such as interviews, mental mapping exercises and video making. Real people are their 'actors' as the design process is has to effectively engage with social concerns and give voice to local communities.

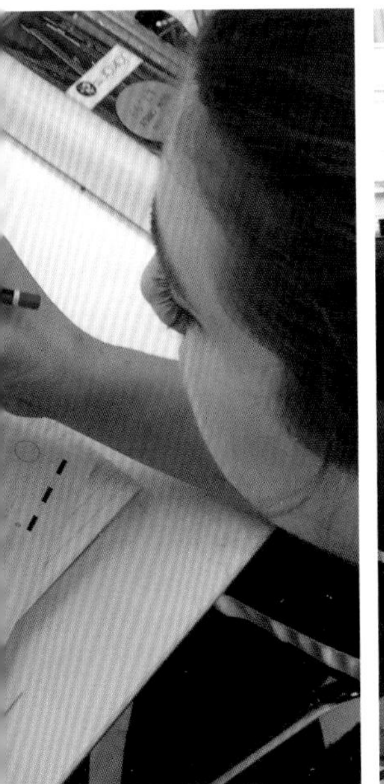

Giulio Verdini & Nasser Golzari

Giulio Verdini *is an urban planner with a degree in Architecture and a PhD in Urban and Regional Development. He has worked as practitioner and academic scholar in Europe, South America and China. He is the Course Leader of the Designing Cities BA.*

Nasser Golzari *is an architect and an academic. He is the principal partner in NG Architects, an award-winning architectural practice based in London. He teaches across a number of undergraduate and postgraduate courses at the University of Westminster.*

Planning for Integrated Neighbourhoods

Students: Elena Ceppo, Clive Cooper Jnr, Shantelle Elliott-Edwards, Vivienne Ezeji, Taishanah Ferris, Martin Miranda Antelo, Lan Pham, Georgia Simondo, Patrycja Wajszczuk, Kareem Wellington

THIS STUDIO-BASED module aims to analyse an inner-city area in London, providing policy recommendations and urban design solutions for ensuring its long term sustainability.

The site selected this year is the area around Euston Station in the London Borough of Camden, which is going to be affected by major redevelopments due to the construction of the new High Speed train between London and Birmingham. This is one of the most central and therefore strategic 'opportunity areas' in London with the potential to accommodate increased densities. According to the area plan adopted in 2015, new mixed-use developments will be mainly concentrated around the current Euston station area. It will surely have an important impact both at the city and the local level. As part of the overall strategy of the city to increase its compactness, a quota of the supply of housing should come from a systematic strategy of urban infill.

Regent's Park Estates, between Regent's Park and Euston Station, accommodate a series of modernist housing compounds built in the 1950s and the 1960s, with the potential of being partially densified and, if carefully redesigned, of improving the system of accessibility and the quality of the public realm.

Based on the group site appraisal, students were asked to design a proposal for a meaningful urban infill and public realm improvement for this neighbourhood. The result of the design research has demonstrated the feasibility of these initial assumptions, redefining at the same time the nature of the private-public space in Camden and providing original and sometimes ludic suggestions for its future functioning.

Special Thanks:
Nick Bailey and Duncan Bowie, for providing useful insights into the topic of urban regeneration and urban growth in London

Patrycja Wajszczuk: *Bringing the Green!*

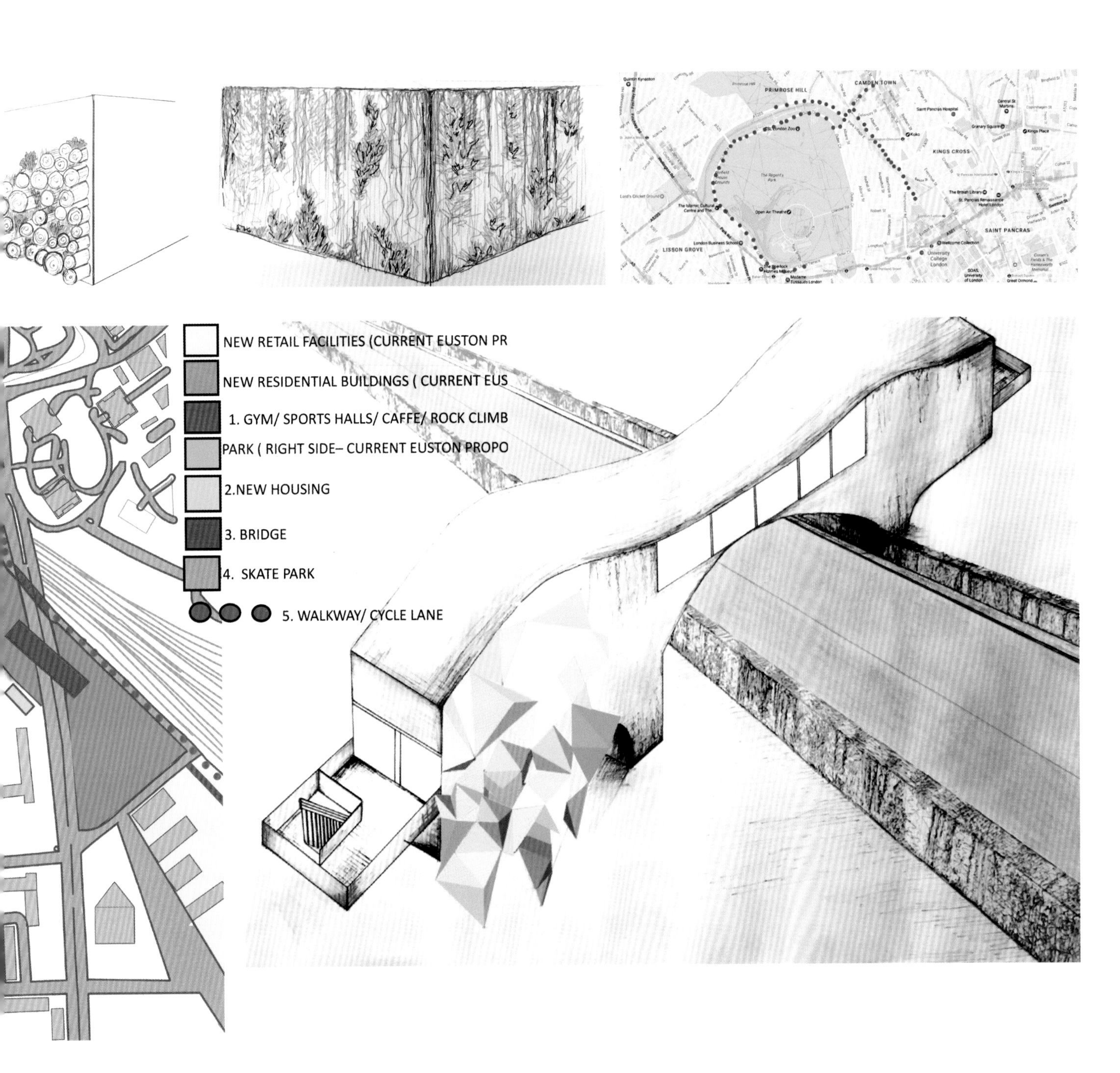
PRIMROSE HILL
CAMDEN TOWN
KINGS CROSS
SAINT PANCRAS
LISSON GROVE
NEW RETAIL FACILITIES (CURRENT EUSTON PR
NEW RESIDENTIAL BUILDINGS (CURRENT EUS
1. GYM/ SPORTS HALLS/ CAFFE/ ROCK CLIMB
PARK (RIGHT SIDE– CURRENT EUSTON PROPO
2.NEW HOUSING
3. BRIDGE
4. SKATE PARK
5. WALKWAY/ CYCLE LANE

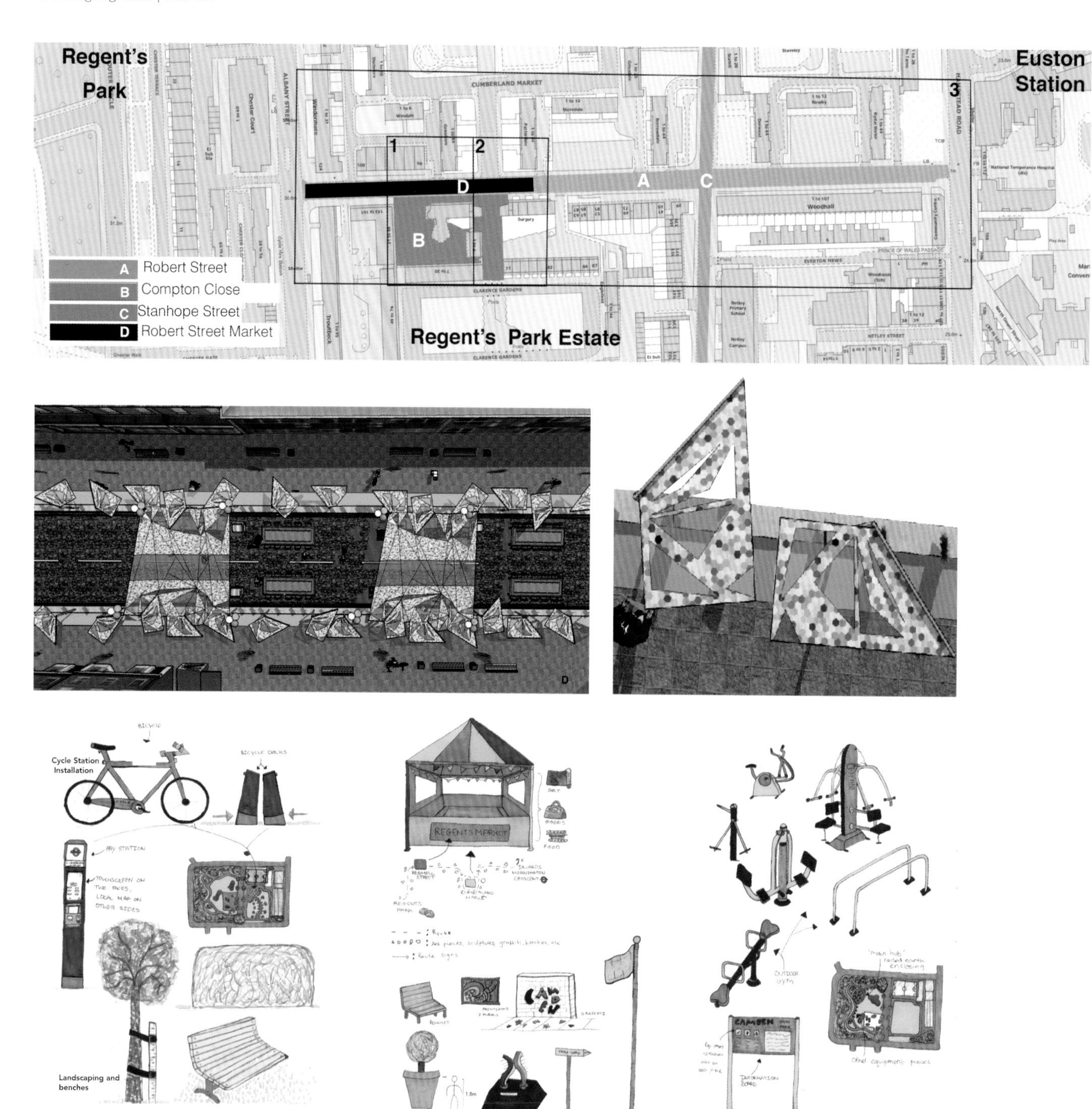

(top & centre) Kareem Wellington: *Robert Street: Open Market and Slow Mobility;* (bottom) Clive Cooper Jnr: *Cumberland Market Area: Playing with Street Furniture*

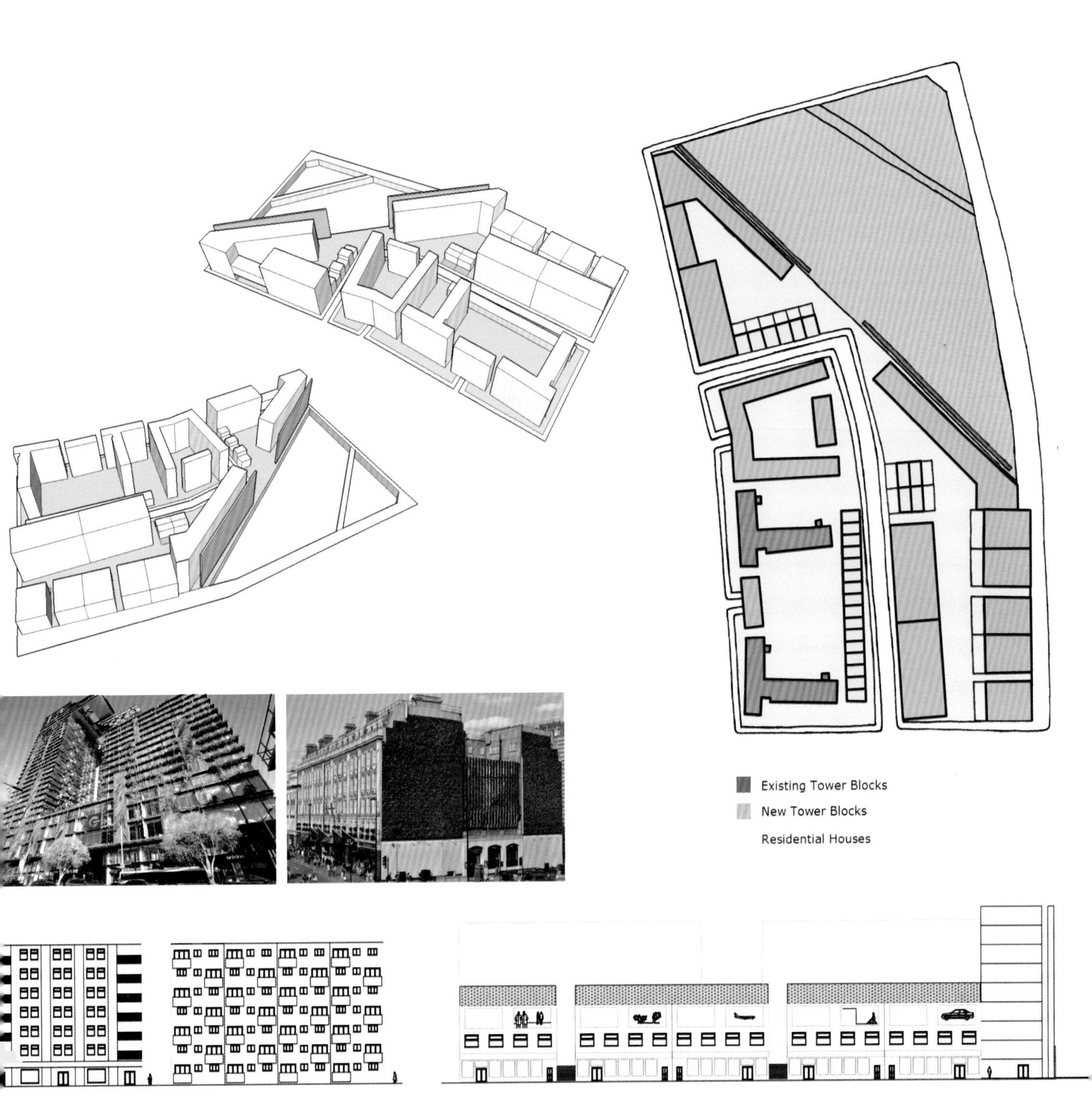

Shantelle Elliott-Edwards: *Urban Infill in Regent's Park Estate*

I WOULD LIKE to extend congratulations to all completing and continuing students: your dedication and the inspiring work you have developed are greatly appreciated by us.

With the strengthening of the year structure, we have begun the process of further integrating design studio and supporting studies, starting in first year with sketchbook studies and technical material exploration work in the Fabrication Lab. A big thanks once again to our dedicated team of MArch students supporting tutors as PALS (Peer Assisted Learners) in first year studio and on building walks.

Second year students developed projects across London for the New River, Peckham Coal Line, Old Street, Whitechapel and Highgate. Starting with Polyark 4, DS(2)5 went on to design and build an Indoor Weather Pavilion for the Imperial College Science Festival. As part of the University's global Latitudes Network, students from DS(2)4 built with snow in Tromsø in a collaboration with the city's Academy of Landscape and Territorial Studies, and DS(2)2 worked with students and staff from CEPT Ahmedabad, India.

The diverse final year studios took on the political, material and social dimensions of architecture. DS(3)1 took up the utopian ideals of Highgate's past, exploring contested land and its future as a shrine for ideas. In Margate, NEETS have been the focus for DS(3)2's creative thinking, gauging the jolly against the economic realities of a town on the periphery. DS3(7) have also been developing proposals for people in the margins in Beijing and London together with students and staff from the Chinese Academy of Fine Art.

DS(3)3 explored montage and allegory through readings and a 15th century painting, generating architectural narratives, and DS(3)4 considered the status of cultural icons and their value in a post-Brexit landscape. DS(3)5 studied the diminishing presence of the crafted artefact in a London under global roll-over with projects exploring the hand-made, whilst DS(3)6 have been building for animals and people in Hampshire and Finland: the latter included the building of a shelter in Lusto in collaboration with the Finnish Institute of London.

Special thanks to Laura Broderick and the RIBA for continuing the mentoring programme collaboration, and to Christine Zarb and Leo Skoutas for their efforts in further developing the highly successful work placements for our final year students, and in establishing an internship programme for the 2nd year.

Julian Williams
Course Leader

BA ARCHITECTURE RIBA Part 1

From local to global, BA Architecture learning is not restricted to the studio:

DS(2)4 snow building with the Tromsø Academy of Landscape and Territorial Studies; DS(2)2 running a workshop for John Donne Primary School, Peckham; and with students from CEPT at a workshop in Ahmedabad, India; DS(2)6 at the MAK, Vienna; and Studio DS(3)7 on the signal tower at the Jiankou section of the Great Wall;

FIRST YEAR ARCHITECTURE STUDIOS

IN SEMESTER 1, the six First Year studios shared the same briefs, beginning with the Lightwall, an exercise exploring the role of the wall in defining space and manipulating the quality of light. 1:2 mock ups of these walls were built in the workshop and displayed in P3. The second brief honed the students' skills in surveying, analysing, drawing and modelling a building. W.A.Gs. (WikiHouse And Games) was the final brief of the term. Students altered, manipulated, and re-imagined a standard WikiHouse structure to accommodate one of six traditional pub games. In semester two, each studio developed their own briefs which are described on the following pages.

Lightwall Construction

GROUP A: Fiona Zisch & John Edwards

Fiona Zisch *is completing a PhD in Architectural Design and Neuroscience at UCL and teaches at Westminster, Innsbruck, and the Bartlett. Her research focuses on experiential qualities and how the mind and brain construct internal worlds in relation to the external world.*

John Edwards *is a practicing architect, once named one of the UK's Top 50 Design Graduates. He works on award-winning projects across the UK. John is currently an Associate at Useful Studio, leading the design and delivery of education buildings.*

Students: Antonio Allegri, Elham Ansaripour, Shivani Bhawnani, Caner Cakmak, Ella Daley, Soraia De Abreu Viriato, Marta Dziuba, Hanane Ferraz, Sarah Hisham, Wojciech Karnowka, Areesha Khalid, Tanzina Miah, Ryan Myers, Stela Nikolaeva, Adrian-Calin Paul, Ecaterina Reabov, Ecaterina Renchez, Zainab Saadat, Anna Terekhova

Many thanks to our Peer Assisted Learners Rhiain Bower and Mihai Chiriac

House for the Apocalypse

ARCHITECTURE IS A profession that deals in futures. It is incumbent upon us to describe a vision of the future, to convince others of a possible world and our designs within it.

Architects have always pondered the future – from utopian technological innovation to dystopian future societies: da Vinci; Lloyd Wright; Archigram; to name a few. Many of the most respected architects have crafted speculative proposals, their success a coupling of rigorous logic with an appealing design.

In this sense the work of architects is not dissimilar to that of sci-fi writers. The Group A brief was framed within an apocalyptic sci-fi scenario: weather/health/political conditions have been magnified to an extreme and the fate of society is at stake. How can architecture respond with environmentally and psychologically considered proposals that will serve as incubators for the next generation without losing sight of what is great about our current world?

GROUP B: Richard Watson and Maria Kramer

Maria Kramer *is a practicing architect who also teaches in second year and on the professional practice part of the course.*

Richard Watson *mainly teaches and works as an artist in his spare time, exhibiting at University of Westminster, the AA and in various shop windows around Hertfordshire.*

Students: Hafsa Adan, Leen Ajlan, Larisa Angonese, Amin Benmoussa, Muniba Choudhury, Daria-Suzanne Donovetsky, Alicja Graczyk, Neslihan Gulhan, Beatriz Jimenez, Marianna Kyriakides, Ivan Levin, Doli Likomanova, Bibiana Malawakula, Larisa Manga, Vanessa Mbadinuju, Cameron McKay, Sulman Muhammad, Dominika Rakoczy, Aya Mousa, Henry Simpson, Mihriban Ustun, Yue Wu

Many thanks to our Peer Assisted Learners Max Martin and Harriet Poweii

Sculptor Studio and Flat

SEMESTER 2 WAS an opportunity for our students to start their first orthodox design project which was to design an Artist's studio and flat in Deptford.

We wanted the students to choose a client who was creative and whose life was well-documented in the hope that some of this would rub off on them.

They could look at the artist's working method, the materials they used, the ideas they were interested in or just their obsession for the subject. For example, Anish Kapoor's use of maquettes or Eduardo Paolozzi's quick early making process, or perhaps the value of the ordinary summed up by Stuart Davis: 'One day I set up an eggbeater in my studio and got so interested in it that I nailed it on the table and kept it there to paint. I called the picture Eggbeater, number such and such…'.

GROUP C: Richa Mukhia & Virginia Rammou

Richa Mukhia *is a director of award-winning architectural practice M.OS Architects. She has extensive experience working in the private and public sector with a particular interest in housing design and standards.*

Virginia Rammou *is Course Leader for BSc Architectural Technology at the University of Westminster. She has extensive experience in practice and is interested in the cross-fertilisation between architecture and technology. Her research focuses on the relationship between architecture, health and palliative care.*

Students: Aleyna Akteke, Sina Bahjat, Nicholas Blacker, Lauren Fashokun, Catalina Guzun, Sharna Johnson, Inna Kurtlakova, Cassie Li, Kamil Mahmoud, Ali Mohammad Vali, Kornelija Nalivaikaite, Natalia Orzel, Andreas Panagiotatos, Marta Rachwol, Yara Samaha, Kelvin-Marc Tolentino, Gia San Tu, Yuechuan Xi

Many thanks to our Peer Assisted Learners Samuel Clarry and Seetul Ghattoara

Deptford (art)Market

THE BRIEF ASKED students to design a space for an artist to live, work and exhibit their work. An intensive programme of talks and visits immersed the students in the complexities of the site (Deptford), the practicalities of the programme and initiated a series of questions that proved to be reoccurring themes throughout the semester.

Students explored questions of objects and value, originality and reproduction, spectatorship, thresholds and boundaries. Where does the private domain of the artist begin and end? What are the thresholds between living and working? When does a passerby become a viewer or perhaps even a muse?

GROUP D: Duarte Santo & Ruth Cuenca

Duarte Santo *is an Architect, Landscape and Urban Designer, Curator and Researcher. Fascinated by the material and the intangible qualities of space, he explores interdisciplinary approaches to architecture, landscape and tourism through spatial, social and cultural reflection and practice.*

Ruth Cuenca *is an Architect and Urban Designer, working between practice and academia. Her practice and research interests focus on architecture with scarce resources, sustainable development, post-disaster recovery and the role of communities in the design process.*

Students: Jannat Alam, Poonam Ale, Denisa Balaj, Handan Bayraktar, Shou Chen, Emil Covasa, William Dunne, Mariam Houta, Polyan Ivanov, Rikesh Kerai, Ramshey Khan, Nicole Langcauon, Polina Novikova, Viktoriia Nozdracheva, Gabriele Pesciotti, Holy Serukenya, Dan Strassburg, Lydia Tryfonopoulou, Boyuan Zhang

Many thanks to our Peer Assisted Learners Zhini Poh and Calvin Sin

Crafting the Future: Live/work in Deptford High Street

'CRAFTING THE FUTURE' asks for the design of a building that can accommodate a live/work space for a small group of skilled artisans and a communal/hybrid space to promote interaction with the local community and engage its members through craft-related activities.

A craft is an activity or profession that requires particular skills and knowledge of materials, tools and techniques. The studio focuses on material and performative aspects of the activity both in space and time. Exploring a specific craft, students are invited to engage with its objects and makers to further expand their research and work into the site, architecture and its users.

Students analysed and interpreted the site and surrounding area, exploring the concept of 'infraordinary', questioning stereotypes and testing ideas through drawings and models, understanding how their intervention could become a catalyst for social interaction in the rapidly changing context of Deptford High Street.

GROUP E: Matthew Stewart & Natalie Newey

Matthew Stewart *is a designer, researcher and writer. His student work received the RIBA CLAWSA prize and runner up in the AR Global Architecture Graduate Award. Matthew has worked with architectural practices in China, South Korea and India on various projects.*

Natalie Newey *is a Senior Lecturer, First Year Leader and SFHEA. She has extensive experience working in practice and is particularly interested in community engagement in the design process.*

Students: Beth Allen, Polina Bouli, Mia Briscoe, Katie-Anne Brown, Yu-Tang Chou, Irgel Enkhsaikhan, Sodueari Graham-Douglas, Matthew Heyna-Francis, Kate Hubert, Aiste Jurgeviciute, Maheer Khan, Faisal Muti, Anna Pawlik, Lavinia Pennino, Zuzanna Sliwinska, Nikoleta Tareva, Midia Veryani, Maciej Worosilak

Many thanks to our Peer Assisted Learners Nouha Hansen, Rafaella Christodoulidi and Marco Catena

House for Sculptor

OUR STUDENTS WERE asked to design a series of live, work and semi-public spaces for a sculptor of their choice, on small sites off Deptford High Street.

In preparation for this we conducted group research into Depford's unique history and urban form, with a wider programmatic analysis of Deptford High Street. Threshold spaces were explored as both physical and social concepts to be introduced to design proposals.

An emphasis was placed on research into their sculptor's particular working process, spatial requirements and daily routine refined through trips to studios spaces in London.

The results were eclectic: a house-cum-brick Swiss mountain for Picasso and his goat; a sorting office studio for Stuart Hogarth; Deptford market junk façades for Tony Cragg; 'Peeping Tom' gizmos for Rebecca Horn and an ethereal house of translucent walls for Naum Gabo.

GROUP F: Corinna Dean & Juan Piñol

Corinna Dean *is a teacher, critical urbanist and curator with an interest in how the urban is communicated, experienced and lived out across cultures. She holds a PhD from the LSE Cities Programme, a collaborative doctoral award with Tate Modern. She launched ARCA, the Archive for Rural Contemporary Architecture.*

Juan Piñol *studied architecture in Colombia, where he taught and worked on master planning and large housing schemes. In the UK he has worked on historic buildings, as well as design and construction of new residential and office buildings.*

Students: Estera Badelita, Smit Baradiya, Eylem Bekam, Navpreet Bolina, Kevin Ferenzena, Joseph Humbert, Sabrah Islam, Manjot Jabbal, Susann Kerner, Daria Kushnir, Omar Khan, Esther Oluwo, Darina Procopciuc, Kenza Salami el Idrissi, Hiloni Sheth, Yana Stoyanova, Catalina Stroe, Reiss Young, Tamas Zuberecz, Egle Zuikaite

Many thanks to our Peer Assisted Learners Anett Beko and Tom Benton

Gallery of the Future

FOR THE FINAL project students were asked to respond to the Deptford site as a space for the Gallery of the Future. Imagining a scenario 30-40 years from now, the students made a selection of what the content would consist of, what might become obsolete or endangered. Or imagine hypothetical scenarios such as online communication becoming debunked, replaced by a return to an analogue means of producing and consuming information – what would such changes mean for buildings as we know them?

Museums and public galleries play a central role in society, not just through engaging with objects but they have become public spaces, spaces in which to question our identity as 21st century citizens.

Students responded with designs encompassing an adaptable relief response which enabled existing buildings to display artefacts, a cultural ethnicity museum which displays cultures of threatened minorities in light of regeneration schemes in the area, and a gallery of endangered plants.

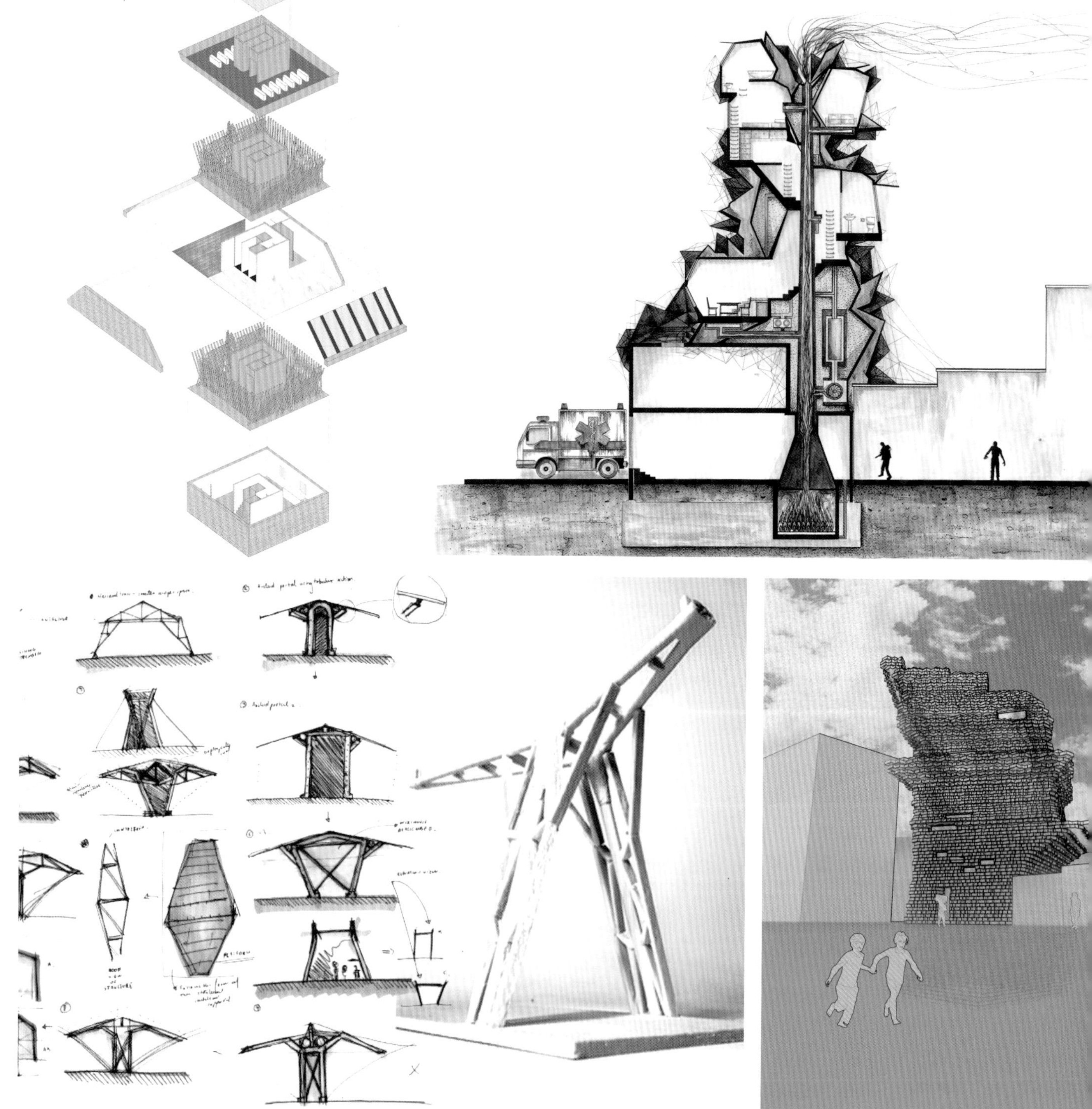

(top left) Tanzina Miah; *(top right)* Ella Daley; *(bottom left)* Adrian-Calin Paul; *(bottom right)* Wojciech Karnowka

The pavilion's connection with the natural environment offers a larger open space around the structure which automatically allows the pavilion in a matter to "extend" the space offered. The open space is primarily used by children in the means of a playground due to their ability to easily move around and be more accessible one with the other.

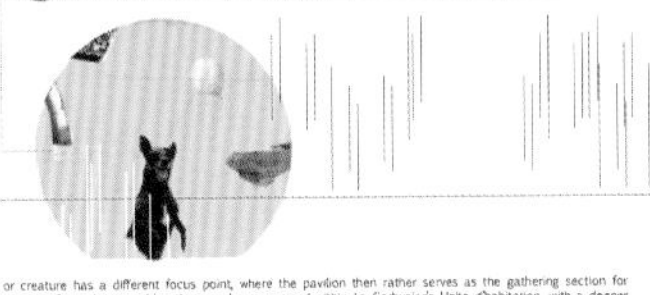

During the day, each individual or creature has a different focus point, where the pavilion then rather serves as the gathering section for a larger vast of communities and types of people, something that can be recognised within Le Corbusier's Unite d'habitation, with a deeper look at the "main street" found within the internal space.

Day in the Life of a Pavilion (Hut with Bench)

During the day the pavilion represented an attraction which can be determined due to the vast amount of people which decided step by to have a further examination of it. The key element which allows the pavilion to be accessed mainly during day is the sun. The sun offers the natural light which when in first contact with the structure, it enables it to offer its rustic beauty. The beauty is primarily offered by the irregular wood pillars, which give a sense of having nature at the core of the pavilion. Another reason for it's popularity during the day has been based on a more human point of view, where due to the sun the temperature rises and therefore, most portions of the park become hotter. The pavilion is found in an enclosed space which is aided by large trees which stop a direct meeting between the light of the sun and the the pavilion, from where automatically, the temperature within the "premises" of the pavilion started to decrease, resulting in a more comfortable environment to be in.

(top) Adrian-Calin Paul; *(bottom left)* Marta Dziuba; *(bottom right)* Marta Dziuba

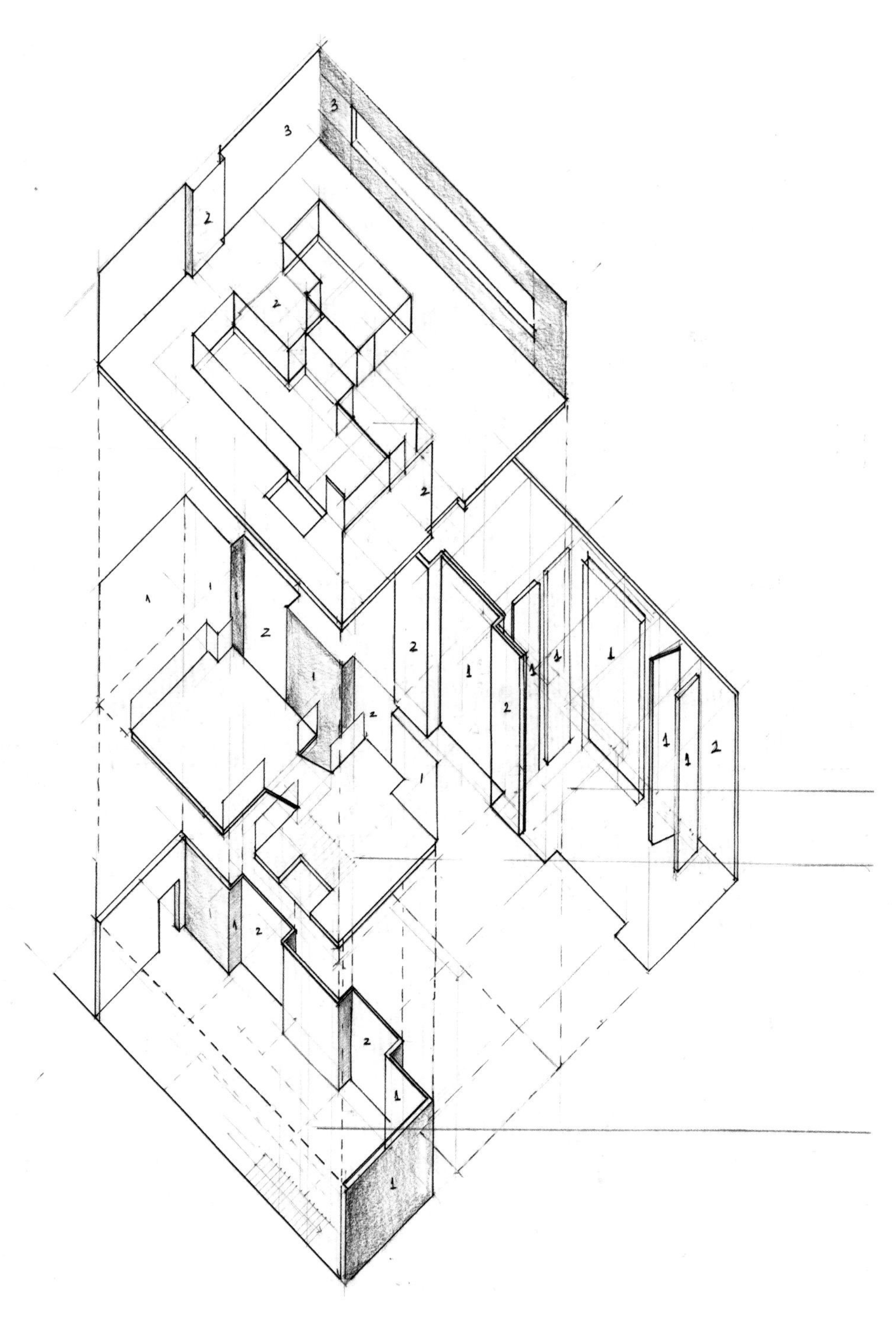

Daria Donovetsky

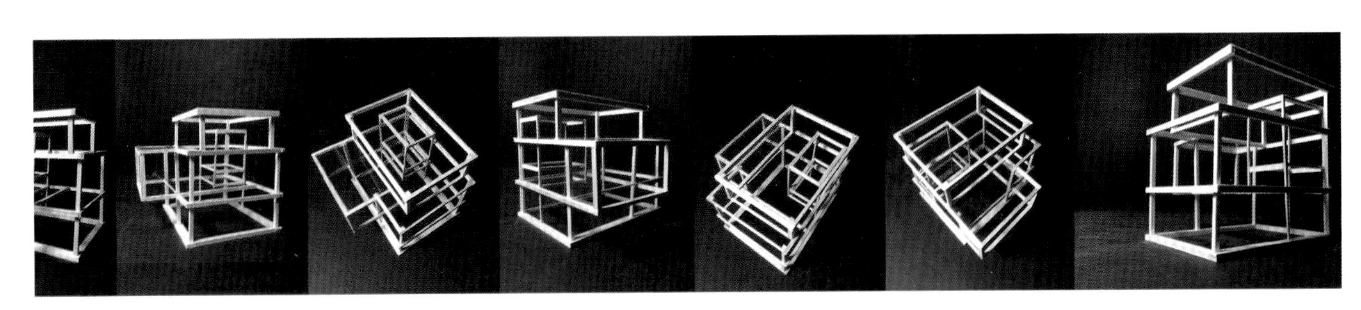

Larisa Manga

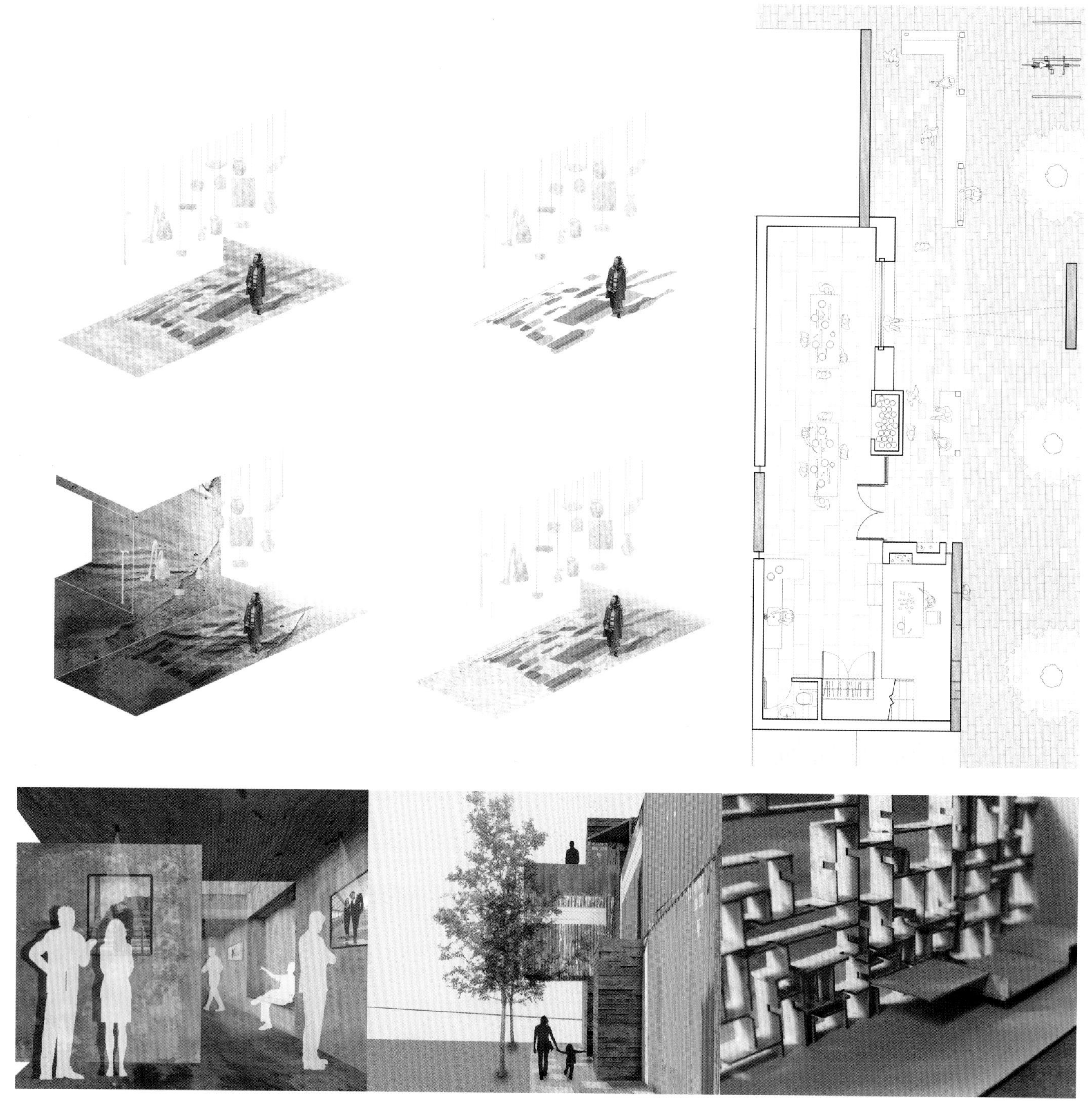

(top left) Lauren Fashokun: *The Deptford Archive; (top right)* Cassie Li: *Market Exchange; (bottom left to right)* Catalina Guzun, Nicholas Blacker, Yara Samaha

(top) Cassie Li: *Market Exchange*; *(bottom left to right)* Catalina Guzun, Yuechuan Xi, Cassie Li

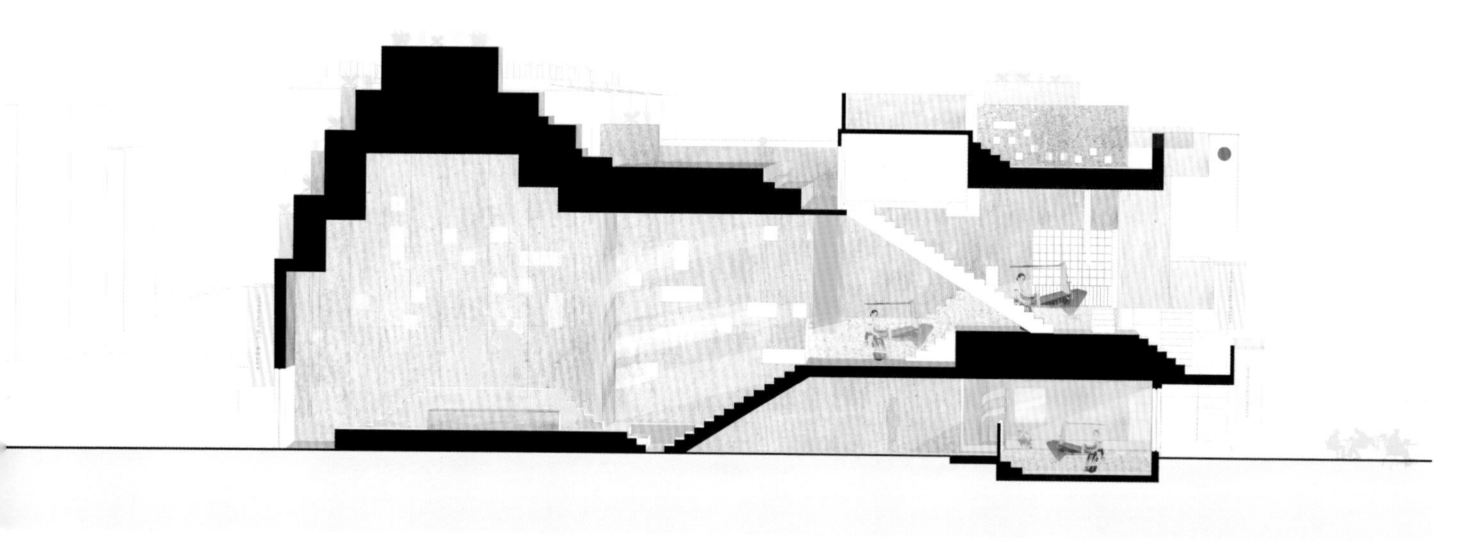

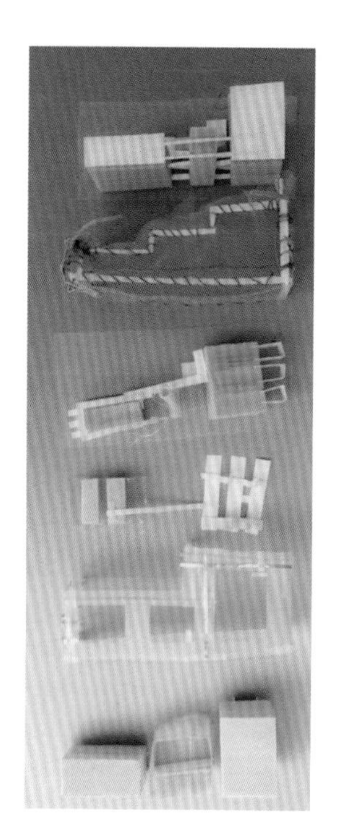

this page (top) **Polina Novikova**; *(bottom left)* **Polina Novikova**; *(bottom right)* **Mariam Houta**;
opposite: (top) **Gabriele Pesciotti**; *(bottom)* **Nicole Langcauon**

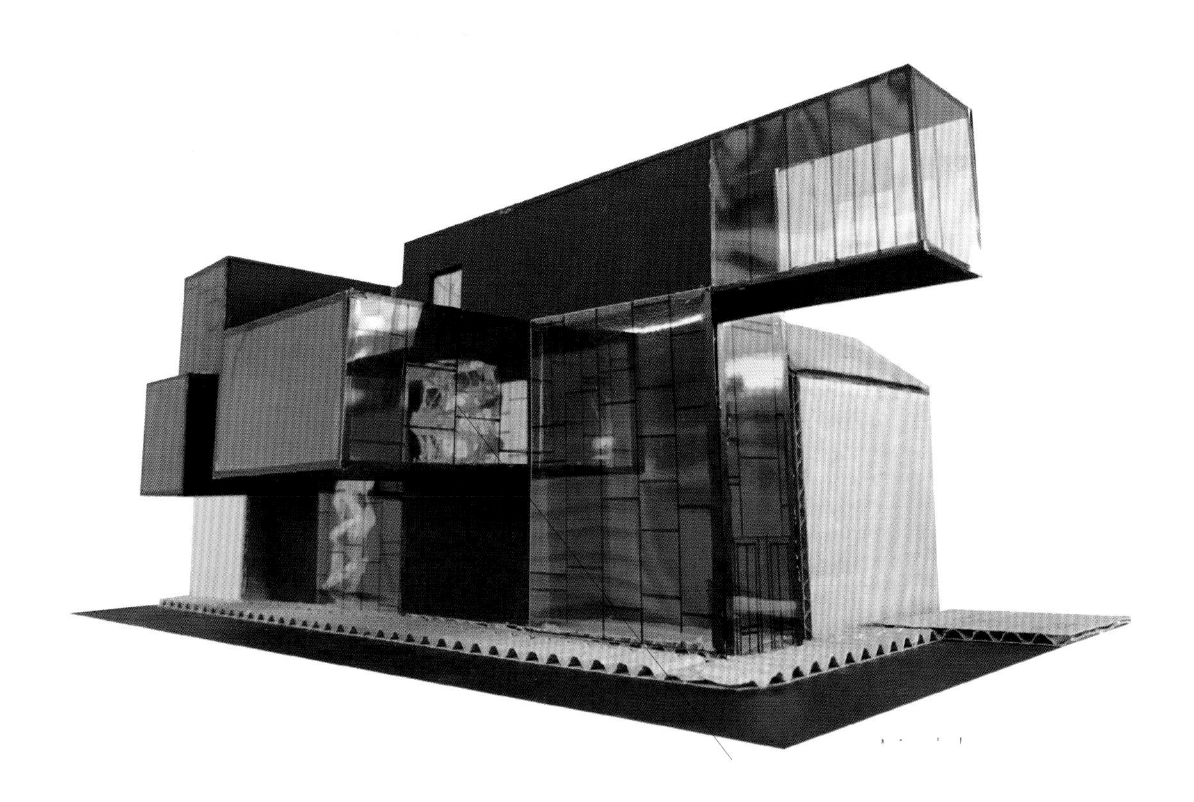

(left) Maciej Worosilak: *Deptford Experiential Collage; (top right)* Maciej Worosilak: *A Sorting Office for Stuart Hogarth; (bottom right)* Zuzanna Sliwinska: *Rebecca Horn Concept Collage*

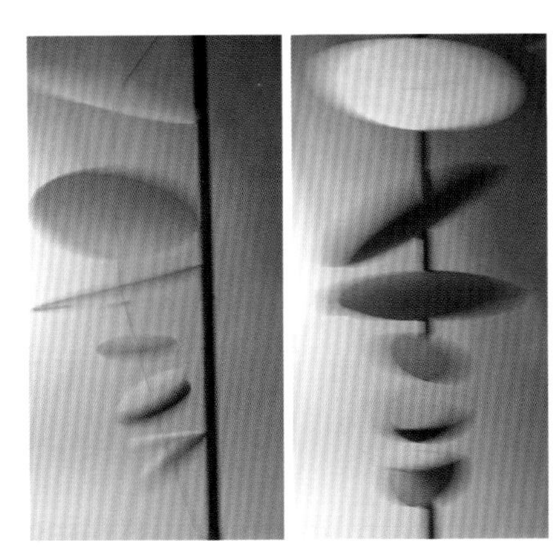

(top left) Mia Briscoe: *Section;* *(top right)* Lavinia Pennino: *Façade Shelving Light Studies;*
(bottom left) Zuzanna Sliwinska: *Peeping Feather Maquette;* *(bottom right)* Polina Bouli: *Naum Gabo Maquette Studies*

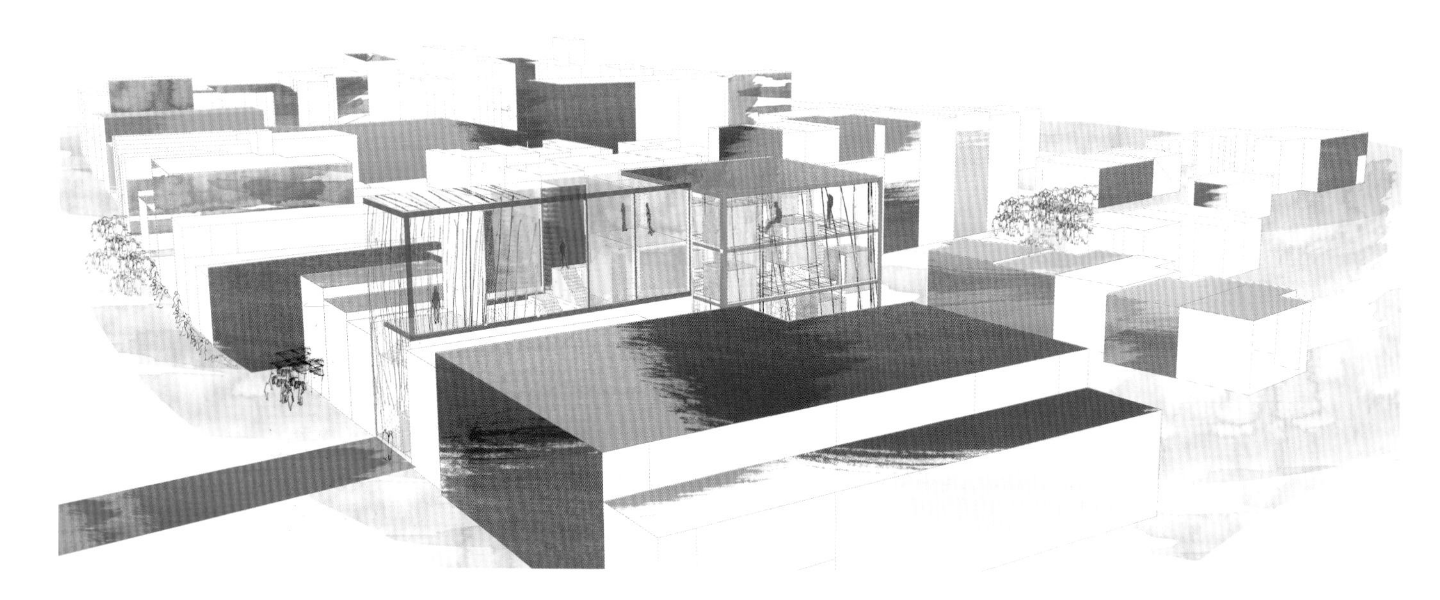

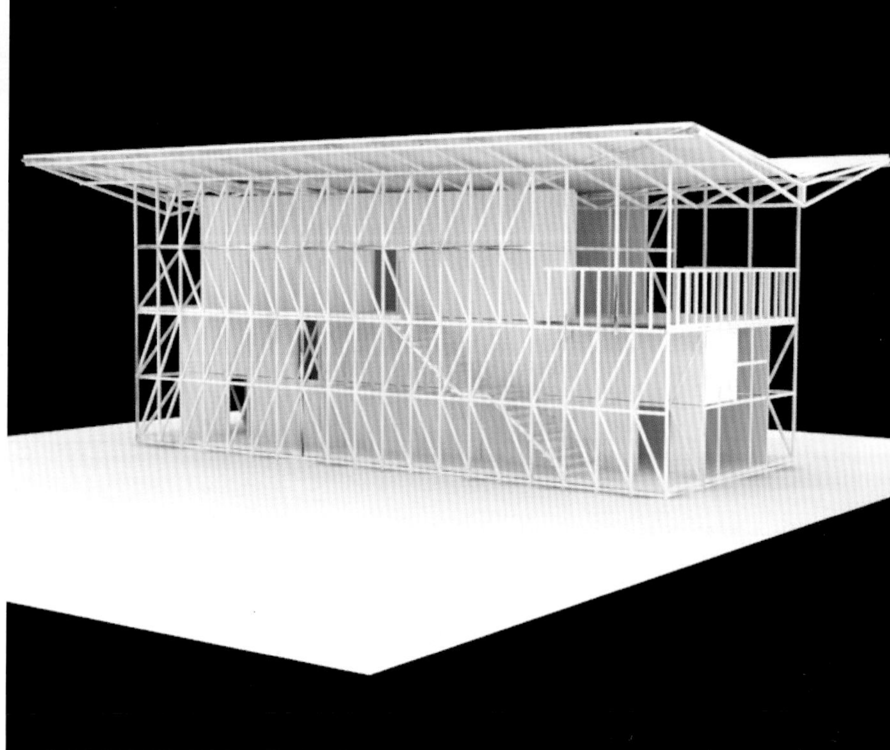

Sabrah Islam

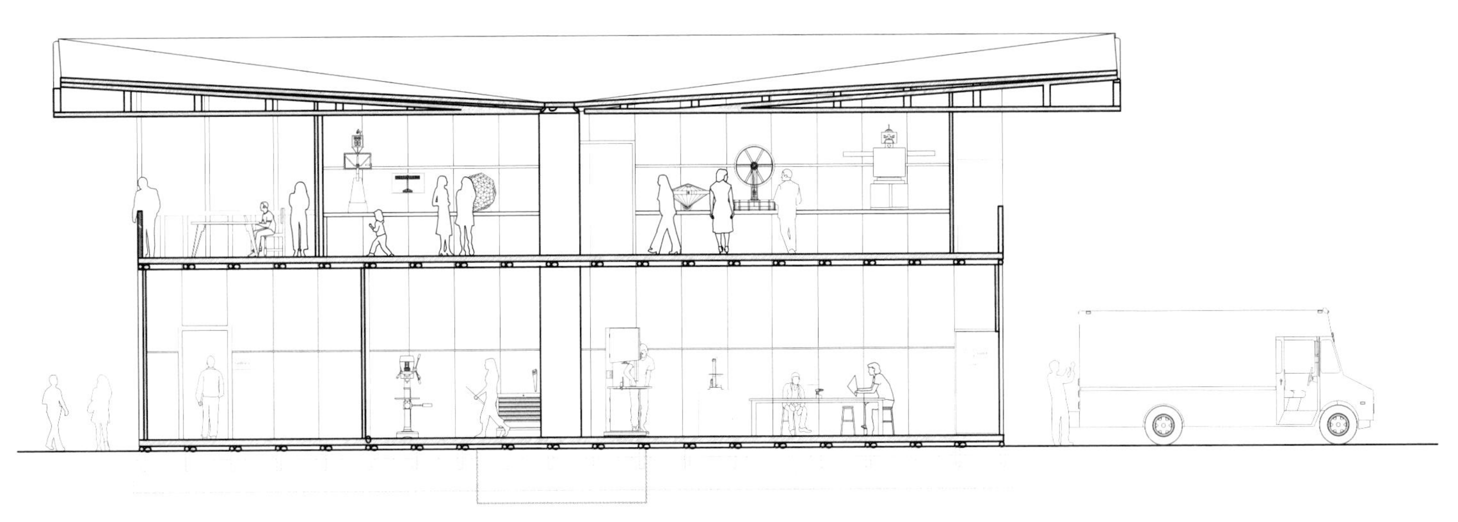

(top) Estera Badelita; *(bottom)* Egle Zuikaite

Elantha Evans & Anthony Powis

Elantha Evans *is an architect and educator. Her practice work with Serrano Evans Partnership included architectural, interior and object design, balanced with site-specific performance and installations. Her current research explores the 'space' for the production of space within the invisible institutional structures of practice and education.*

Anthony Powis *is an architect and researcher with interests in public space, urban nature, and hybrid landscapes. He has taught at the University of Westminster since 2015.*

DS(2)1: Urban Ghosts: redundant/reimagined

Students: Ishma Ahmed, Mustafa Akkaya, Aristides Apatzidis Jones, Jasdeep Atwal, Alexandra Badea, Sabina Blasiotti, Jeffrey Chan, Hannah Clarke, Stefan Dean, Yasemin Evmez, Mattia Faraci, Zuzanna Grodzka, Yasemin Kose, Philip Longman, Clarissa O'Driscoll, Jaroslaw Owsianny, Signe Pelne, Joshua Ricketts, Guy Sinclair, Gade Smith, Monifa Yasmin

OUR STARTING POINT for the year was exploring the course of the 'New River', constructed to bring fresh water into central London from Hertfordshire. This territory offers diverse physical context and enabled an exploration of the idea of resource: from public utilities and parks, to social services and health service provision; for the city, the neighbourhood, and the individual. Developing an understanding of the 'urban' as shaped by manifold historical and material structures, we ask: how can architectural projects leverage, augment, and articulate existing resources to reimagine particular sites and offer new places?

The study visit to Madrid, Chinchón, Ávila, and Toledo in Spain paid particular attention to the ways in which institutional buildings sit within urban fabric, how they affect public and private space and what presence – literal and symbolic – they have in the city.

Domestic Sanctuary/everyday moments

The brief in semester one required the development of a 'social hub' on one of three sites, each having a particular relationship to the New River and linking in with existing health facilities: social prescribing, conduct disorder and hydrotherapy. The sites chosen were clustered around this expansive but redundant waterway as it progresses through Haringey and Hackney, bisecting streets and defining odd and unexpected urban pockets. Notions of sanctuary, domesticity and human interactions were considered key as part of knitting the proposals into a modified urban journey.

Civic Sanctuary/everyday asylum

In semester two, proposals for a 'civic cog' were made on a choice of two liminal sites: one in the former peripheral 'village' of Stoke Newington, and the other on a layered, historic site near Aldgate, located next to the former London Wall. The brief incorporated a public space, charity headquarters, and small-scale support services. Successful projects demonstrate clarity in social agenda and programme; linking historical context, existing built fabric and institutions; and responding to current socio-political needs.

Guest Critics:
Stefania Boccaletti, Dusan Decermic, Jenny Dunn, Clare Hamman, Hwei Fan Liang, Natalie Newey, John Ng, Andrew Peckham, Emma Perkin, Claire Priest, Shahed Saleem, Jeanne Sillett, Matthew Stewart

Stefan Dean: *New River/Harringay Ladders*

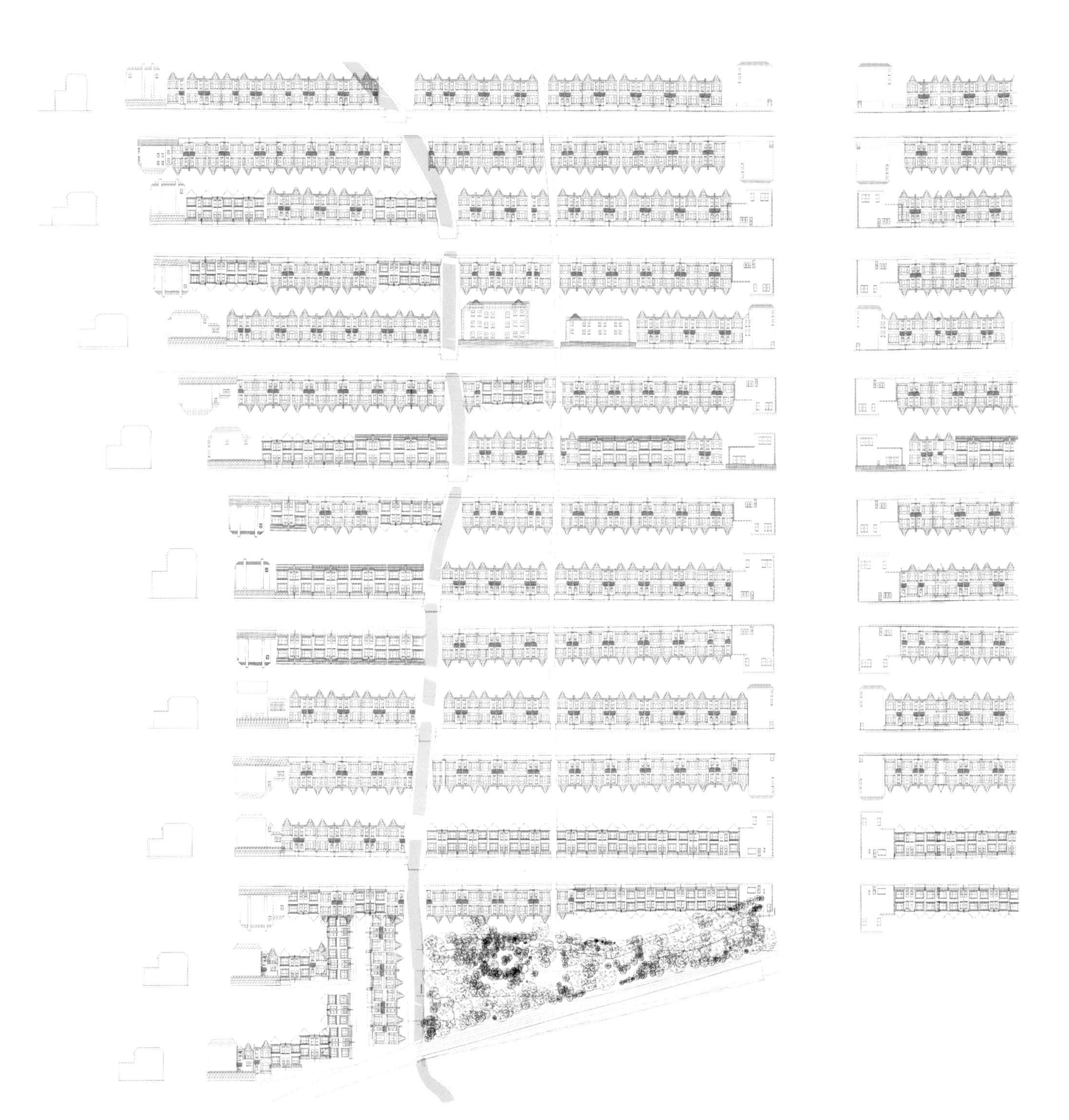

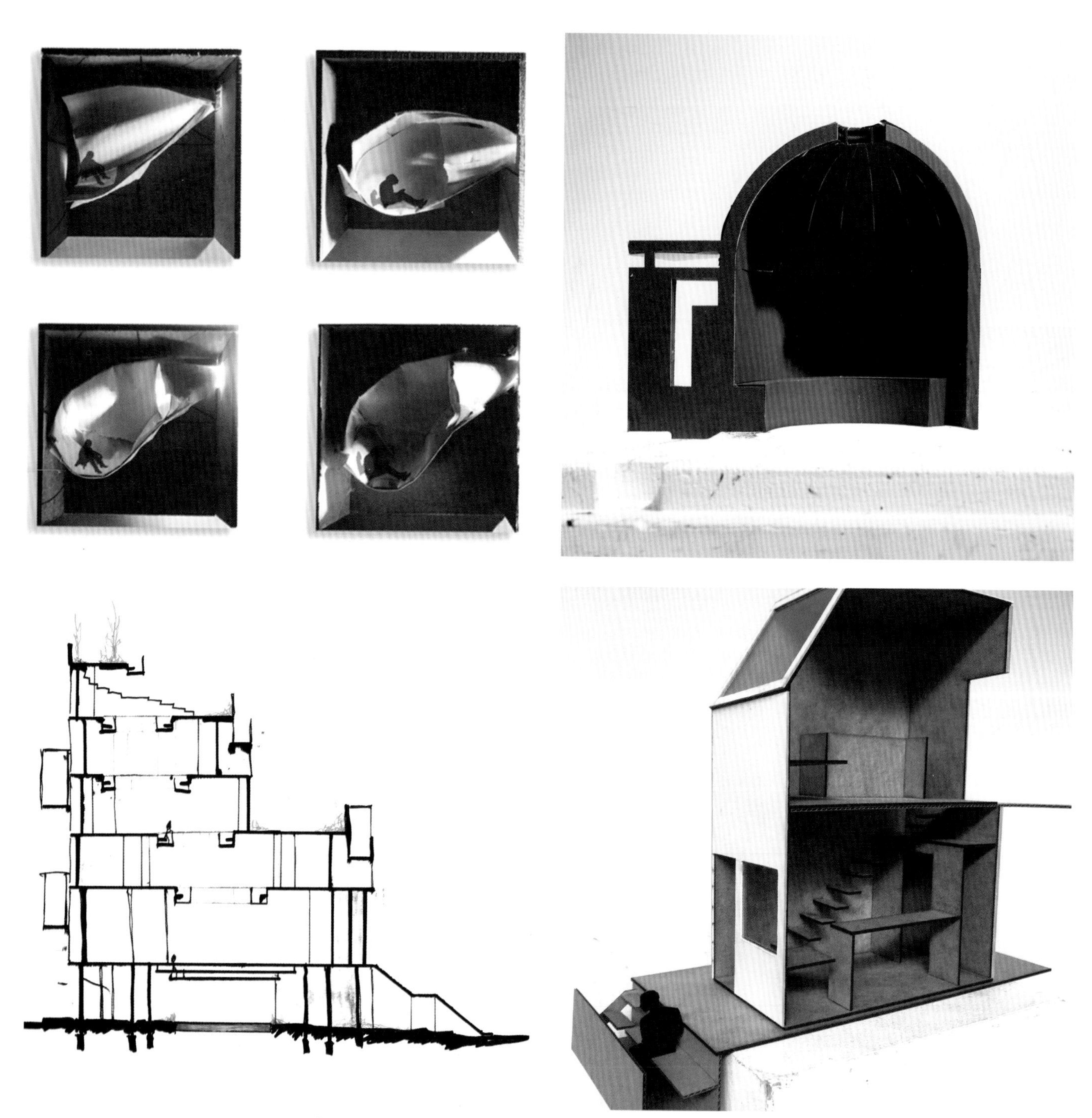

(top left) Stefan Dean: *Embryonic Sanctuary; (top right)* Guy Sinclair: *Viewing Seat; (bottom)* Signe Pelne: *Migrant Living Hub*

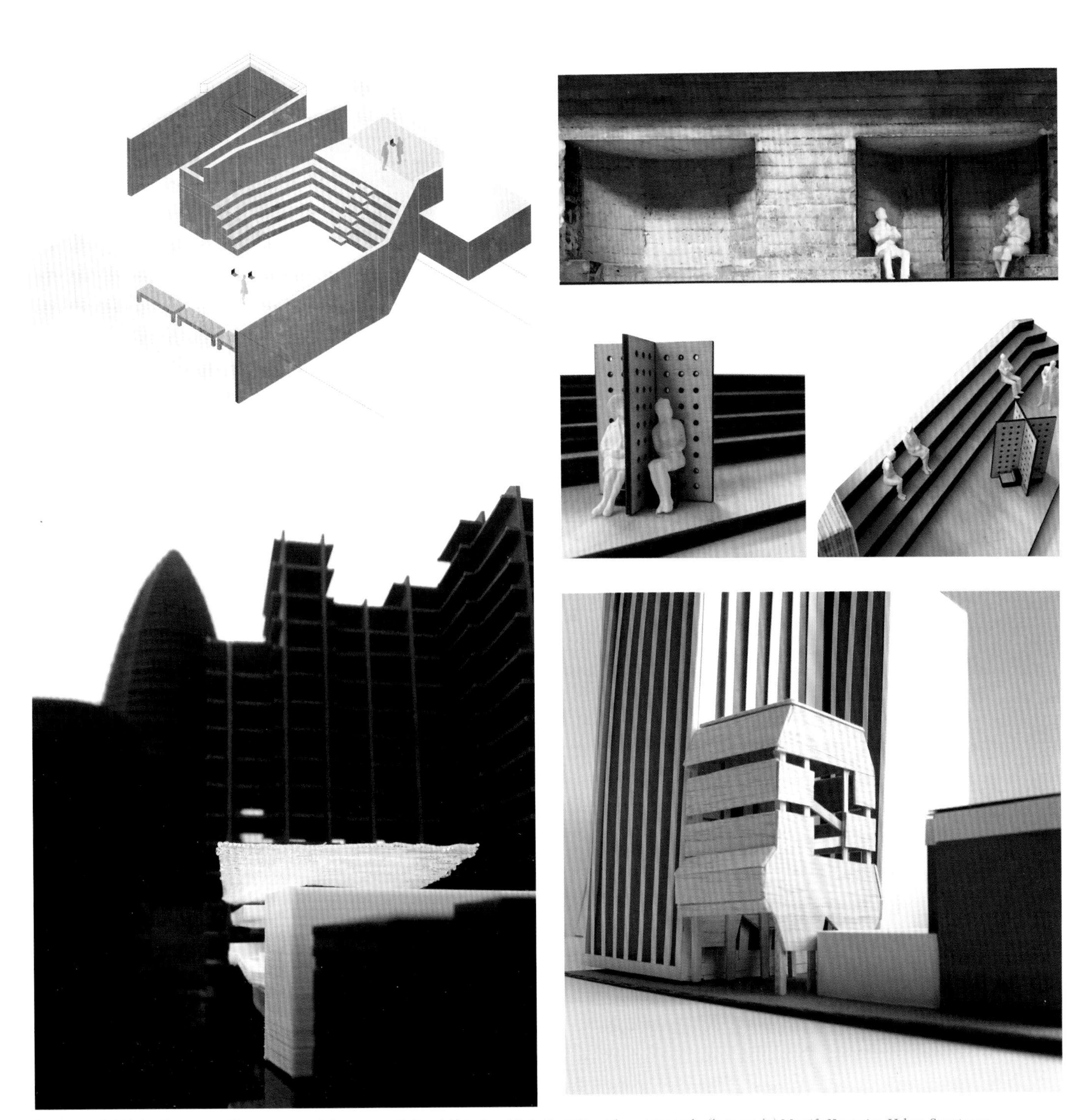

(top left & right) Philip Longman: *Transparency & Screening*; *(bottom left)* Joshua Ricketts: *Mitre Place Approach*; *(bottom right)* Monifa Yasemin: *Urban Sanctuary*

Natalie Newey & John Zhang

Natalie Newey *is a Senior Lecturer and SFHEA. She has extensive experience working in practice and is particularly interested in community engagement in the design process.*

John Zhang *is a practicing architect and an Associate at DSDHA. He is also currently working on a PhD at the Royal College of Art on the topic of contemporary Chinese architecture.*

DS(2)2: Made in Peckham

Students: Oliwia Bisaga, Kryzta Castillo, Sanya Chadha, Eugene Dubovoy, Petter Elverum, Rebecca Foxwell, Gabija Gumbeleviciute, Enes Karakus, Kirill Menshikov, Daniel McNally, Teodora Neagoe, Zlatina Nedeva, Matthew Rea, Vittoria Rega, Raluca Rimboaca, Mark Tsenov, Ryan Wu, Fan Xingye, Yiwen Zhou

WE WENT BACK to Peckham this year, where the broad mix of people and built environment provide rich territory to explore the studio's interest in how design is informed by a meaningful engagement with local communities. Our briefs developed around the relationship we have cultivated with the Coal Line project and local community groups including John Donne, a local primary school. Chance and opportunism have long played a part in the development of this vibrant neighbourhood, but in recent years gentrification has become a growing threat which the local community is determined to control. The studio has explored this issue as part of our year's briefs.

As a means of getting to grips with the site, the students began by inventing *'Field Instruments'* which they used to explore the qualities of the sites chosen. Their inventions included tools for measuring vibration, mechanisms for listening to conversations, devices for containing and emitting smells, and wearable viewing machines. We shared our inventions with the students at John Donne, who provided excellent advice and inspiring feedback. Research into local community projects then lead to designs for Pop-Up Community Hubs, part of a proposal for a summer festival along the proposed Coal Line.

A trip to Ahmedabad, India in January was a highlight of the year, organised around a workshop with students at CEPT University. We investigated local community projects, analysed through sketches local landmark buildings, and explored the urban fabric of this ancient city. On our return to London, students developed briefs for alternative educational facilities with the help of the John Donne student body. On a site next to the proposed Coal Line, schemes were developed that attempted to knit together disparate site elements, enhance community connectivity and create inspiring facilities for encouraging wider knowledge and fostering curiosity among the students and the community.

Many thanks to our critics and collaborators:
Peckham Coal Line project group, especially Louise Armstrong; John Donne School staff, particularly Cindy MacDonald; CEPT University, especially Urvi Desai and her students.

Scott Batty, Stefania Boccaletti, Almudena Cano Pineiro, Andreas Christodoulou, Elantha Evans, Morgan Graboski, Will Mclean, Lucy McWeeney, Laura Nica, Isis Nunez Ferrera, Ralph Parker, Dragan Pavlovic, Shahed Saleem, Laylac Shahed, Tszwai So, Matthew Stewart, Ozan Toksoz-Blauel, Mike Tuck, Jean Wang, Victoria Watson, Julian Williams

(top left) **Xingye Fan:** ***Fun Palace;*** *(top right)* **Petter Elverum:** ***Peckham Observatory;*** *(bottom)* **Petter Elverum:** ***Peckham Observatory***

(top left) Teodora Neagoe: *Wind Drawing Instrument*; *(top right)* Muyu Wu: *Engaging Studios*; *(bottom)* Muyu Wu: *Engaging Studios*

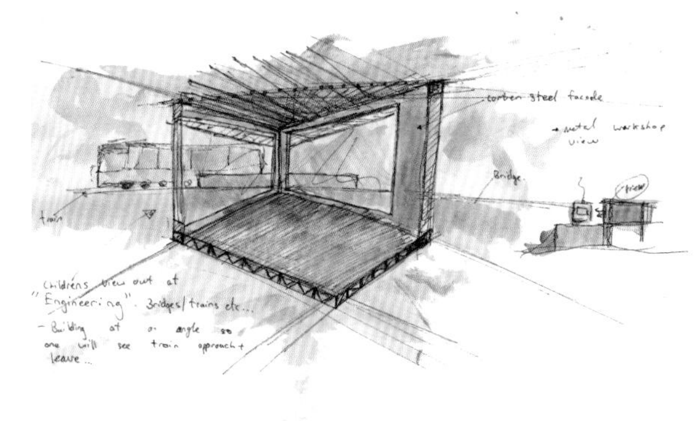

(top left) ***India Visit;*** *(top right)* Daniel McNally: *Crafting Education;* *(bottom)* Raluca Rimboaca: *Theatre of Life*

Shahed Saleem & Michael Rose

Shahed Saleem *is a practising architect and researches and writes on architecture's relationship with cultural identity, heritage and nationhood. He works regularly with Historic England and is a Senior Research Fellow with the Survey of London.*

Michael Rose *has been teaching architecture for over forty years. He explores how architecture can enhance human experience and well-being, from the physical to the emotional, intellectual, and spiritual. He aims to instil in students a clear understanding of the design and making process.*

DS(2)3: Intercultural Encounters in Architecture

Students: Arwa Al-Nasrawi, Betool Amier, Gentrit Bunjaku, Samiye Cifci, Ahmed Elmasri, Faustine Ghislain, Samar Green, Michaella Hadjihanna, Aloys Heitz, Joyce Hui, Pooja Kerai, Unnati Mankad, Zahra Mansoor, Aleksandrs Manza, Jaesung Nam, Setareh Nosrati, Christina Petridou, Elena Ryskute, Fatema Salim, Alexander Tyrwhitt, James Wraith

THIS YEAR WE asked what kind of architecture is required for an intercultural city. Our projects were located in Spitalfields and Whitechapel, and ranged from small-scale temporary installations to a civic institution, in the form of a library and public space.

Interculturalism describes a type of social encounter that reappraises the multi-cultural model of managing diverse societies which was pioneered in the 1980s. The drawback of multiculturalism was that it created a 'false sense of harmony' by encouraging culturally and spatially distinct communities thus leading to alienation and disconnection with wider society and with other cultural groups. Apart from this being problematic in terms of social cohesion, it was also out of touch with the experience of more recent migrant and post-migrant communities who were forging new and often hybrid identities.

Through our design projects we asked what an intercultural space is and what kind of cultural encounter does it encourage; what sort of contact and relationships can architecture instigate between diverse people and what does meaningful contact mean?

Our major project explored this question through an intercultural reappraisal of the established typologies of the library and public space. These are complex social programmes and we endeavoured to make sensitive and insightful observations about them. How does public space create and manage relationships in a diverse society? How does the library, and the forms of knowledge that it contains, enable a range of people to access and relate to it, and what is the role of public space in this process? What is meaningful contact between culturally distinct people, and how can this happen through our proposals?

Through our projects we found that intercultural encounters constitute new ways in which the city is being inhabited and urban space is being negotiated. Architecture can respond to, and accommodate, this new reality through a process of close observations followed by considered propositions.

Guest Critics:
Damion Burrows (Darling Associates), Elizavet Dimitriou, Elantha Evans, Khuzema Hussain (Collective Works), Joseph Hyman, Edward Ihejirika (DCUK), Natalie Klak, Daniel Leon (Square Feet Architects), Urna Sodnomjamts, Anshu Srivastava (MRA Associates), Julian Williams

Special thanks:
JW3 Jewish Community Centre, The Nomadic Gardens, Iakovos Dimitriou, Iris Papadatou, Sarah Milne, Laura Vaughan

(top) **Faustine Ghislain:** ***Intercultural Theatre;*** *(bottom)* **Gentrit Bunjaku:** ***Viewing Platform***

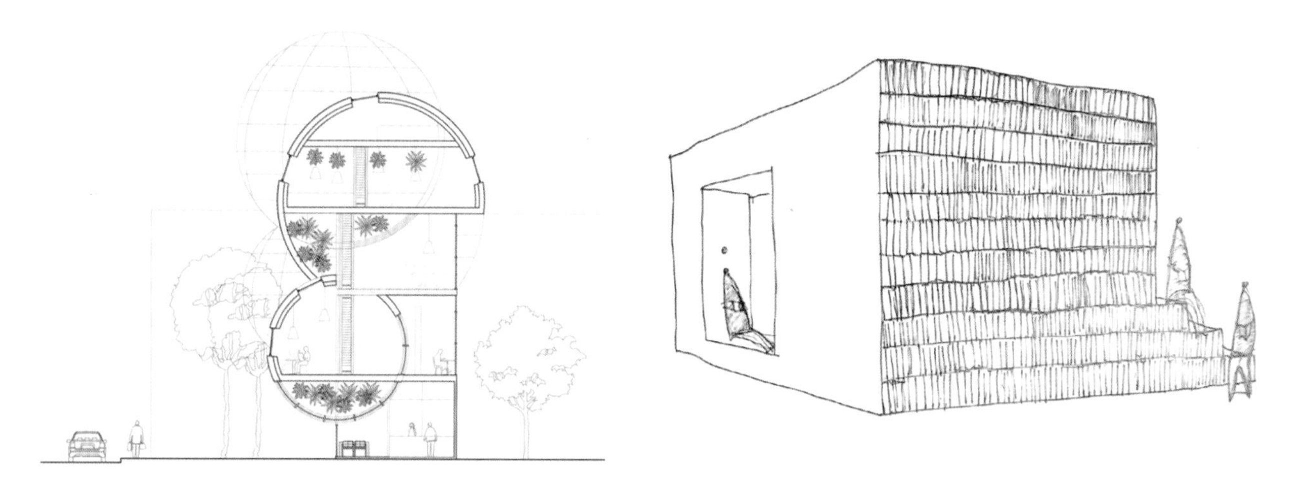

(top left) **Elena Ryskute:** ***Intercultural Library;*** *(top right)* **Samar Green:** ***Intercultural Library;*** *(bottom)* **Aloys Heitz:** ***Soundscape***

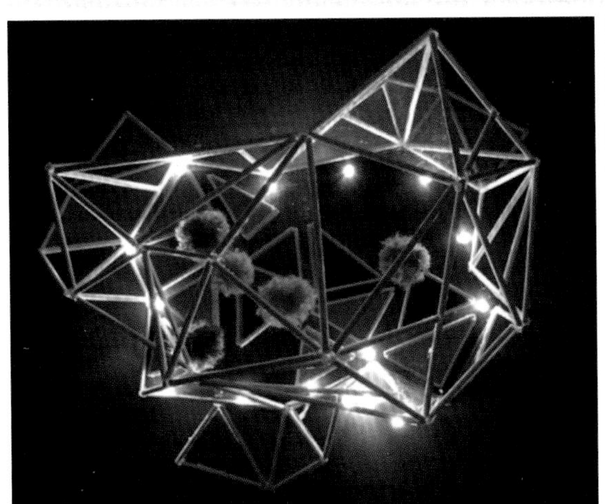

(top) Setareh Nosrati: *Intercultural Library;* *(bottom left)* Fatema Salim: *Nomadic Garden;* *(bottom right)* Alex Tyrwhitt: *East End Archive*

Julian Williams & Maria Kramer

Julian Williams *worked as a project architect for 20 years before moving into full-time teaching. Ten of these were spent at muf architecture/art, collaborating with artists on public realm landscape works and projects for young people. His current research is on the experience of LGBT professionals, and the study of public housing landscapes.*

Maria Kramer *is an architect and has been in practice for more than 15 years. She was a partner and co-managed leit-werk before setting up her own studio, Room 102, in 2011. Maria teaches on the Part III Professional Practice course and in MArch studio DS12.*

DS(2)4: Landscapes of the Eye, and of the Mind's Eye

Students: Hamza Abbas, Francesca Benetti Genolini, Simon Dendere, Deane Dizon, Dilan Kalayci, Hyun Kim, Ugne Kiseliovaite, Amirreza Kiyaniyan, Helena Klenovski, Remi Kuforiji, Wangyan Liu, Illia Marynin, Aamirah Munshi, Magdalena Ochal, Zoe Power, Patrycja Smola, Maciej Sobieraj, Amy Wallace, Nabla Yahya

THE STUDIO DISCUSSED what it means to live and learn outside, to explore landscape as a cultural artefact, an educational resource, and in architectural dimensions. Our students tried out Bharat Cornell's exercises for sharing nature with children, drew the woodland canopy and went on to design two projects for the emerging Forest School movement. This advocates getting children and young people out of the classroom by teaching the regular curriculum in an outdoor 'natural' setting, using simply available natural materials and the immediate surroundings as starting points for scientific, literary and cultural learning.

Nature Nook

For St Michael's School in Highgate, our students examined the funding problems confronting the maintenance of school grounds, and the factors limiting outdoor playing and learning. They developed landscape strategies to respond to this context; designed a 'Forest School' space; and a shelter for teaching in a landscaped setting and storing teaching materials and equipment. They speculated on how Forest School ideas could be extended as an ambitious architecture, not just in a rural setting but within the challenges of the inner suburbs.

Queen's Wood Retreat

We listened to expert allotment growers, Forest School practitioners and school teachers, and then developed designs to transform a brownfield site adjacent to Queen's Wood Highgate into a centre for Forest School practice. Escaping to the wilds at the end of a twenty-minute bus ride rather than a two-hour coach journey. Through the child's eye we understood the importance of the journey of discovery from the bus-stop to the camp fire, making Forest School residentials accessible to the most hard-pressed, with space to stay and learn far away from the classroom timetable.

Guest Critics:
Jorge Beroiz, Stefania Boccaletti, Rui Carvalheiro, Liz Elston, Caterina Frizone, Omar Ghazal, François Girardin, Paul Grover, James Lai, Natalie Newey, Lucy O'Reilly, Alicia Pivaro, Nic Pople, Shahed Saleem

(top) Remi Kuforiji: *Eien No (Eternal): Landscape Strategy;* *(bottom)* Liu Wangyang: *Embracing Nature*

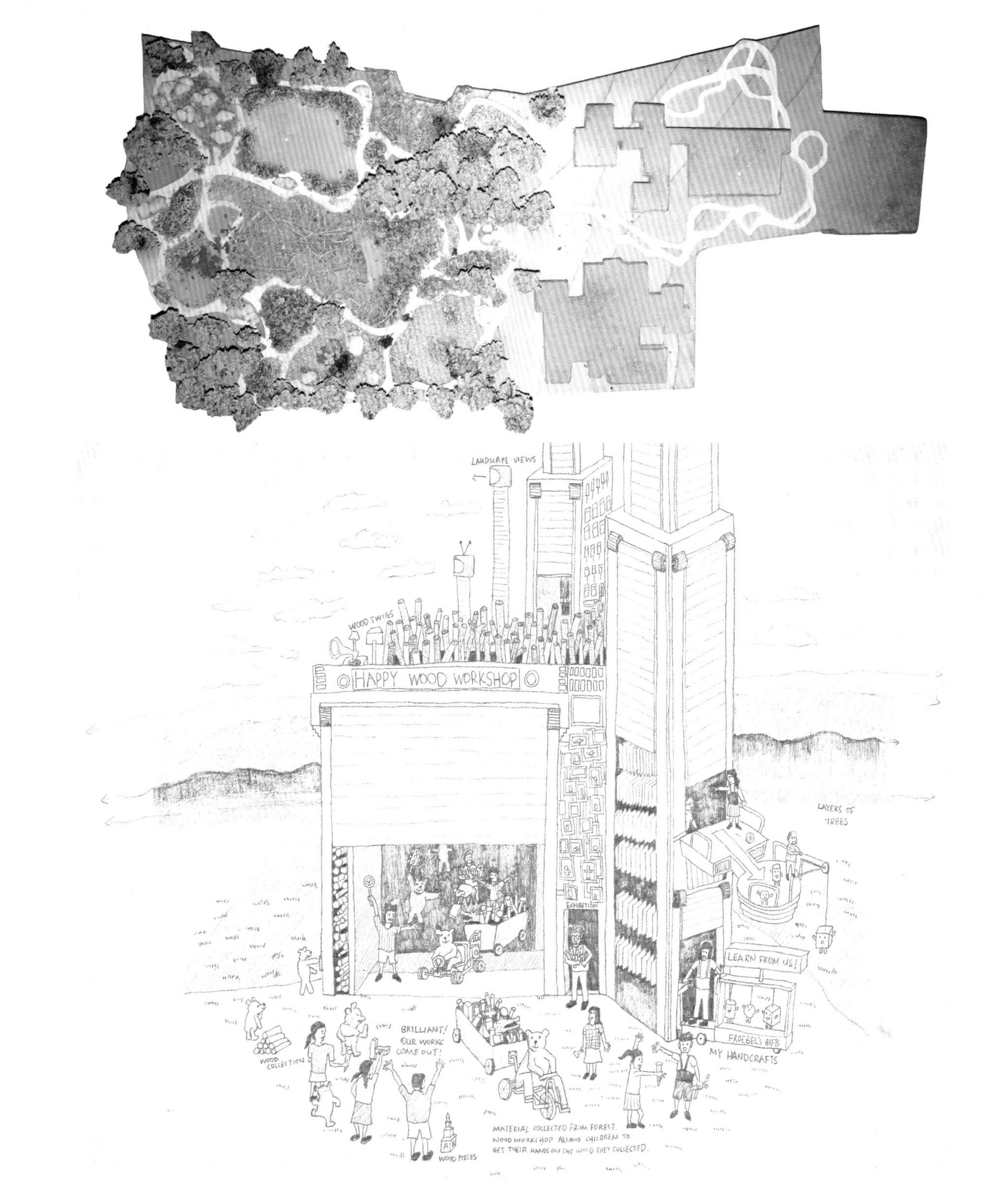
LANDSCAPE VIEWS
WOOD TWIGS
HAPPY WOOD WORKSHOP
EXHIBITION
LAYERS OF TREES
LEARN FROM US!
FROEBEL'S GIFTS
MY HANDCRAFTS
BRILLIANT! OUR WORKS COME OUT!
WOOD COLLECTION
MATERIAL COLLECTED FROM FOREST. WOOD WORKSHOP ALLOWS CHILDREN TO GET THEIR HANDS ON THE WOOD THEY COLLECTED.
WOOD PIECES

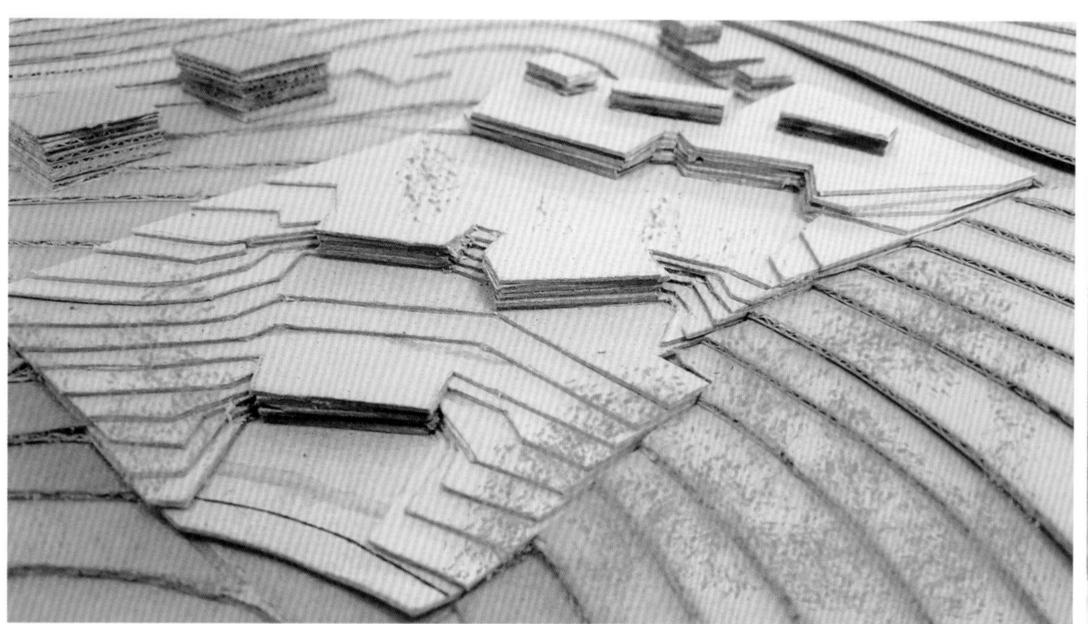

(top left) Patrycja Smola: *Into the Woods: Landscape Study Model*; *(top right)* Remi Kuforiji: *Eien No (Eternal): Landscape Study*; *(bottom)* Liu Wangyang: *Embracing Nature: Long Section*

(top left) Ugne Kiseliovaite: *Forest Gardens;* *(top right)* Francesca Benetti-Genolina: *Concrete Façade Studies;* *(bottom right)* Francesca Benetti-Genolina: *Story-telling Room*

Camilla Wilkinson & Emma Perkin

Camilla Wilkinson *is an architect and lecturer, who has worked in Germany and UK for leading architects Allies and Morrison, Sauerbruch & Hutton, Will Alsop. Her current research is into Dazzle Camouflage as Experimental Practice.*

Emma Perkin *is director of Emil Eve Architects and a co-founder of Voluntary Design & Build. She has worked in architecture practices in London, Paris and Edinburgh and taught at Edinburgh University and UCA.*

DS(2)5: Fun Palace Futures: Laboratory of Fun

Students: Gaia Buscemi, Ben Daughtry, Dominic Din, Aaron Fernandes, Danyal Goudarzirad, Adam Kramer, Miao (Owen) Lin, Andreas Makris, Aesha Mehta, Federico Minieri, Muhtasim Mojnu, Esi Plaku, Arshaq Rahim, Ramzi Ramzi, Robert Siggins, Remigijus Sliakonis, Cyrus Stephen-Smith, Youjung Won

'everyone an artist, or a scientist'

Joan Littlewood

WE TOOK THE programme for Polyark 4: Fun Palace Futures, as an opportunity for students to make connections between the brief – the communication of scientific research – and the process of experimentation in architectural design. We set two speculative projects:

1 Indoor Weather

A pavilion for Imperial Festival – a temporary pavilion housing a weather condition that enables scientists to engage the public in their area of scientific research.

2 Laboratory of Fun, Hackney Wick

A laboratory that spawns ancillary spaces for public use or laboratories that transform into public space.

Experimentation through making and drawing is central to the studio design process. Large scale experiential weather drawings, 1:20 structural concept models, and 1:50 sections were developed as ways to propose, test and communicate architectural ideas – before being refined into a more formal architectural language. We held tutorials in the café's of great buildings in London – and Paris. The Pompidou served as the nearest accessible experiment on the theme of movement and time in architecture and represented the Fun Palace for many of our students.

On our tour of research space at the Blizard Institute we learnt that nothing interesting comes out of a tidy laboratory.

Guest Critics:
Scott Batty, François Girardin, Clare Hamman, Samantha Hardingham, Will McLean, Ross Perkin, Catherine Phillips, Giles Smith, Mike Whitfield, Julian Williams, Fiona Zisch
From DS15: Ciaran Linane, Max Martin, Connor Page; *DS (3)1*: Fiona Tmava

Special thanks:
Imperial College and James Romero, Imperial College Research Events Officer, for inviting us to exhibit our Indoor Weather pavilion designs at Imperial Festival 2017;
Professor Denise Sheer, Blizard Institute, Queen Mary, University, London

Ben Daughtry, Miao Lin, Aesha Mehta, Muhtasim Mojnu, Esi Plaku, Robert Siggins, Youjung Won

LIBRARY

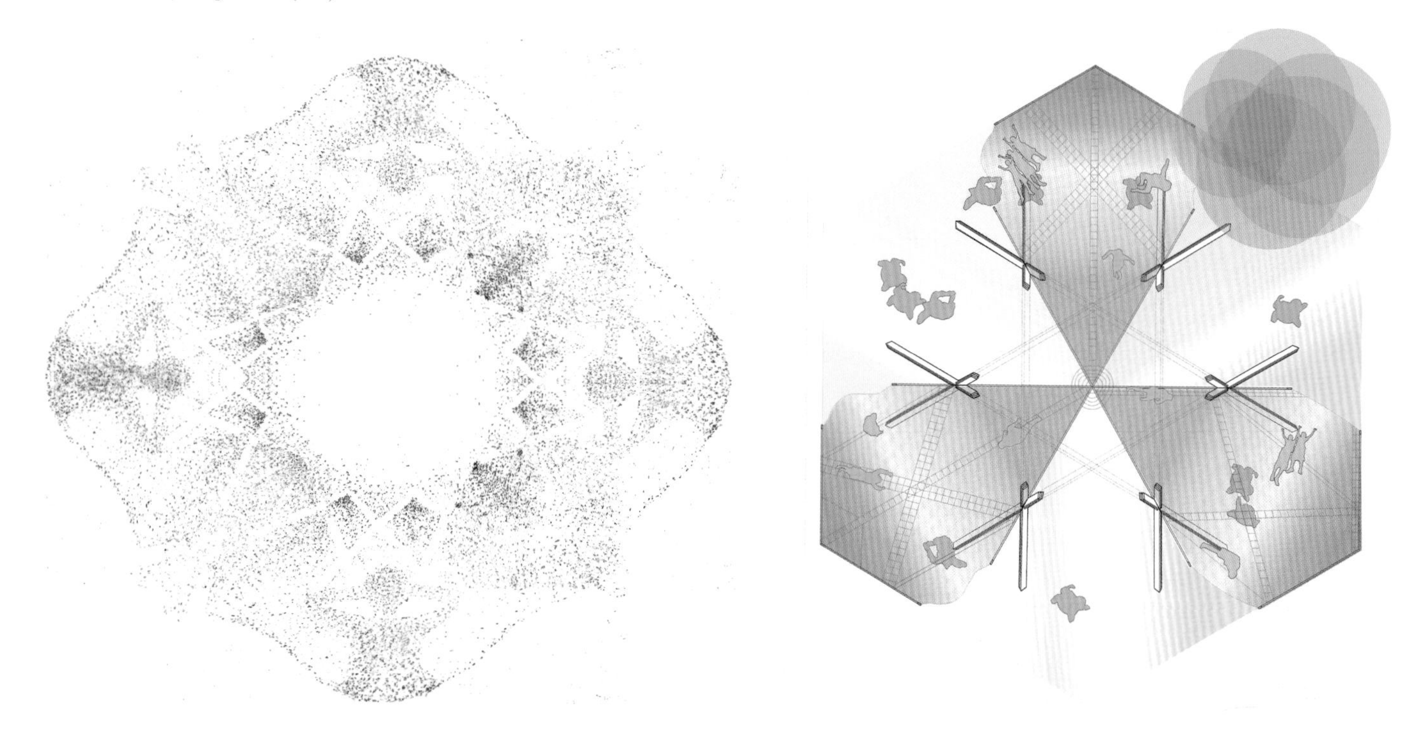

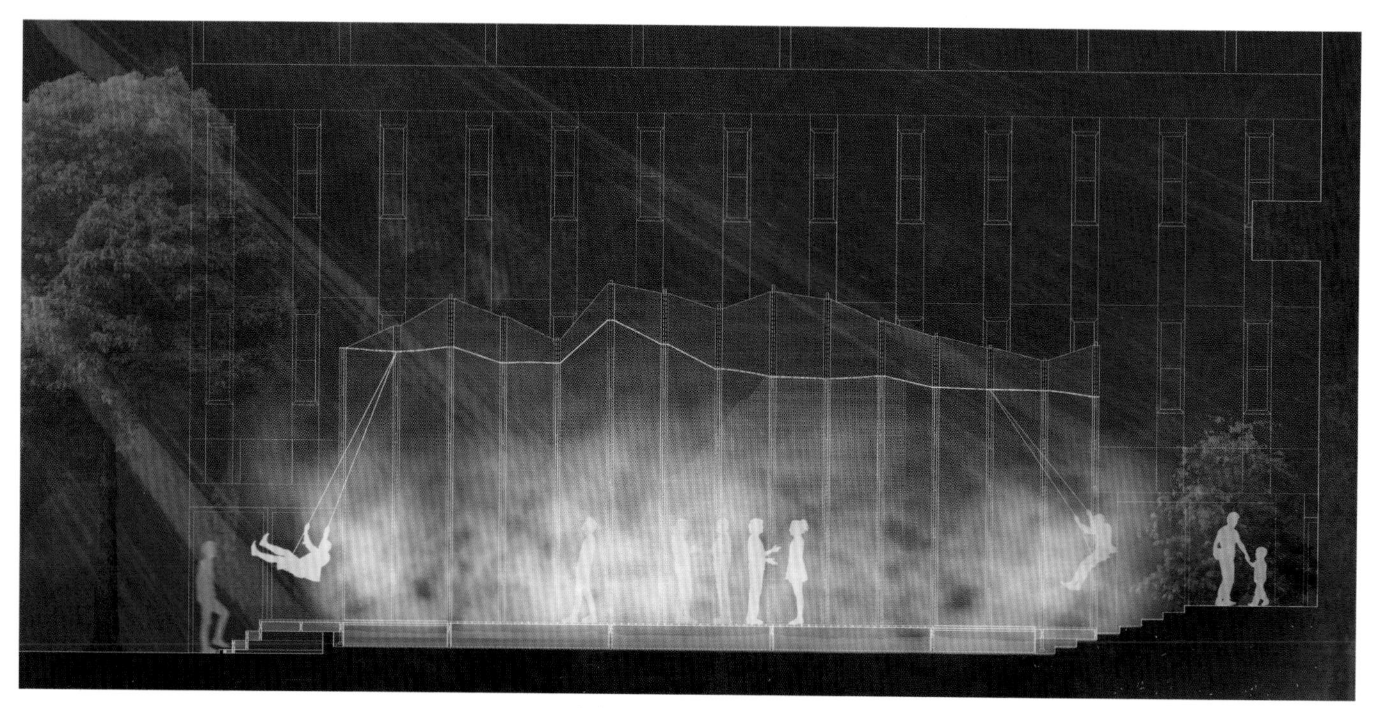

(top) Youjung Won: *Sunshine in Shadow Pavilion;* *(bottom)* Miao (Owen) Lin: *Fog Collector Pavilion*

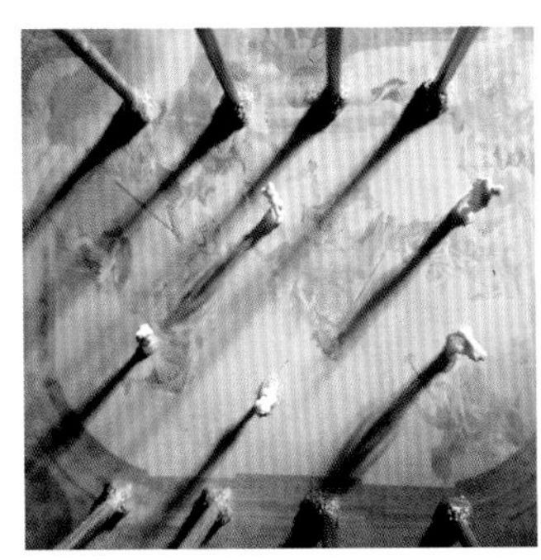

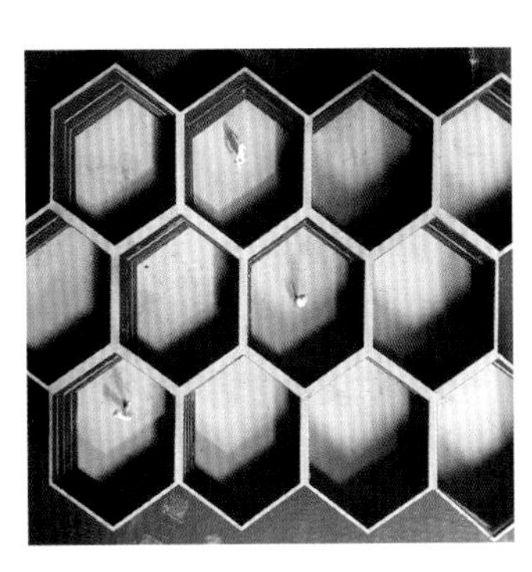

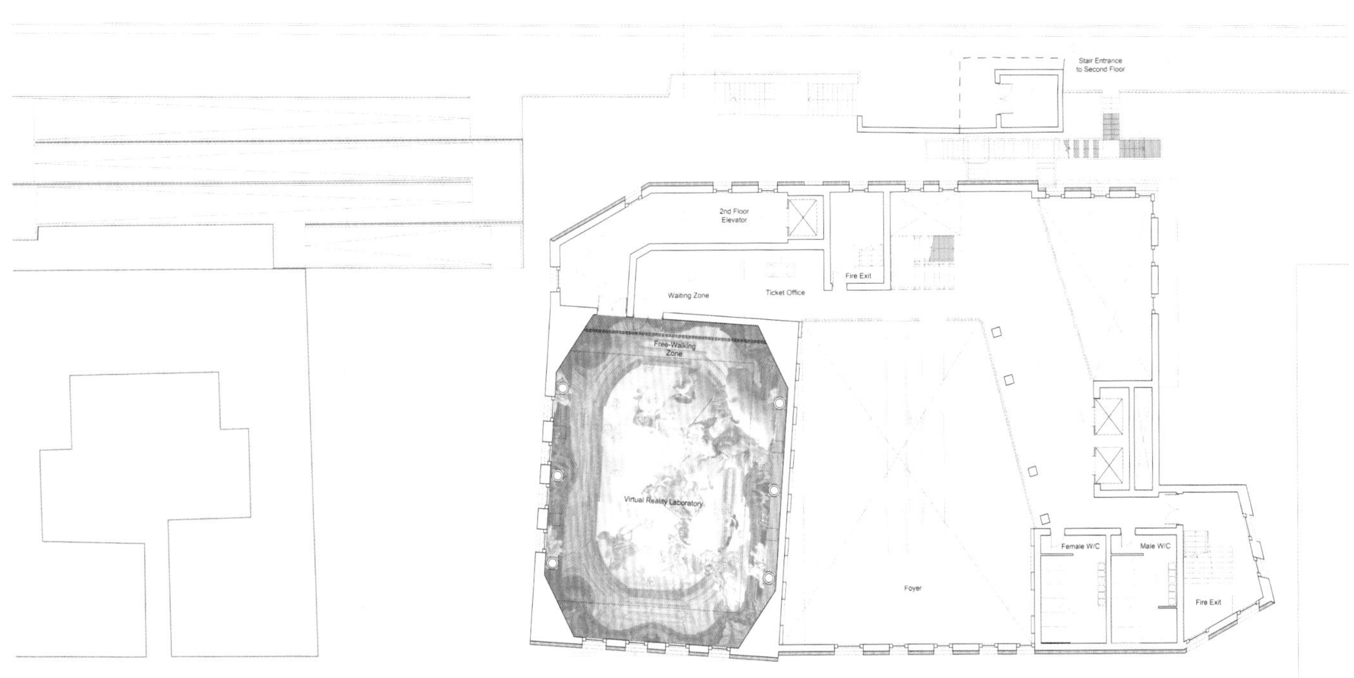

Muhtasim Mojnu: *The Mind Palace*

Stefania Boccaletti & Fiona Zisch

Stefania Boccaletti *studied, practised and taught Architecture in Italy, Canada, and England. Throughout her career as a practitioner and academic she has developed an interest in the impact of digital tools on the design and fabrication process in the field of architecture.*

Fiona Zisch *is completing a PhD in Architectural Design and Neuroscience at UCL and teaches at Westminster, Innsbruck, and the Bartlett. Her research focuses on experiential qualities and how the mind and brain construct internal worlds in relation to the external world.*

DS(2)6: Smart Spaces

Students: Bibissara Alpys, Nikola Babic, Anderson Barbosa Sales, Lyba Fatima, Thomas Grunberg, Dasha Illarionova, Zhangeldy Kaupynbayev, Dominyka Kybartaite, Amir Hamed Mahdianzad, Simon Mclanaghan, James Mould, Asile Mussa, Amir Noori, Pawel Obuchowski, Alexander Onufriev, Gilberto Paolucci, Alexander Roos, Diana Sacco, David Volodin, Drew Yates, Luka Ziobakaite

IN 2009 THE United Nations released a report announcing that the world's population will pass the 9 billion mark by 2050. Based on the same study, by 2030 60% of the world's population will live in cities: increasing urbanisation is inevitable. Considering that today's cities use two-thirds of the world's energy and are responsible for 70% of the world's CO_2 emissions, it is imperative that cities are designed as integrated, sustainable solutions for the production of energy, collection of water, and production and transportation of food and waste.

Design Studio (2)6 set out to investigate how agriculture can be inserted into highly urbanised areas as small-scale resource-saving systems. In the process of developing their designs, students queried both how urban agriculture has been transforming through the integration of new technologies and how to combine the myriad architectural requirements (e.g. responsive systems linking user and building, environment and building, and user and environment) with the needs, ambitions, and practicalities of 21st century food production.

During the first semester, students identified and developed these ideas through the design of a smart greenhouse. Proposals emerged first as abstract constructs integrating technologies already used in food production and spatial requirements. The final proposals were tested in Torrington Square, London. Students explored how different technologies could be combined to create new and complex spatial opportunities enabling the growth of crops in urban settings.

The second semester saw students further develop their research/theme and test it on more complex architectural proposals resulting in buildings housing start-up companies. The site was located in East London's Tech City. Through their proposals, students considered the relationship between the innovative production of food in an urban setting, new modes of production coming from its by-products, and the consumer's/public's experience, merging the artificial with the natural.

Guest Critics:
Panagiota Adilenidou, Constantina Avramides, Scott Batty, Tom Benson, Roberto Bottazzi, Mihai Chiriac, Francois Girardin, William Mclean, Adi Meyer, Laura Nica, Rosa Schiano-Phan, Julia Schütz, Cid Schuler, Calvin Sin

Special Thanks:
Clemens Plank and Philipp Zluga (Studio 2, Institut für Gestaltung, University of Innsbruck)

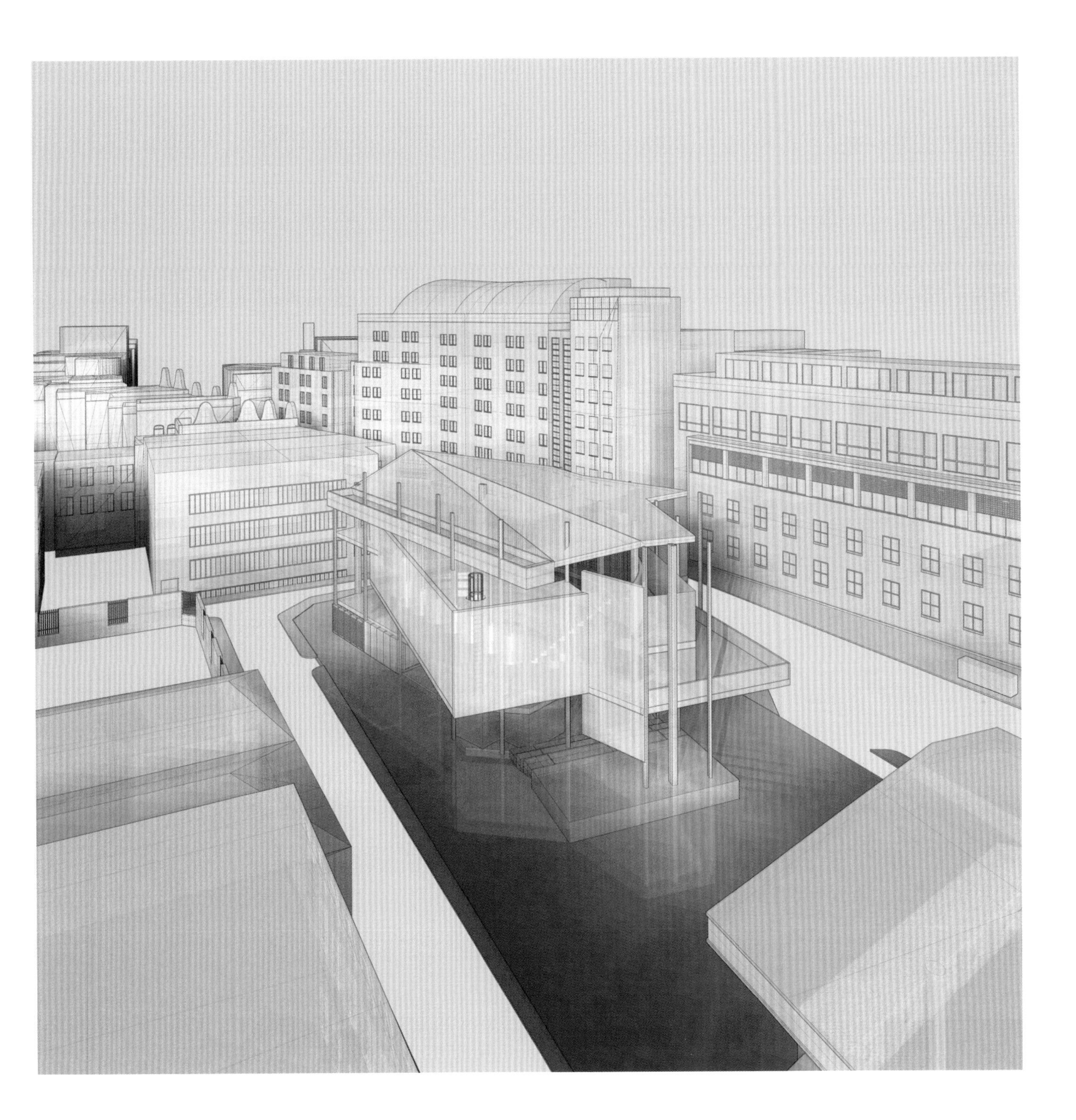

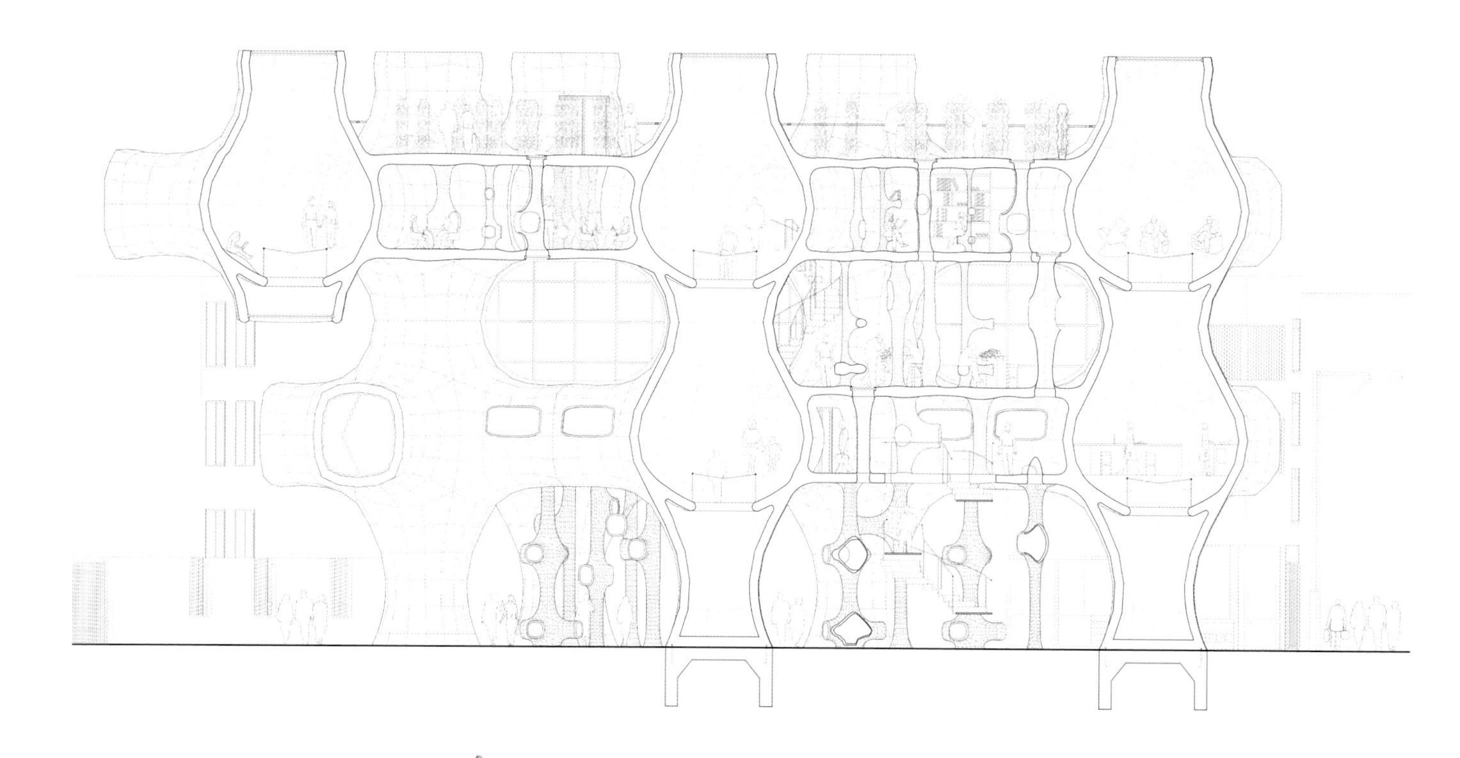

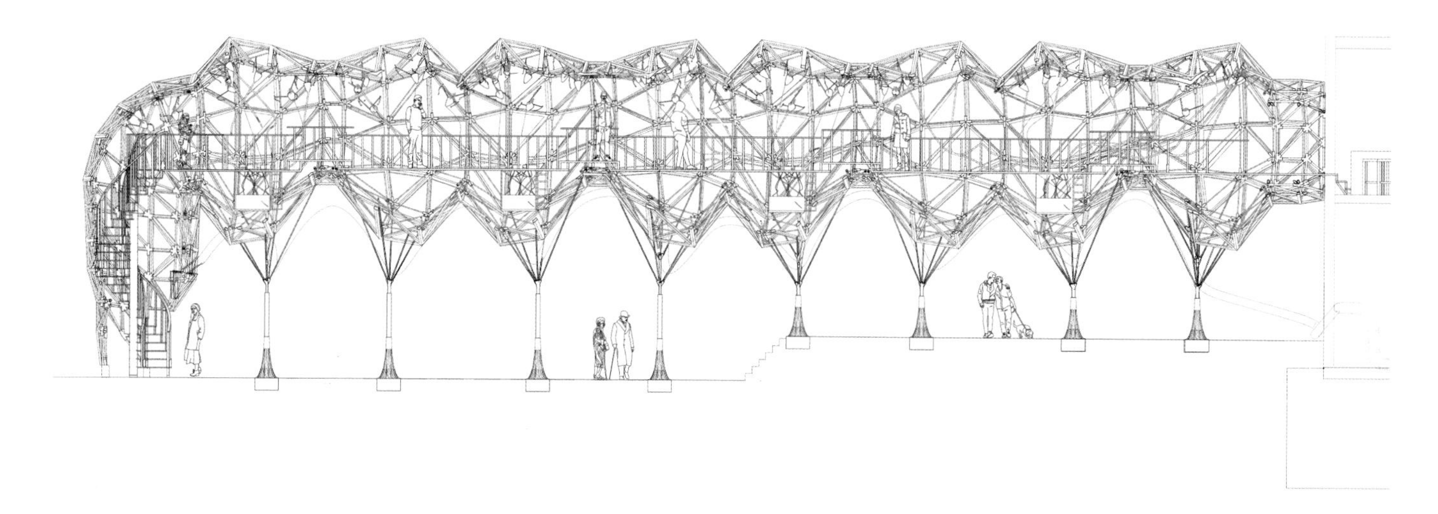

(top) Diana Sacco: *The Soy Clinic: An Alternative Health Centre*; *(bottom)* Drew Yates: *The Smart Greenhouse: Extension of the Department of Biological Sciences*

(top left) Drew Yates: *The Smart Greenhouse: Extension of the Department of Biological Sciences; (top right)* Bibissara Alpys: *B House: Research Centre for Children's Development; (bottom left)* Alexander Onufriev: *Spuds and Studs: A Self-sufficient Leisure Centre; (bottom right)* Luka Ziobakaite: *Soy Ink: An Alternative Publishing House*

Jane Tankard & Alicia Pivaro

Jane Tankard *is a full-time member of staff and BA Year 3 leader, studio supervisor for DS(3)1 and UG Professional Studies coordinator. A registered architect, she is particularly interested in architecture 'against the grain' and the relationship between space and politics. She is currently researching aspects of late 20th century architectural education.*

Alicia Pivaro *is an urbanist, artist, community activist and gardener. After training at the Bartlett, with an MSc in History of Modern Architecture she held a number of key positions at leading organisations: Arts Council of England, RIBA, and Architecture Foundation. She now teaches and crits at Westminster, CSM and LSA and promotes community-led urbanism.*

DS(3)1: Architecture + Anarchy

Students: Jadene Aguilar, Sheikh Tanim Ahmed, Ziadoon Azeez, Veronica Cappelli, Lai Chan, Simrath Diocee, Ioana Dumitrasc, Alison Edwards, Daniel Gee, Abdulrahman Hassan, Ronahi Kaplan, Myungin Lee, Eleanor Lucock, Ani Markova, Aikaterini Petsali, Maria Ribalaygua, Amirah Suhaimy, Janice Yee Tai, Fiona Tmava

THE NOTION THAT anarchy or self-determination has the potential to be central to architectural design and production was the focus of studio DS(3)1's explorations this year. Addressing the role of the architect and the representation of modernist ideology in film, we examined the dichotomy of a utopian ideal versus everyday life. By attempting to gain some understanding, through choreographic drawing and model-making, of the political and social contexts of post-war modernism, we began to develop a programmatic and representational language with which we might interrogate or inscribe the landscape of the city.

Our site, the 'Highgate Bowl' in North London, was until recently a left-over, secret, ad-hoc world of nature, and small- and low-scale activity. The local community has found themselves pitched against developers who want to build super-high spec houses for those who wish to buy into a world being eroded by the people who will sell them their dreams – at a price. Through research into local utopians – past and present – we unravelled narratives and histories that informed individual programmes for a landscape and museum/intervention that embodied the values of these visionaries; from Francis Bacon's New Atlantis to Ray Davies' lyrics.

In semester 2 each student determined their own programme, manifesto and architectural ambition. Using the utopian values identified in semester 1, and their landscape strategies as a masterplan, propositions were formulated for alternative developments for the Bowl with community, education and exchange central to their evolution. Using a series of cumulative multimedia drawings, print release and sketch models, along with an understanding of the local authority Unitary Development Plan, the design process manifested in propositions including experimental, high yield food production enabling The Good Life to become a reality, a sanctuary and memorial to the mothers and children forcibly separated at birth by the Nuns of St Pelagia's Convent, and a 'Forest School' for deaf and hearing children.

Guest Critics:
Michelle Barratt and Trevor Morriss (SPPARC Architects), Steve Bowkett,
Ben Brakspear Battle (McCarthy Architects), Georgie Day and Tim Rowson (FACtotum),
Tom Grove (Simon Bowden Architecture), Christos Kakouros, Maria Kramer

Special Thanks:
Paul Monaghan (AHMM)

Ani Markova: ***Utopia 1: Forest School***

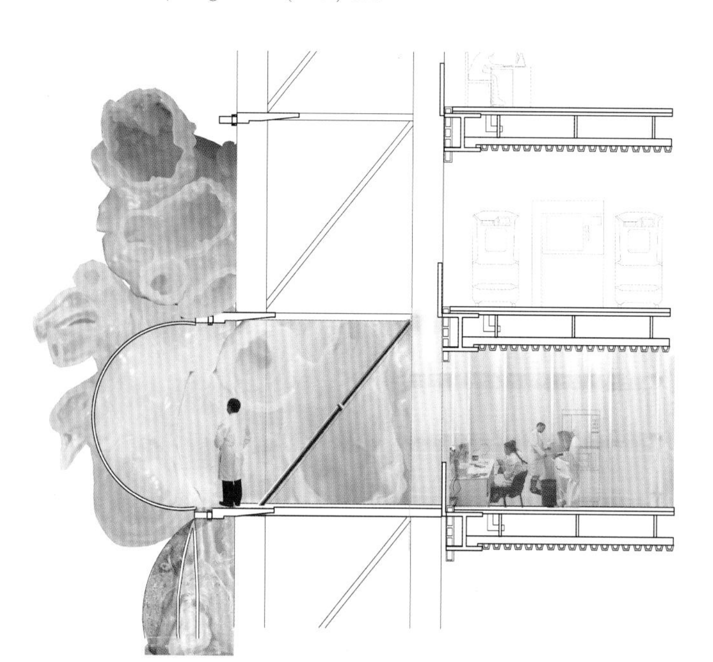

(top) Abdulrahman Hassan: *Utopia 3: Replacement Joint Factory*; *(bottom)* Jadene Aguilar: *Utopia 2: Off-grid Settlement for Homeless Teenagers*

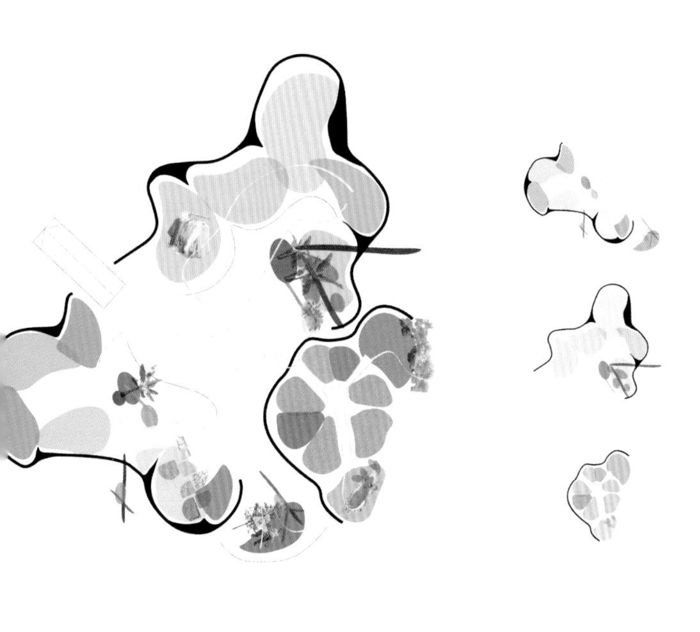

(top) Myung Lee: *Utopia 4: Sanctuary for Trafficked Domestic Slaves*

Alison Edwards: *Utopia 5: The Good Life: Tom and Barbara's 21st Century Utopian Settlement*

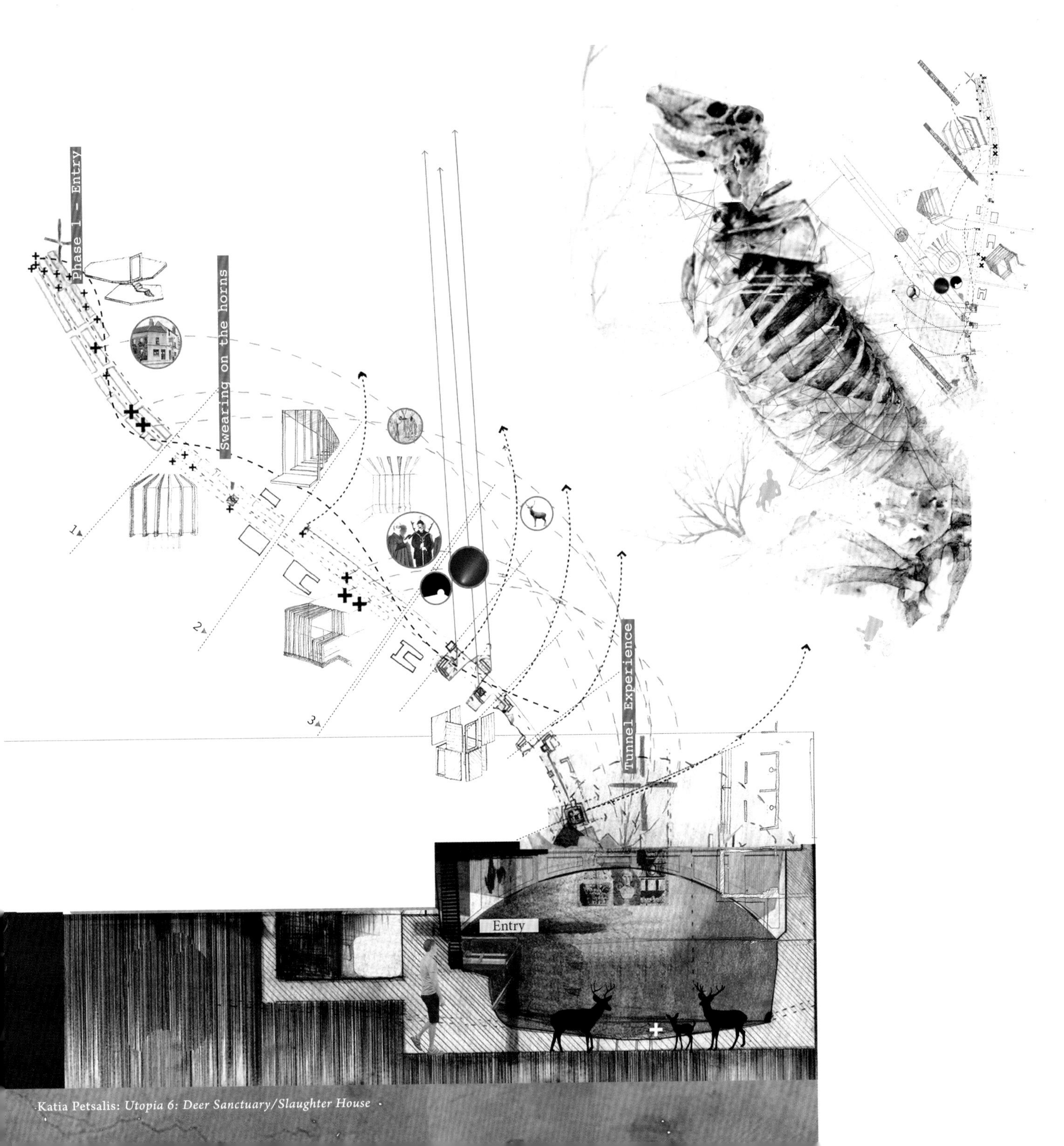

Katia Petsalis: *Utopia 6: Deer Sanctuary/Slaughter House*

Giles Smith & Anthony Engi Meacock

Anthony and Giles *are co-founders of the architectural collective Assemble. Founded in 2010 to undertake a single self-built project, Assemble won the Turner Prize in 2015 and has since delivered a diverse body of built, social and research-based work at a variety of scales.*

DS(3)2 *is obsessed with money: for the last three years the unit has been dedicated to exploring the relationship between architecture and capital. Our studio favours a critical realist approach: innovative responses to real-world issues, developed through a mixture of critical thinking and hands-on making.*

DS(3)2: Cultural Capital

Students: Sarah Ahmad, Sneha Baptista, Stefania Barbera, Lemar Darien-Campbell, Elisavet Dimitriou, Ilar Farrokhzad, Lucy Fincham, Jamie Goring, Emily Hadley, Magdalena Harmacinska, Matthew Jackson, Clovis Keuni, Marie Magnien, Borislav Merdzhanov, Hayden Mitchell, Tommaso Scarlato, Aleksandria Stosio, Anastasia Zabarsky, Rukhsar Zahid, Shirin Zhaparalieva

Coastal towns in the UK, with their crumbling infrastructure and social ills, need more to transform their futures than sparkly new vanity projects.[1]

THIS YEAR, WE'VE taken our interest in architecture and economics to the English seaside. That forever nostalgic land of soft-serve, soggy chips, and steely swimming in icy, grey water.

The coast has suffered a precipitous decline, with local industries dwindling and indigenous tourists abandoning Margate for Magaluf. Coastal towns now form many of the most deprived areas in the UK: modern poverty within fading Victorian grandeur.

The previous Labour government sought to alleviate this by transporting the policy of culture-led regeneration from our city centres to our coastal resorts. Towns from Southend to Southampton have spent the last decade chasing Richard Florida's 'Bilbao Effect'. But do these capital injections into 'culture' result in sustainable change experienced across the demographic spectrum, or are we just expanding a displacement-led model of gentrification?

This year we took Margate as our site in order to explore this relationship between coastal capital and coastal culture, and the distinctive architecture that these both generate. Working from a highly situated reading of the town, we developed projects to question the current policy of culturally-led redevelopment.

These propose a series of new models of (creative) industries, ranging from housing for old-age entrepreneurs through to a basketball academy for Margate's disenfranchised youth.

Bring your bucket and spade, raincoats and critical thinking, we're going to the seaside.

[1] Tracy McVeigh, 'Where are the real towering ambitions to help coastal towns?' *The Observer*, August 2016

Guest Critics:
James Binning, Stefania Boccaletti, Shumi Bose, Roberto Bottazzi, Coyan Cardenas, Clare Carter, Oli Chambers, Matthieu Courtade, Amica Dall, Alice Edgerley, James Green, Jane Hall, Phineas Harper, Alexander Hills, Chris Kennedy, Chee Kit Lai, Mathew Leung, Morgan Lewis, Maria Lisogorskaya, Daniel Marmot, Max Martin, Manon Mollard, Alice Moxley, Ed Ponti, Kester Rattenbury, Tom Raymont, Fiona Stewart, Ben Stringer, Marcus Todd, Emma Tubbs, Elly Ward, Percy Weston, Julian Williams

Special Thanks:
Sam Causer, Chris Hibbert, Niall Hobhouse, Andy Mason, Molly Molloy, Terry Pinto, Rick Stewart, Geoff Stow, Tim Trevenna

Marie Magnien: *Ashtray*

(top) Stefania Barbera: *The Guild of Crafts; (bottom)* Jamie Goring: *Community Bounce*

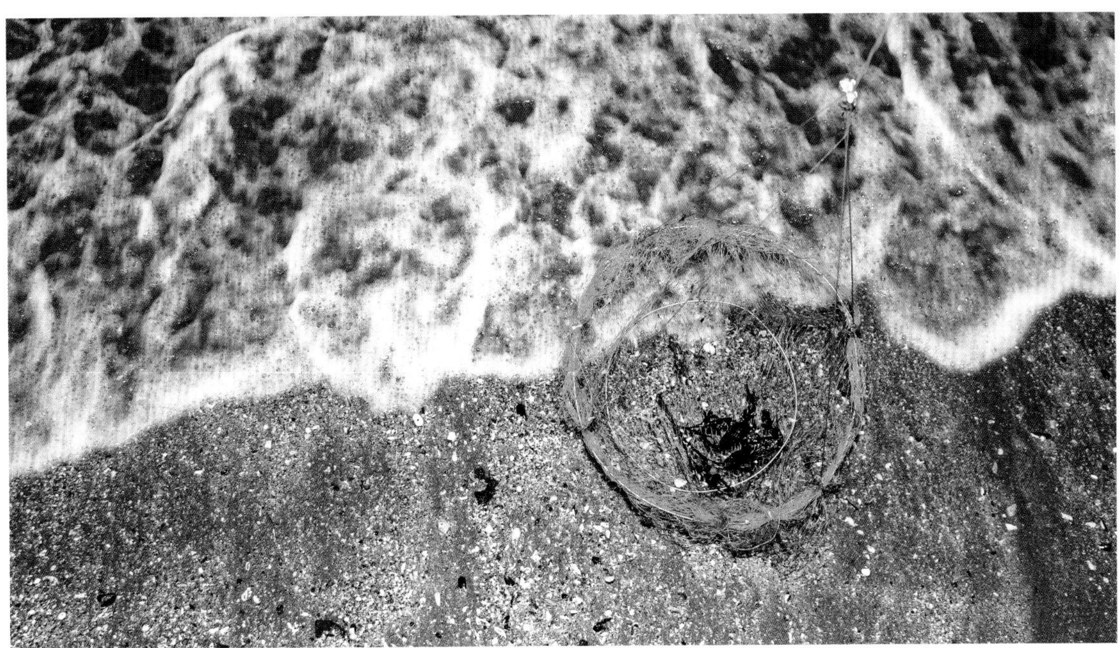

(top left) Emily Hadley: *Club Culture;* *(top right)* Marie Magnien: *Hotel Margate;* *(bottom)* Sneha Baptista: *Sea Forager's Tool*

(top) Lucy Fincham: *Marcade;* *(bottom)* Shirin Zhaparalieva: *Market Play Park*

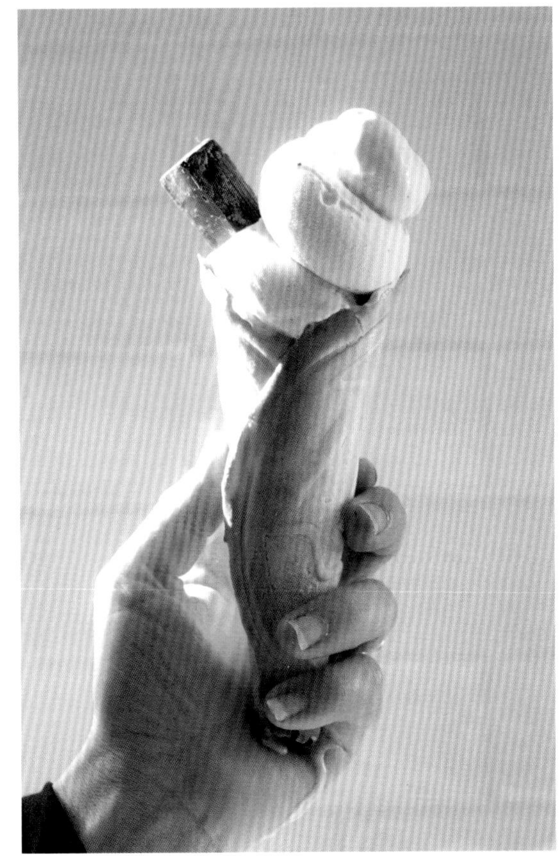

(top) Aleks Zabarsky: *Urban Agriculture College;* *(bottom left)* Matt Jackson: *In With the Old;* *(bottom right)* Hayden Mitchel: *Margate Cone*

Constance Lau & Alison McLellan

Constance Lau *practices and teaches architecture in London and Singapore. The studio's research interests in multiple interpretations and narratives are explored through the techniques of montage as well as notions of allegory. Narrative as an ongoing dialogue in architectural design is further articulated through projects in the book* Dialogical Designs *(2016).*

Alison McLellan *teaches and practices architecture. She founded Form_art Architects having worked with internationally acclaimed practices Stirling Wilford and Stanton Williams. Delivering museums, galleries, visitor and performing art centres, teaching is a natural continuation of Form_art's work with artists and galleries, namely their current engagement with the Tate.*

DS(3)3: The Techniques of Montage

Students: Ali Bash-Imam, Patricia Bob, Neophytos Christou, Shahriar Doha, Esra Gonen, Emma Hartley, Harry Hughes, Andreea Istratescu, Humaira Keshtmand, Enioreoluwa Majekodunmi, Wilza Silva Mendes, Deren Mustafa, Kyu Sung Pai, Lara Saad, Bisher Tabbaa, Na-Pat Tengtrirat, Martin Vasilev, Lukas Virketis, Khoa Minh Vo, Lucy Wellman

IN *THE OPEN WORK*, Umberto Eco discusses the capacity for user intervention to shape the reading of the work.[1] This concept is also demonstrated in Walter Benjamin's *The Arcades Project*, described as 'the blueprint for an unimaginably massive and Labyrinthine architecture'.[2]

These ideas and arguments inform the studio's interest in multiple interpretations, and especially the search outside architecture to inspire architectural design. The architectural narrative is further constructed as a design tool to integrate the different facets of research material during the working process.

First semester's **Building the Arnolfini** explores the complex use of signifiers and perspective views by Jan van Eyck to portray the apparent narrative of a wedding. In pursuit of 'openness' this geographical, cultural and site-specific portrait was explored through the notion of an architectural montage where different readings radiate from a singular source. This created infinite opportunities for the work to be completed by the user.

The argument for different ways to approach the reading and meaning of a piece of work is furthered in semester two's **Artefice and Artefact**. While the provenance of the Arnolfini portrait appears straightforward, this trajectory is not shared by many of the British Museum's acquisitions. In this instance, ideas of ownership, authorship as well as the accommodation and display of highly contested items are explored. Hence the way the host is perceived is as important as the understanding of the artefacts which includes conventional concepts of 'protector', as well as the United Kingdom's post-Brexit image. The argument that 'there is always a history of drawings, objects and buildings within and against which an architectural work can be seen' is important.

These readings allow the proposals for a new museum typology to address the ensuing shifts in the current disparate landscape of the British Museum's chronologically, geographically and culturally displaced items.

[1] Umberto Eco, *The Open Work*, trans. by Anna Cancogni (Cambridge, Mass.: Harvard University Press, 1989).

[2] Walter Benjamin, *The Arcades Project*, ed. by Rolf Tiedeman, trans. by Howard Eiland and Kevin McLaughlin (Cambridge, Mass. and London: Belknap Press of Harvard University Press, 1999). Eiland, 'Translators' Foreword', in *The Arcades Project*, pp. iv–xiv (p. viiii).

Guest Critics:
Alessandro Ayuso, Harry Paticas (Arboreal Architecture),
Loreta Lukoseviciene (Edward Williams Architects)

Special Thanks:
Sotirios Varsamis (Coventry University), Kyriakos Eleftheriadis

Na-Pat Tengtrirat: *The Depository of The Society of Architectural Historians of Great Britain*

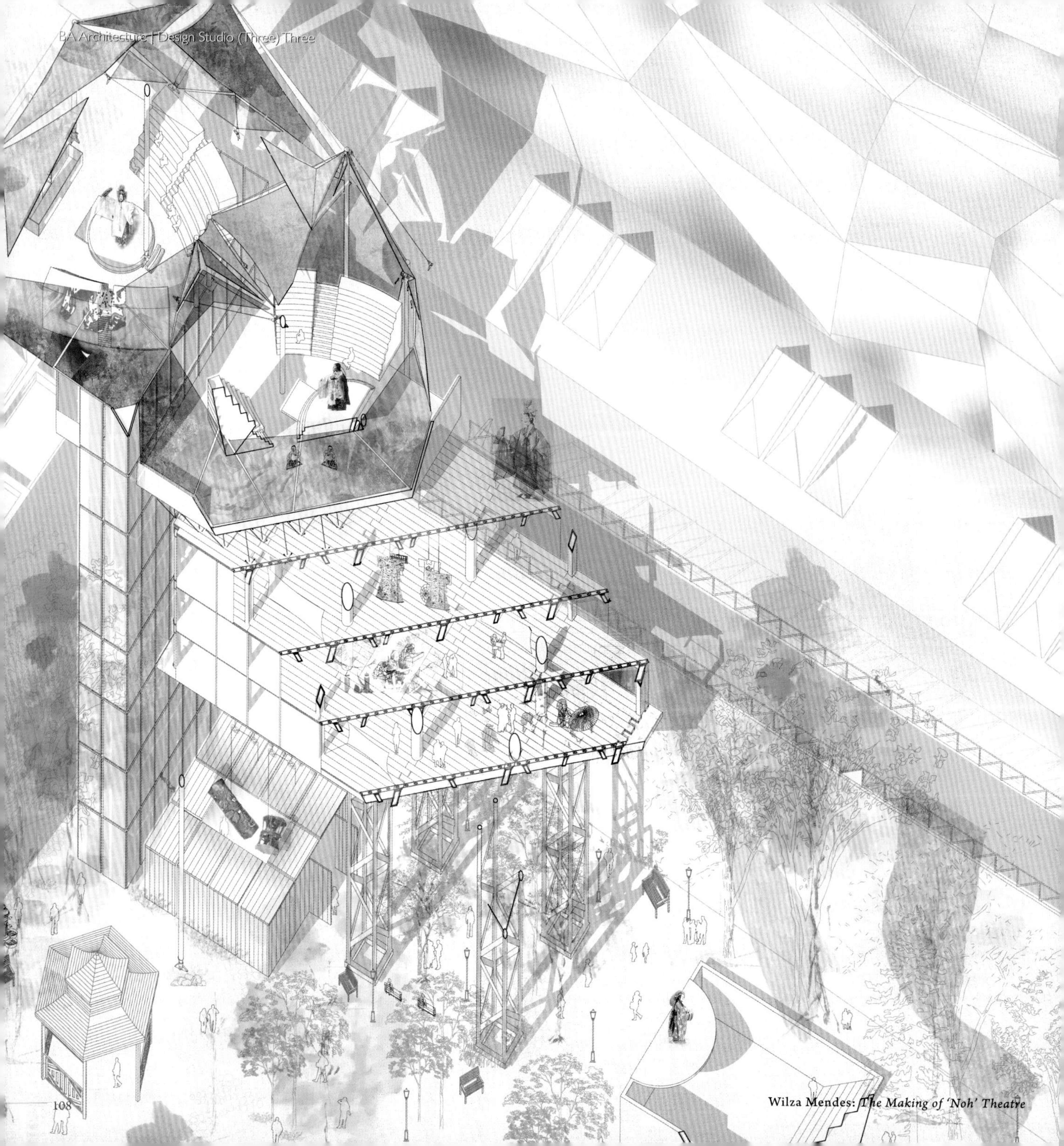

Wilza Mendes: *The Making of 'Noh' Theatre*

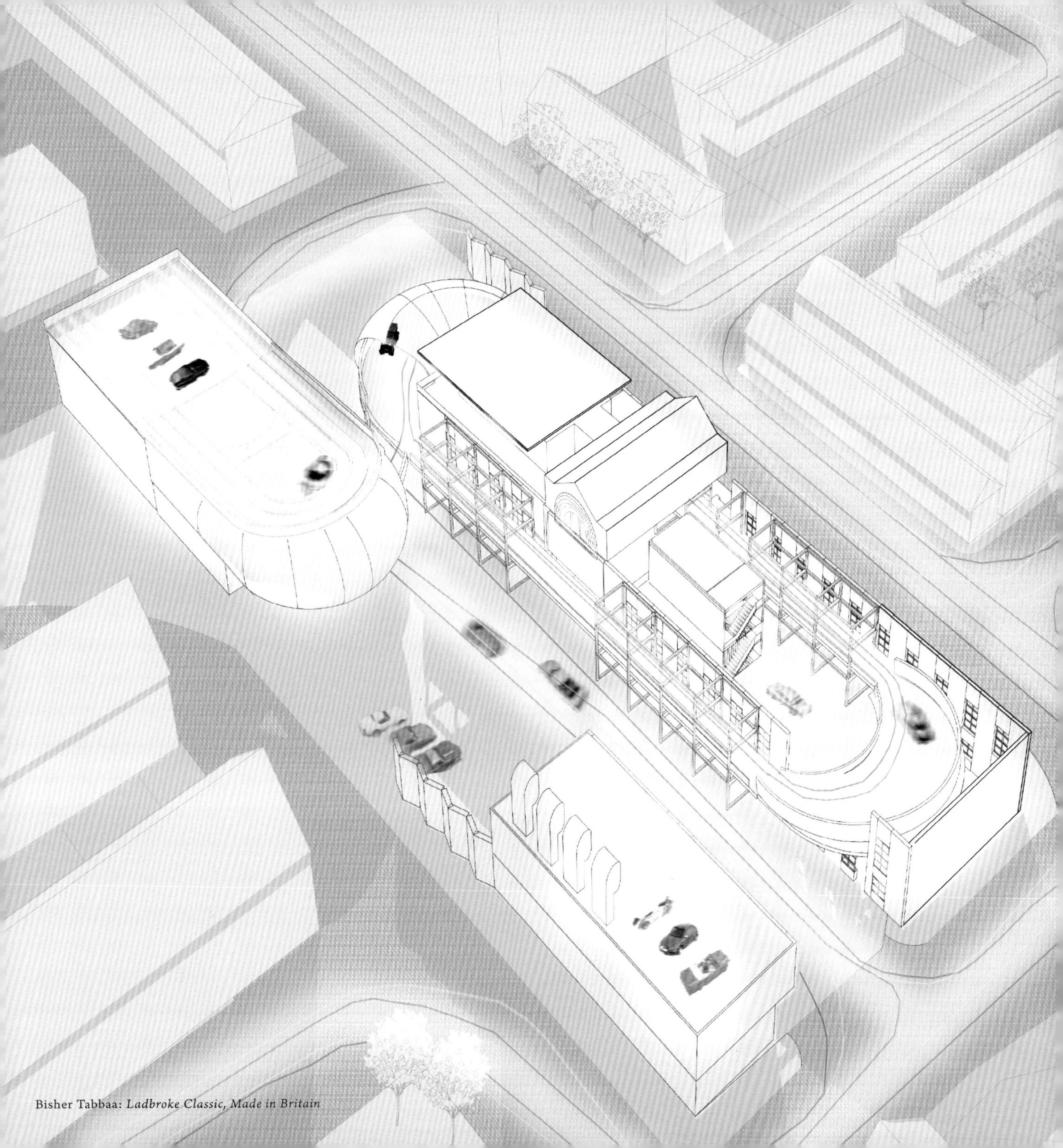

Bisher Tabbaa: *Ladbroke Classic, Made in Britain*

(this page) **Enioreoluwa Majekodunmi:** ***The Plant Museum;*** *(opposite)* **Emma Hartley:** ***Soane's Chandelier***

Elly Ward & Jonny Fisher

Our studio *is interested in cultural identity, British-ness and popular contemporary culture. Elly's practice focuses on cultural projects and she has recently designed exhibitions for the V&A at the Venice Biennale 2016 and the Royal Academy along with a number of public art installation projects in Los Angeles. Jonny is a fully qualified architect with over 15 years experience as a designer and project manager working on a variety of both large- and small-scale residential, commercial and public realm projects.*

DS(3)4: Island State Of Mind

Students: Zahraa Al-Subeiti, George Davies, Safia Gay, Kiril Georgiev, Joe Hyman, Sooyeon Jeong, Anisha Kureembukus, Chris McManigan, Sana Mir, Anis Mohamad Khairi, Jade Newman, Zoe Okuns, Mohammud Salamut, Fatema Sulemanji, Asa Vassallo

IN JUNE 2016, the UK voted to detach both physically and philosophically from the EU with no clear idea how this island nation would continue to operate without collaboration with our European counterparts.

In response to this lack of a manifesto, our studio has spent a year speculating on how the future of British architecture might look in a post-Brexit Britain. Together, we considered the concept of A Nation at Sea, the Edge Condition, and how statements such as 'Taking Back Control' and 'Making Britain Great Again' impact on debate and our cultural frame of reference.

Collectively we undertook a critique of contemporary exemplar British architecture and each student became an expert in one particular building category. We curated a Great British Expo, and designed exhibition pavilions to test initial ideas.

We then embarked on a contemporary Grand Tour of Europe in search of art, culture and contemporary Western civilisation, to discover, explore, exchange and steal ideas for our speculative designs. Back in the UK, we continued our quest for cultural exchange and searched for ways to maintain and nurture cultural relationships with other nations in a post-Brexit Britain.

Finally, students developed a series of significant architectural proposals for the appropriation of a major redevelopment at Silvertown Quays in the Royal Docks, London. The history of the Royal Docks is embedded in global trade and exchange. When it opened in 1855, the Victoria Dock was the largest man-made expanse of water in the world and one of the great visionary schemes of the Victorian era.

Silvertown Quays is now set to become a new gateway for the UK, shaped by its transformative heritage embedded in global trade and the rapidly changing needs of the modern city. It will be a place for contemporary cultural exchange, to offer opportunities for visitors to trade with local workers and residents through exemplary new architectural typologies of the future through these projects.

Guest Critics:
Laura Allen (Smout Allen), Peter Allen (Platform 5 Architects), Amanda Callaghan (aLL Design), Phil Coffey (Coffey Architects), Ed Crooks (Royal College of Art), Emma Elston (Project Orange), Alex Ely (Mae Architects), Ioana Gherghel, Saba Ghorbanalinejad (Duggan Morris Architects), Glykeria Gkoudkoudi (Studio Gkoudkoudi), Wayne Head (Curl La Tourelle Head Architects), Timo Heidrich (Haptic Architects), Elena Lledo (Duggan Morris Architects), Claire McKeown (Platform 5 Architects), Joe Morris (Duggan Morris Architects), Sam Page (UCL), Polina Pencheva (Duggan Morris Architects), Alicia Pivaro, Sanna Rautio (DMA), Giles Smith (Assemble), Jane Tankard, Tom Wilkinson (Architectural Review)

Special Thanks:
Brendan Cormier (Victoria & Albert Museum)
Finn Williams (Greater London Authority)
Charlotte Béasse (BHSF Architekten)

Jade Newman: ***Conceptual Study 'Freedom of Movement'***

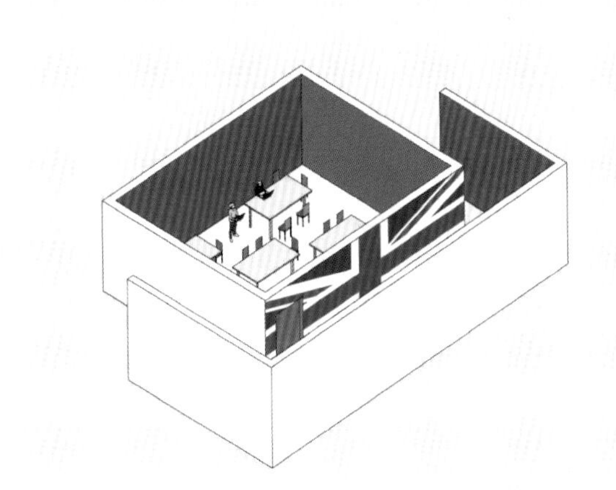

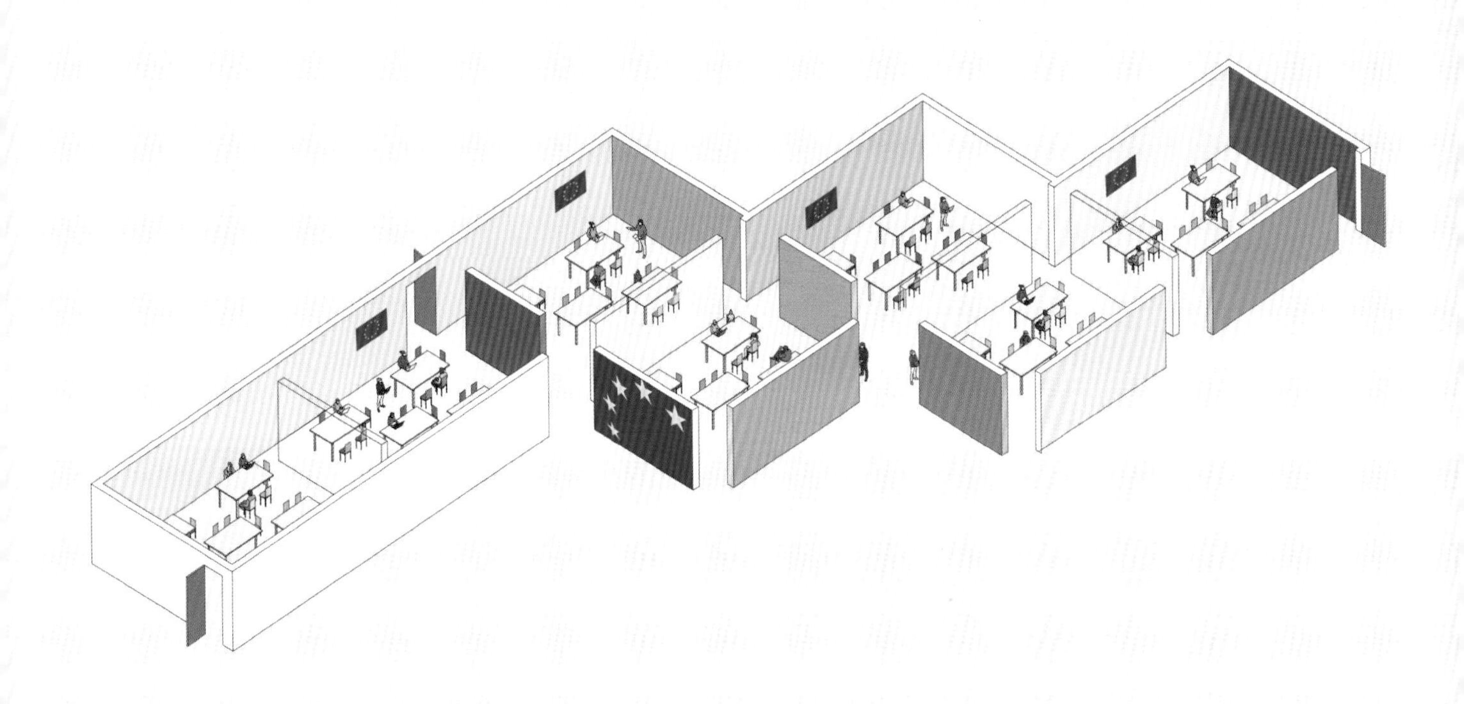

(top) Joe Hyman: *Cultural Appropriation Study 'The Many Manifestations of Nefertiti'*;
(bottom) Anis Mohamad Khairi: *Cultural Appropriation Study 'Elevational Possibilities'*

Zahraa Al-Subeiti: *Site of Cultural Exchange 'The Life Cycle Community Market Place'*

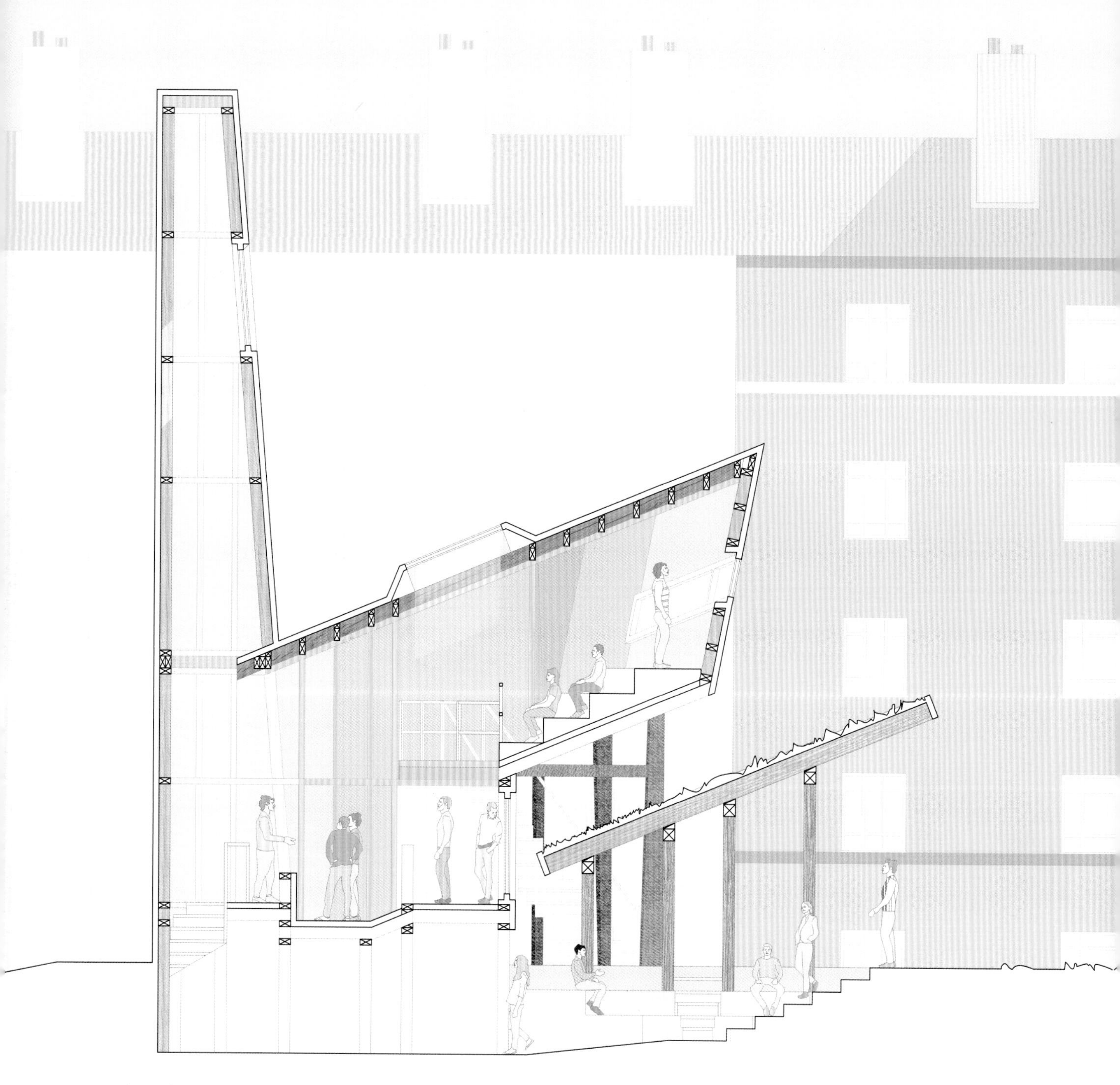

(*this page*) Chris McManigan: *Site of Cultural Exchange 'Cyclical Ideas Debating Pavilion'*; (*opposite*) Kiril Georgiev: *Site of Cultural Exchange 'The People's Lido'*

Bruce Irwin & Catherine Phillips

Bruce Irwin *studied art and architecture at the Bartlett and Rhode Island School of Design and has lived and worked in New York and London. His practice combines design, teaching and curating.*

Catherine Phillips *studied architecture at the Bartlett and Manchester University, and art at City and Guilds of London Art School. Her practice combines architecture, teaching and art.*

DS(3)5: Fleeting Encounters

Students: Justine Aguilar, Cassandra (Thuong) Duong, Vicky Carrillo Mullo, Denitza Dimitrova, Cristina Gelagotellis, Daniel Gloambes, Maciej Jungerman, Evita Katsiani, Darina Keane, Natalie Klak, Esther Medina Llamas, Yianna Moustaka, Ksenitza Pejovic, Christos Sevastides, Sandra Sidarous, Urna Sodnomjamts, Vicky Theocharous, Elina Zampetakis, Xingyu Zhou

When I start, my first idea for a building is with the material. I believe architecture is about that. It's not about paper, it's not about forms. It's about space and material.

Peter Zumthor

One can say that the city itself is the collective memory of its people, and like memory it is associated with objects and places. The city is the locus of the collective memory.

Aldo Rossi

WHAT IS THE relationship between urban form, material memory and public space? If time is embedded in material, form and use, what does erasure allow or leave out? London development favours a blank slate, a site cleared of all trace of prior occupation, particularly at a large scale. This is an economic reality, but entails a form of forgetting. What happens when a city loses what it physically was? Is there an alternative?

During 2016/17 DS(3)5 investigated two London sites on the Grand Union Canal – in Camden Town at Castlehaven Road and at Corbridge Crescent adjacent to Mare Street and Cambridge Heath Road. One of these sites has been largely erased and is currently undergoing high density development; the other is under threat of erasure.

Our studio practice proposed procedures of artistic investigation – drawing, printmaking, sculpting, shaping – to help bridge the gap between material research and practice, and between intuition and analysis. Themes of process and iterative/series work were emphasised and encouraged. Students developed and expanded skills of visual, spatial and material reasoning.

In Term 1 each student defined a personal brief around investigations of site history and form, and informed by a specific material research.

In Term 2, working over layered site maps and informed by observation, research and intuition, students expanded this research to include wider social and community topics based on individual observation and site discoveries.

Guest Critics:
Luísa Alpalhão, Dinah Bornat, Oscar Brito, Carlos Jimenez Cenamor, Tristram Fetherstonhaugh, Marco Godoy, Samantha Lee, Francois Lefranc, Hwei Fan Liang, Angela Marquito, Sol Perez Martinez, Patrick Morris, Edward McCann, Nic Tuft, Keith Winter

Special Thanks:
Phillip Springall, Omar Manshi

Ksenija Pejovic: *Axonometric Massing Study, Camden Town*

PRIVATE
ENTRANCE
PUBLIC
ENTRANCE
CAMDEN HIGH

(top) Natalie Klak: *Corbridge Crescent Yoga Centre Section*; *(bottom left)* Natalie Klak: *Interior View, Section Model Studies*; *(bottom right)* Maciej Jungerman: *Theatre*

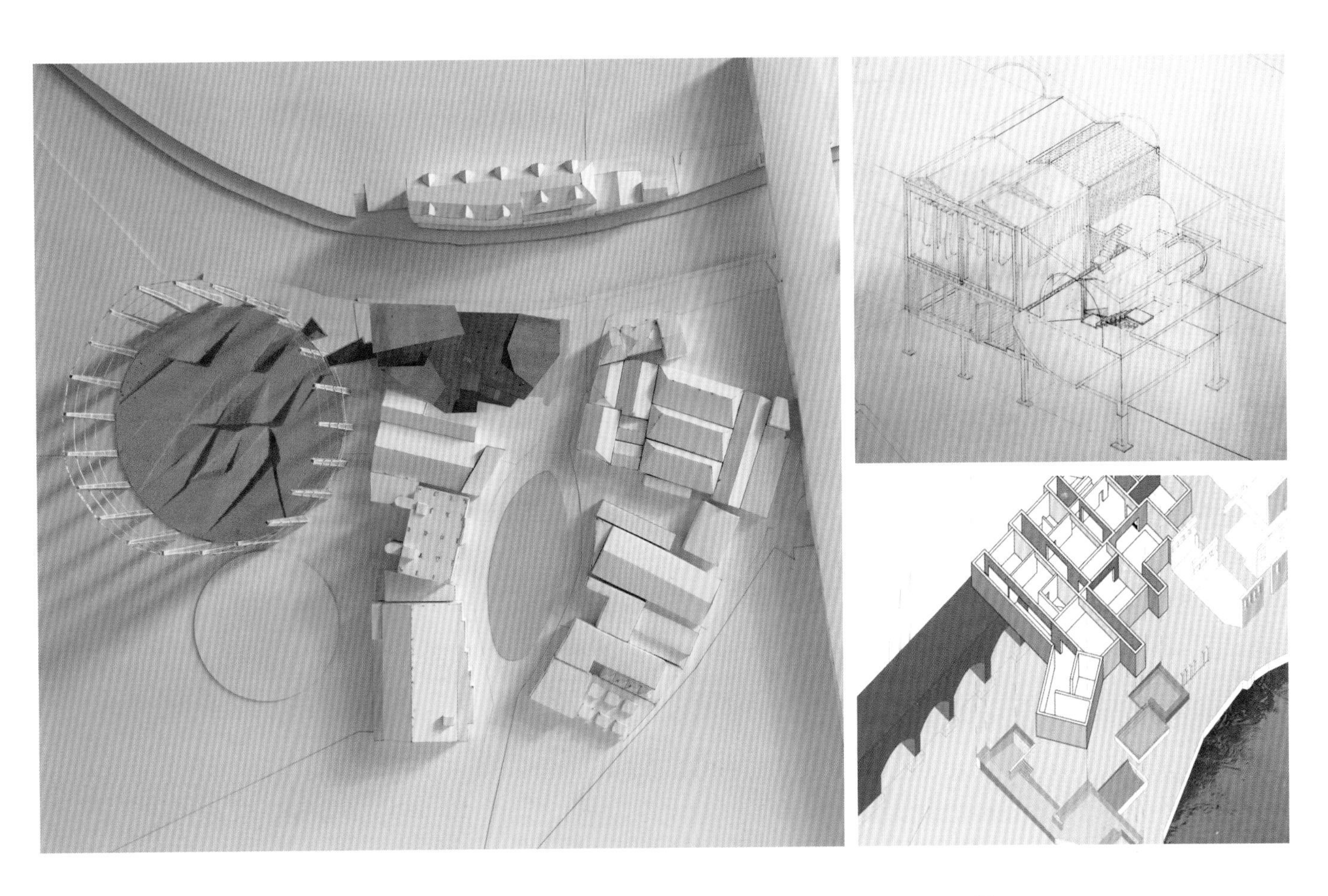

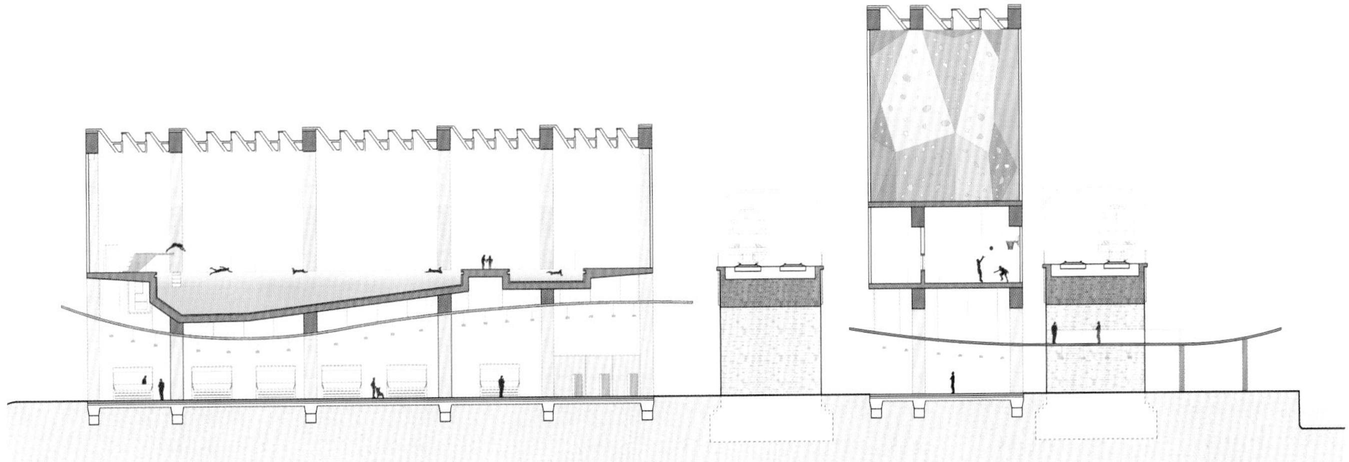

(top left) Elina Zampetakis: *Inhabited Landscape: Film Studios + Park*; *(top right)* Christina Gelagotellis: *Paper Research Studio*; *bottom)* Sandra Sidarous: *Camden Town Swimming Pool + Market*; *(centre right)* Uangua Sodnomjamts: *Camden Baths Spa*

(top) Christos Sevastides: *Corbridge Crescent Student Housing*; *(bottom)* Darina Keane: *Camden Arts Centre*

(top) Xingyu Zhou: *Camden Dance School*; (centre) Paraskevi Katsiani: *Camden Photographic Archive*; (bottom) Esther Medina Llamas: *Camden Studio Residency*

Harry Paticas & Tom Raymont

Harry Paticas and Tom Raymont *are directors of Arboreal Architecture, an ecological architecture practice that combines high technical performance with engaging spatial experiences of built and natural environments. Their work spans across the usual barriers between natural and man-made systems to envision a unified future free from waste, carbon emissions and non-renewable energy sources. Their projects have won awards for innovative use of timber construction, exemplary building performance and ecological retrofit of historic buildings.*

DS(3)6: Regenerative Habitats

Yr3: Aftab Ahmed, Deep Balloo, Jessie Bath, Josh Corden, Tudor Cristescu, Alberto De Castro, Ana Diaconu, Allaster Grant, Ola Hjelen, Carla Hora, Amad Hussain, Ronahi Kaplan, Robert Rusu, Maryam Saleemi, Felix Thiodet, Wan Wong , Yagmur Yurtbulmus

WE BEGAN THIS academic year in Epping Forest and ended it in the woods of Punkaharju, Finland. Along the way we discovered the forest as a complex ecosystem, a regenerative source of building material and a repository of cultural, mythical and design narratives.

In semester one students proposed an intervention into the woodland at The Sustainability Centre in Hampshire that enhanced the habitat for one particular species as well as bringing human beings into closer, more mutualistic relationships with that animal. Projects sought to reintroduce rare or extinct species such as the red squirrel or lesser spotted woodpecker and provide ways to observe and interact with them for either scientific or educational purposes. Others found ways to juxtapose animal and human activities, such as the lifecycle of butterflies bringing a sense of transitory beauty to a funerary chapel.

In semester two students returned to London and turned their Naturalists' lenses on to the Doon Street car park site behind the National Theatre. Here they re-imagined London as a regenerative city, creating communal dwellings that worked to renew and restore the ecosystems that underpin London's existence. Their projects proposed architecture as a dynamic process (rather than a commodified product) defining the narratives of where materials come from, how they are used, how they decay and can then be reprocessed in industrial or biological metabolisms.

We concluded the year in the Punkaharju Forests of Finland where we spent nine days collectively designing and building a timber shelter with the architect Sami Rintala. We built by hand with no power tools, using wood cut from the forest nearby, to produce an intimately site-specific, permanent public gathering place. This small building forms part of the Mobile Home project organised by The Finnish Institute in support of the Finland 100 celebrations.

Guest Critics:
Oscar Brito, Harry Charrington, Peter Corbett (Corbett & Tasker), Gary Grant (Green Infrastructure), Sophia Gravina, Nick Hayhurst (Hayhurst & Co), Martha Lagess (Lama Studio), Constance Lau, Michael McNamara (Lama Studio), Anthony Meacock (Assemble), Michael Pawlyn (Exploration Architecture), Yaneev Peer (Exploration Architecture), Greg Ross, Giles Smith (Assemble), John Zhang

Special Thanks:
Harry Charrington, Eero Knaapi (Lusto Forest Museum, Finland), May Mackeith, Kara Moses (Rewild Everything), Niklas Nabb (The Finnish Institute), Sean Reeves (The Sustainability Centre), Sami Rintala (Rintala Eggertsson), Christine Seaward (The Sustainability Centre), Richard Shackleton (British Embassy, Helsinki), Pauliina Ståhlberg (The Finnish Institute), The forests of Punkaharju, Finland

Group Construction Project to Build a Timber 'Laavu' in Finland (Photo: Ola Hjelen)

Top roof layer
Lower roof layer
Horizontal nailing boards for roof attachment
Roof beams
Chamfered edgeboard surrounding the hearth
Floor boards
Fishscale wall with horizontal cladding boards
Seating

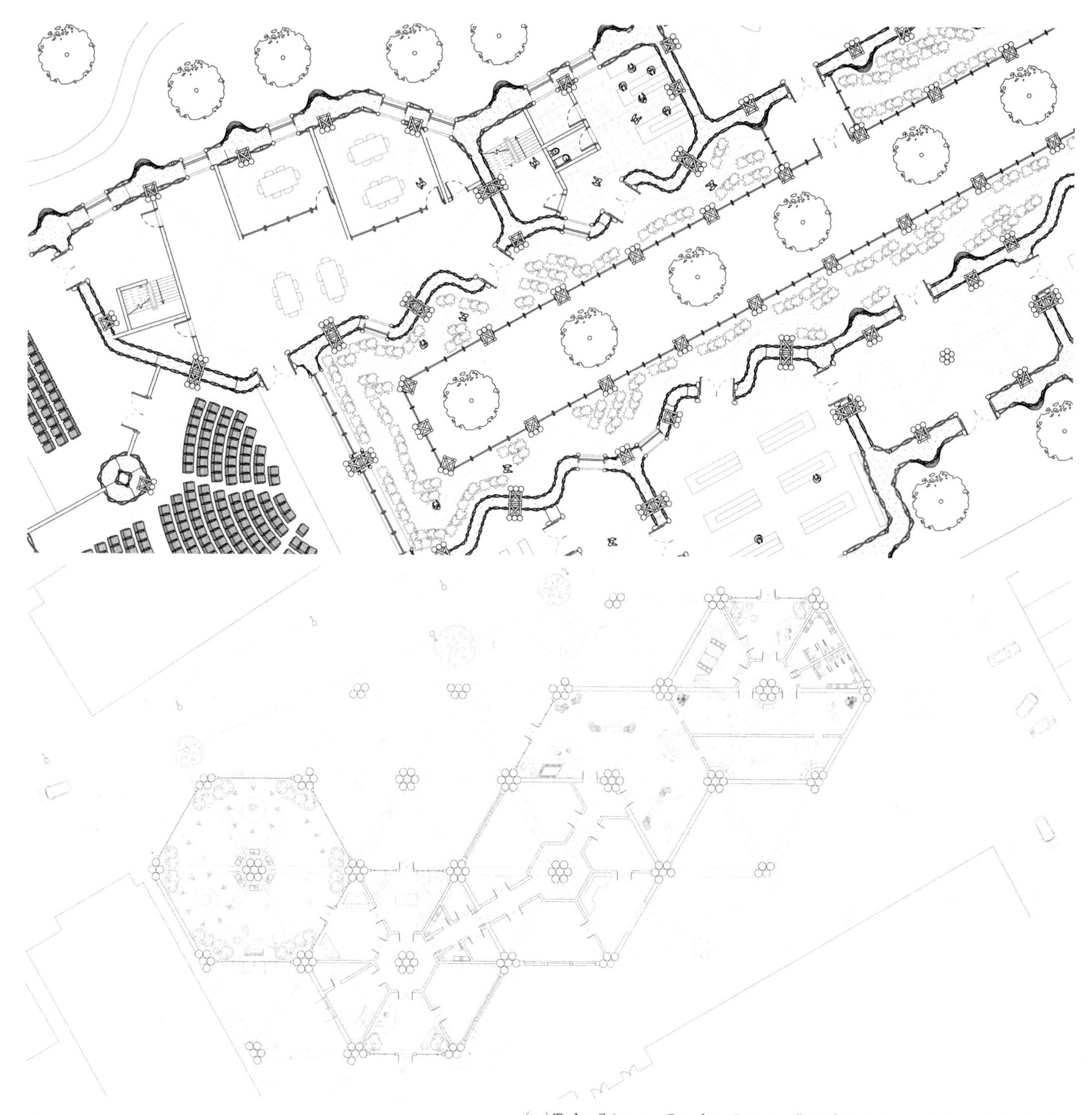

(top) Tudor Cristescu: *Greenhaus Institute*; *(bottom)* Carla Hora: *The HempArt Collective*

(top) Josh Corden: *Moth Cathedral;* *(bottom)* Maryam Saleemi: *Don't Judge a Crow by its Cover*

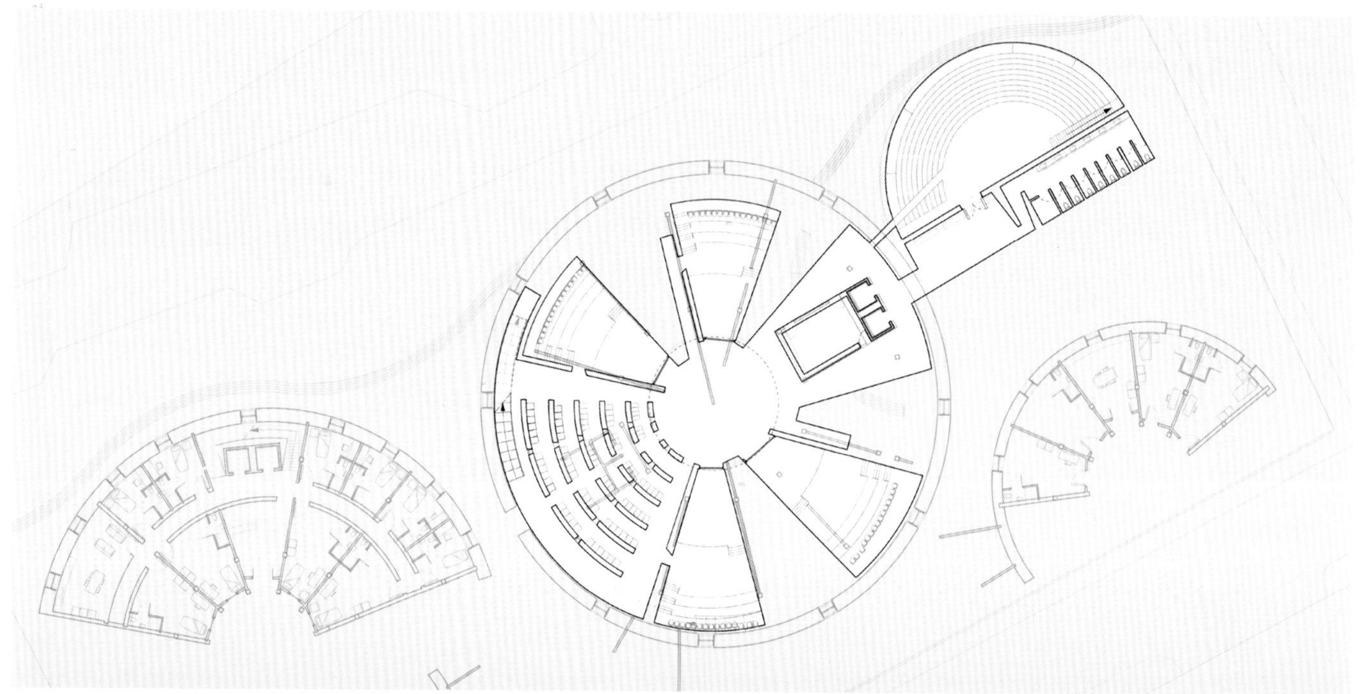

(top) Allaster Grant: *Thames Tulous;* *(bottom)* Yagmur Yurtbulmus: *Woodpecker Echo Chamber*

(top) Amad Hussain: *Red Squirrel Reintroduction*; *(bottom)* Wan Wong: *Gall Ink Collector*

John Zhang & David Porter

John Zhang *is a practicing architect and an Associate at DSDHA. He is also currently working on a PhD at the Royal College of Art on the topic of contemporary Chinese architecture.*

David Porter *is an architect, writer and educator. He was a partner in Neave Brown David Porter Architects, and currently holds a Professorship at the Central Academy of Fine Art, Beijing.*

DS(3)7: Happy Together

University of Westminster Students: Irina Bodrova, Anissa Colaço Souza, Zuzanna Osiecka, Jasmine Montina, Bryan Espinoza Ortiz, Heenah Pokun, Hugo Shackleton, Karol Wozniak

CAFA Exchange Students: Shi Zeyuan, Zuo Dan

USING BEIJING AND LONDON as our test beds, this joint studio with Central Academy of Fine Arts in Beijing, (CAFA), seeks to explore how diverse communities of citizens can live together in the city.

Key to the studio's approach is the focus on the thresholds between public and private, between the inside and the outside, and between the neighbourhood and the city. We advocate an architecture that engages the global context, and not a Eurocentric one. We are a global community of diverse individuals seeking answers to the same questions.

In semester 1, a two-month long exchange programme at CAFA anchored the term and facilitated the students in the analysis of a series of urban 'threshold' conditions, before moving to an ex-industrial site in Fengtai, Beijing. Here the students developed strategic designs for a community housing scheme that dealt with the emergent demographic demand that the students identified from their research.

In semester 2 the students consolidated the lessons learnt from Beijing, developing a comprehensive architectural proposal for a hybrid housing scheme in Bermondsey on an under-utilised car park site that sits on the threshold between the Shard, Guys Hospital, King's College, Bermondsey High Street, and the densely populated residential neighbourhoods around Snowsfields. The students were asked to identify and understand the end users, their socio-economic conditions, their specific housing needs, and their personal idiosyncrasies. Through a tectonically-led process, informed by model-making, the students were asked to explore the spatial, material, and experiential qualities of the proposed spaces, accompanied by a clear understanding of the appropriate construction approaches and structural principles.

Guest Critics:
Cheng Dapeng (DO), Martijn de Geus (TAFH), He Keren (CAFA), Constance Lau, Li Hu (OPEN Architecture), Li Lin (CAFA), Liu Siyong (CAFA), Douglas Murphy (RCA/Central St. Martins), Edward Simpson (Karakusevic Carson), Wang Hui (Urbanus)

Special Thanks:
Han Tao (CAFA, Beijing), He Keren (Central Academy of Fine Arts, Beijing), Kong Lingyue (CAFA, Beijing), Liu Siyong (CAFA, Beijing)

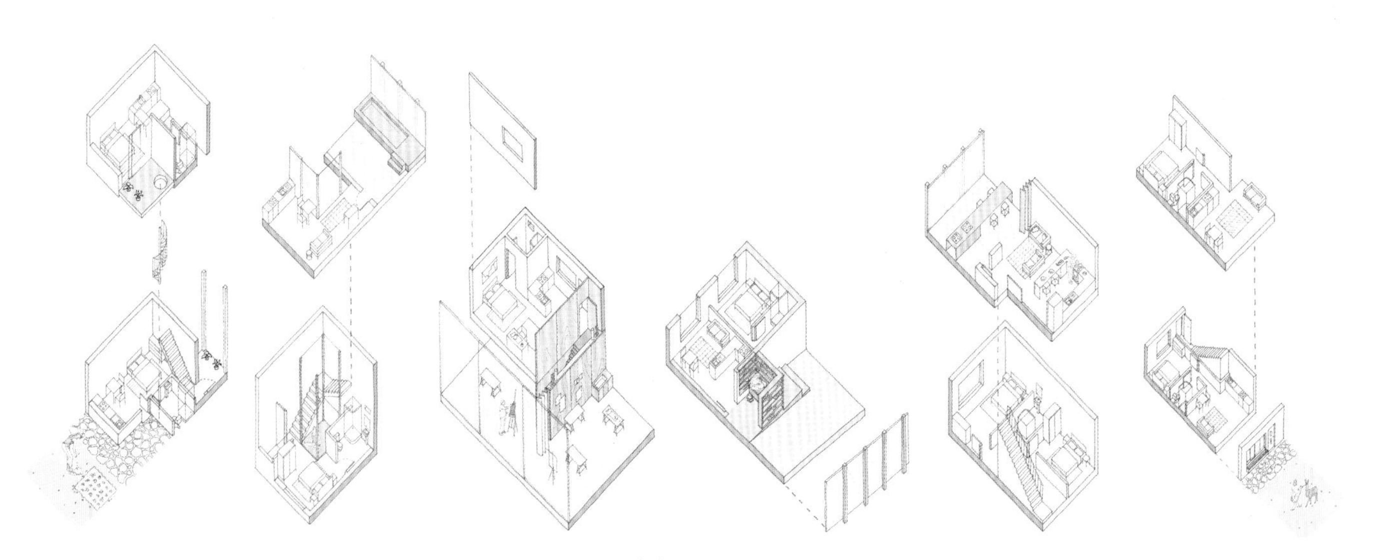

(top) **Bryan Espinoza:** ***Adaptable Artist Housing;*** *(bottom)* **Heenah Pokun:** ***Living as Therapy***

(top) Heenah Pokun, Irina Bodrova, Anissa Colaço Souza: *1:20 Model Interiors;* *(bottom)* Hugo Shackleton: *Pensioners & Medics Co-Housing*

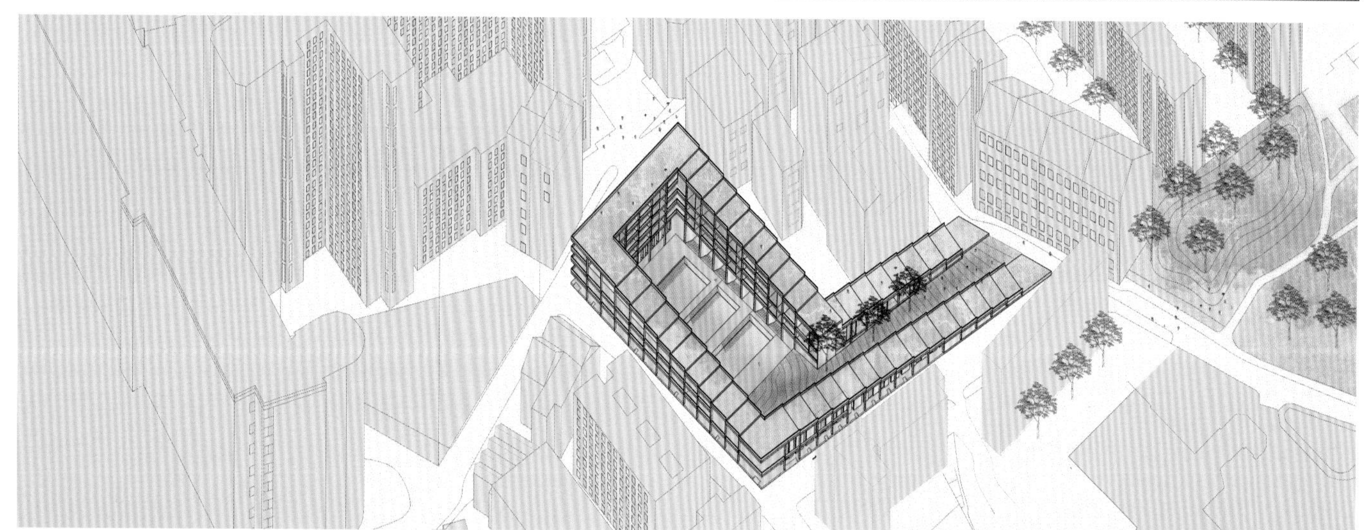

(top) Jamine Montina: *House of Rebirth;* *(middle)* Irina Bodrova: *Post-Op Rehab Housing* *(bottom)* Zuzanna Osiecka: *Beijing Thresholds*

Karol Wozniak: *Naturehood*

Speculative Realism

THE MARCH PROGRAMME is underpinned by critical agendas which, through its studio culture, are explored as speculative realities. The diverse range of themes presented in the following pages captures the extent of those speculations in 2016-17. The evolving nature of the city, environmental intervention, digital craft, cinematic investigations of space, chance operations, spaces of conflict, industrial regeneration – these are just some of the themes explored by staff and students.

The relevance of the teaching offered by the MArch also extends beyond the design studio into non-studio modules. Promoting critical and reflective practice, these courses become increasingly professional as students transition between first and second year. In year 1, discrete bodies of knowledge (Digital Design, Professional Practice, Environmental Technology, and History and Theory) are introduced in a linear sequence. In turn this broader awareness supports design ability and critical know-how. This interaction between studio and non-studio courses (thought and action) defines an important cycle of integration encountered during the first year of the MArch programme.

In addition to being critically informed, the MArch studios are identified by their design intelligence. In broad terms, the purpose is to encourage interplay between design and research. This implicit (tacit) cycle of design thinking is equal in rigour to more cognitive, critical knowledge. Here design is structured as a non-linear process, allowing research frameworks to evolve into embodied skill and reflective practice.

The second year of the MArch culminates in the production of three specialised components: the Strategic Report, Applied Technical Studies, and a Design Thesis. At this level, students are expected to fluidly move between thinking and making, where the goal is a form of synthetic judgement that provides a platform for future professional practice. This process expands into a more outward-facing attitude, achieved by using technological and environmental performance, complimented by legislative frameworks and procurement models, as constraints to be negotiated by speculative design practices.

Darren Deane
Course Leader

MArch ARCHITECTURE RIBA Part 2

Exploring and discussing architecture of all scales and forms from within and without:

DS20 drawing inspiration from Pier Luigi Nervi's Palazzo del Lavoro, Torino;

MArch students participating in an Urban Design charrette at Giovanni Michelucci's studio in Fiesole;

DS11 exploring texture and scale;

DS21's chance discovery in a Torino courtyard; the creativity of the studio space;

and DS15 interrogating their designs.

Toby Burgess & Arthur Mamou-Mani

Toby Burgess www.tobyburgess.com - *is the director of Toby Burgess Design Ltd and teaches at postgraduate level at the Architectural Association and the University of Westminster, with a focus on the funding and delivery of student projects.*

Arthur Mamou-Mani www.mamou-mani.com - *is a French architect and director of architecture practice Mamou-Mani Ltd. He is a lecturer at the University of Westminster and UCL-Bartlett and owns a digital fabrication laboratory called Fab.Pub.*

DS10: WeWantToLearn.net

Yr1: Anett Bako, Christine Cai, Maialen Calleja, Stefano Casati, Matthew Chamberlain, Eleanor Cranke, Mirela Maria Fournaridi, Georgina Gilbert, Alexandra Goulds, Alex Horsman, Sarah Jones, Min Kang, Ed Mack, Sylvia Plumridge, Tia Shaker, Ana Sidorova, Christopher Thornton, Ola-Aleksandra Wojciak

Yr2: Jonathan Pilbeam, Ben Roake

> *Instead of doing art about the state of society, we do art that creates society around it.*
>
> Larry Harvey, co-founder of Burning Man

DS10 BELIEVES THAT architecture should be fun and is obsessed with giving the students the opportunity to build their own projects in the real world. We dare to be naïve, curious, and enthusiastic. For us, architects should think like makers and act like entrepreneurs. We like physical experiments tested with digital tools for analysis, formal generation and fabrication. We value combinations of conceptual bravery matched with architectural reality, and seek an architecture of playfulness and beauty which responds intelligently to its environment, and sits within the wider cultural and environmental context.

BRIEF ONE: FROM SYMBOLS TO SYSTEMS - PAVILION PROPOSAL

Students studied the 10 guiding principles of Burning Man, analysing the philosophy behind the event. They looked at symbols, and chose one to play with. These were sacred, profane, mystical or even corporate. They extracted and understood the meaning behind the symbols and through digital and physical exploration, twisted, contorted, multiplied, fractalised and amplified the symbol into a sketch proposal for Burning Man 2017.

BRIEF TWO: PAVILION CONSTRUCTION

Further developing and understanding their proposals, students costed every screw, bolt and LED light, looking at each aspect of the project from budget to logistics. Students diagrammed fabrication and assembly sequences and produced the construction drawings needed to build their pavilions as well as making a refined 1:5 model of the entire proposal with LED lighting. As per previous years, students submitted a grant application to compete for a Burning Man Art Grant. This year Eleanor Cranke won funds to build Celestial Field this summer.

BRIEF THREE: THE BIG PLAN

Following the studio's study trip to the utopian city of Auroville and the many temples of Hampi Valley, we were seeking a reflection of the notion of utopian cities, and the role of central or decentralised architectural 'temples' as focal points of radical forms of urban development that inform and influence the city around them, similarly to Burning Man. Students proposed a city, or a city state, or a city in one building, that offered a critical reflection on the current state of the world.

Special Thanks:
Ross Cairns, Harry Charrington, Roisin de Cogan, Peter Cogger, Elena Corchero, Selvaraj Damotharan, Nancy Herms, Edward Lancaster, Vladimir Marinov, Geoff Morrow, Next Limit, Alex Rowling, David Scott, Pete Silver, SimplyRhino, Alex Smith, Henry Unterreiner

Guest Critics:
Anthony Boulanger, Lindsay Bremner, Darren Dean, Richard Difford, Andrew Peckham, Gabby Shawcross, Ben Stringer

Maialen Calleja

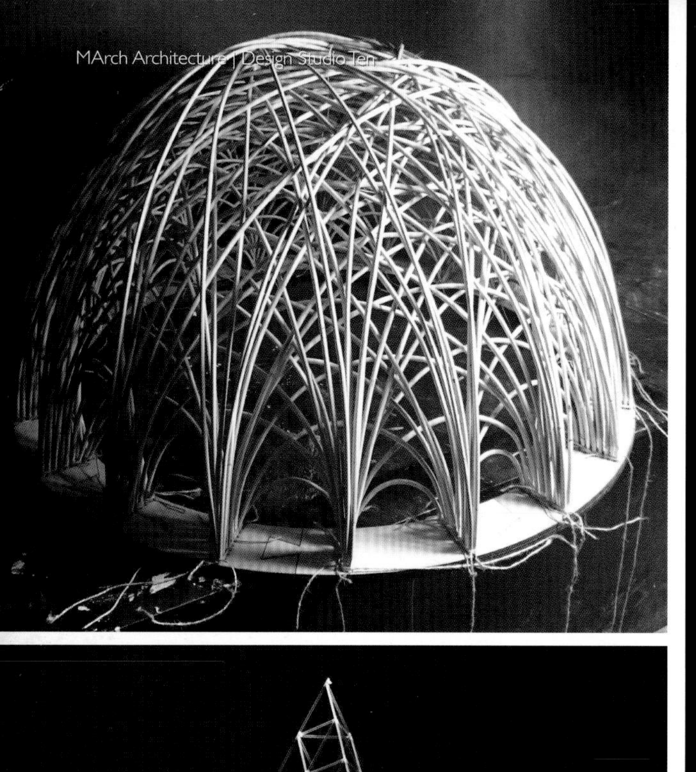

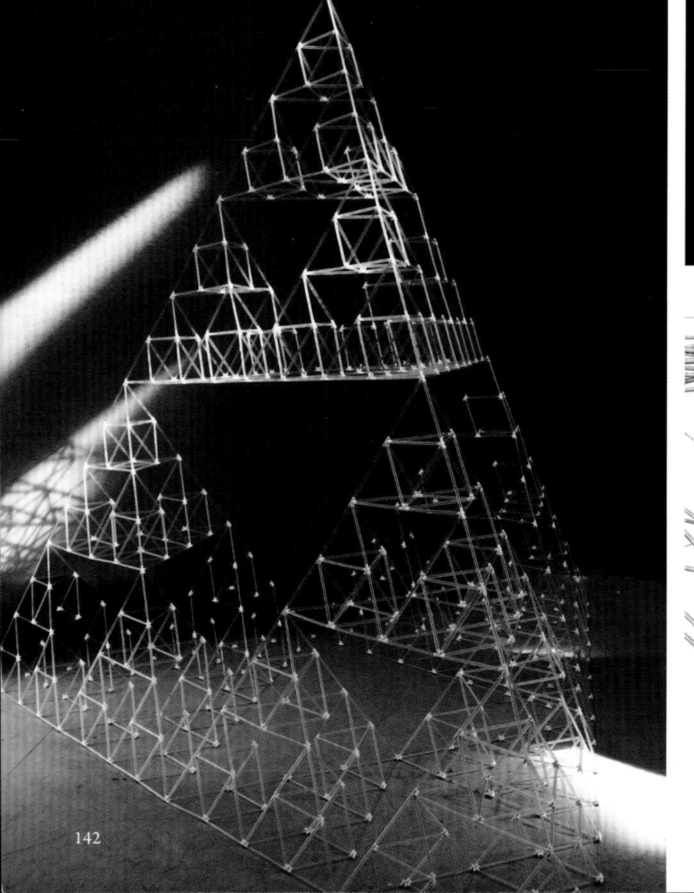

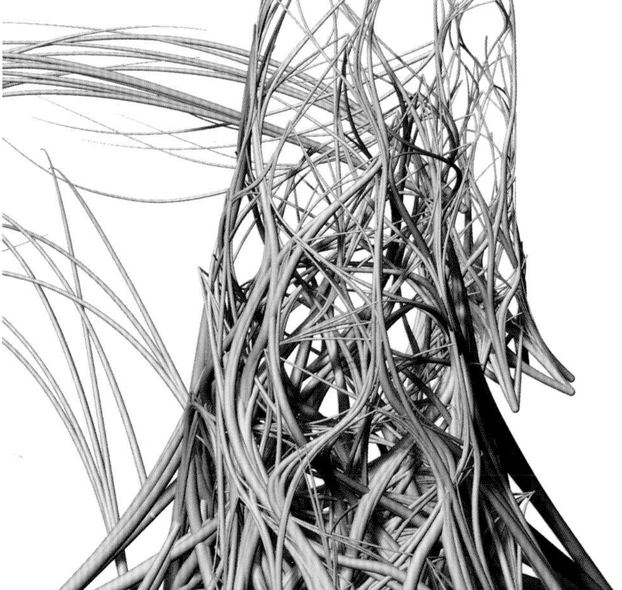

osite: (top left) Sarah Jones; *(top right)* Min Kang; *(bottom left)* Alexandra Goulds; *(bottom right)* Annett Bako;
page (top) Maialen Calleja; *(bottom)* Sarah Jones

(left) Stefano Casati; *(right)* Ola Wojciak

Andrew Peckham & Dusan Decermic with Elantha Evans

The DS11 *studio is best visualised as an open framework of investigation, setting out the terms in which students operate and local research is done: examining mores of design, and the social life and the urban history of particular cities. Resisting a consistent content or focus on applied 'research', our interest is structural; examining how non-linear patterns emerge to inform design procedures. Short studies and collective projects prompt an inquisitive mode of working, and a questioning of assumptions in examining a variety of urban conditions.*

DS11: Budapest: Twin Cities

Yr1: Duncan Catterall, Jamie Gallienne, Siyao Huang, Wenhao Li, Oana Oncica, Ruth Pearn, Christian Peel, Crista Popescu, Peter Sienkowski

Yr2: Sam Giles, Jasmine Hayden, Laura Hill, Loreta Lukoseviciene, Kristel Nurmsalu, Fredrika Rees, Isheeta Sachdeva, Rosemary Sonnenschein, Manodha De Silva, Jonathan Snell

> *There are two ways of describing the city of Budapest: you can speak about 'the form of the city', that is about its topology, the relationship between centre and periphery, kernel and outskirts, working-class and upper-class districts, about nature and culture (in the city), and all this would be no different from those images we see with half-shut eyes after long and aimless days of roving, and which we might call geometric fantasies…*
>
> Peter Esterházy

THE CHOICE OF Budapest as the location and focus of our studio projects this year related to an initial interest in the constitution of twin cities, where 'twinning' as a theme might be understood at different scales: from a transnational context to that of the city itself, its urban districts, buildings and interiors. If 'twinning' denotes similarity, then 'singularity' promotes contrasts and conditions the dialogue between extremes suggested by our subtext: 'architectures of stasis and flux'.

The studio developed three short study and project themes: 01) The World of the Interior: *the recess* – drawing, casting and wrapping; *psychoanalysing the room* – repressed surfaces; 02) Taking (to) the Waters: *Danubian* – the river, urban flow and flux, the dynamic of the city; *the pleasures of stasis* – the pool and its depths, taming flow; 03a) Water Table (year one): *reclaiming the underground* – subterranean space, levels below and their micro-ecologies; *geothermal conditions* – drilling down and drawing up, heat transfer, sustainable technologies; and 03b) Catalogue (year two): *hierarchy and construct* – manifest and thesis, collecting, analysing, categorising and archiving; *on the wall* – graphic currency, wall-paper, poster-wall, publication. The main Year One design project: Reconfiguring the Baths, and the Year Two design 'thesis' associated with Architectures of Stasis and Flux, were introduced before visiting Budapest and conducting a city survey.

Year One subsequently pursued their interpretation of the 'water' themed project (bathhouse, spa or island), while Year Two's 'catalogue' provided a springboard for their design thesis (film district, factory, urban densification, recycling/power plant, reconfiguring the 'centre', communal folk narrative, re-making the suburb, museum of the Danube, and twin buildings).

Guest Critics:
Lucy Brooke, Aya Dibsi, Liz Ellston, Tom Grove

Special Thanks:
Professor András Ferkai (MOME), Head of Institute and Associate Professor Ákos Juhász (MOME), Associate Professor Árpád Szabó (UTE Dept. of Urban Planning and Design) and Dr Károly Teleki

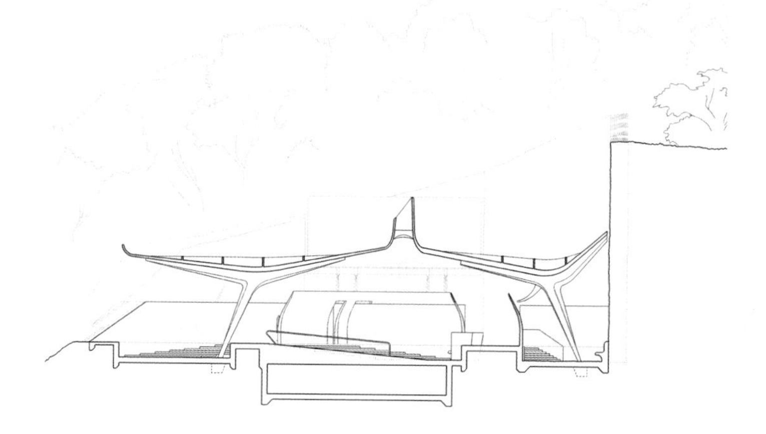

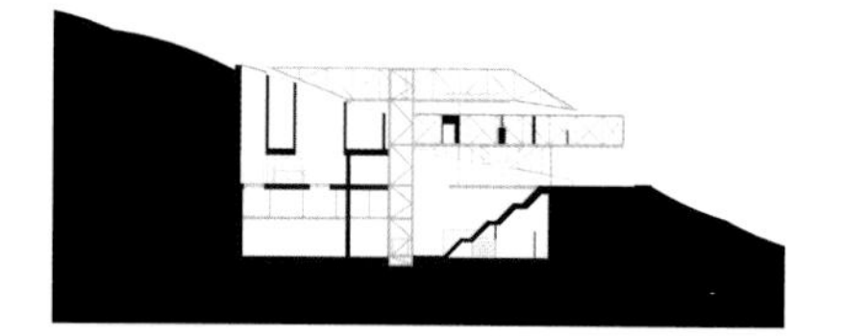

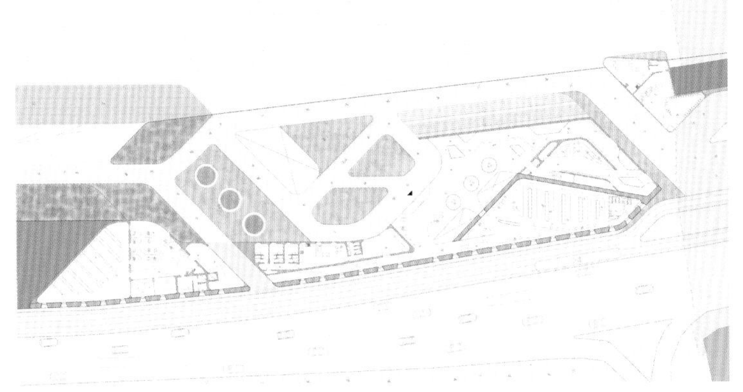

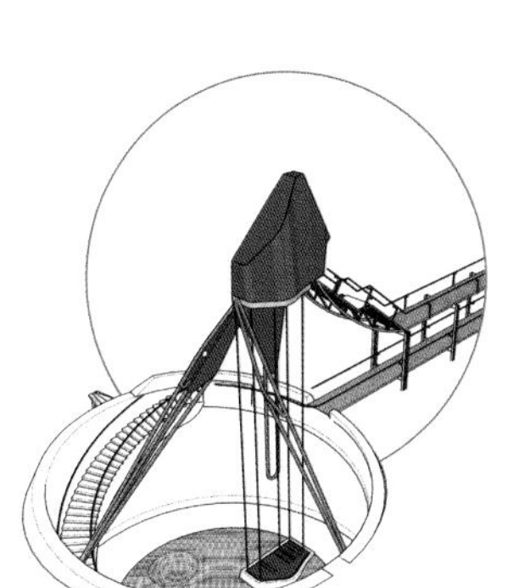
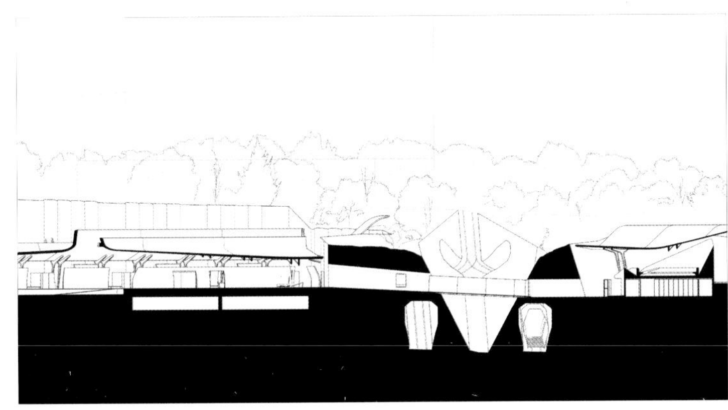

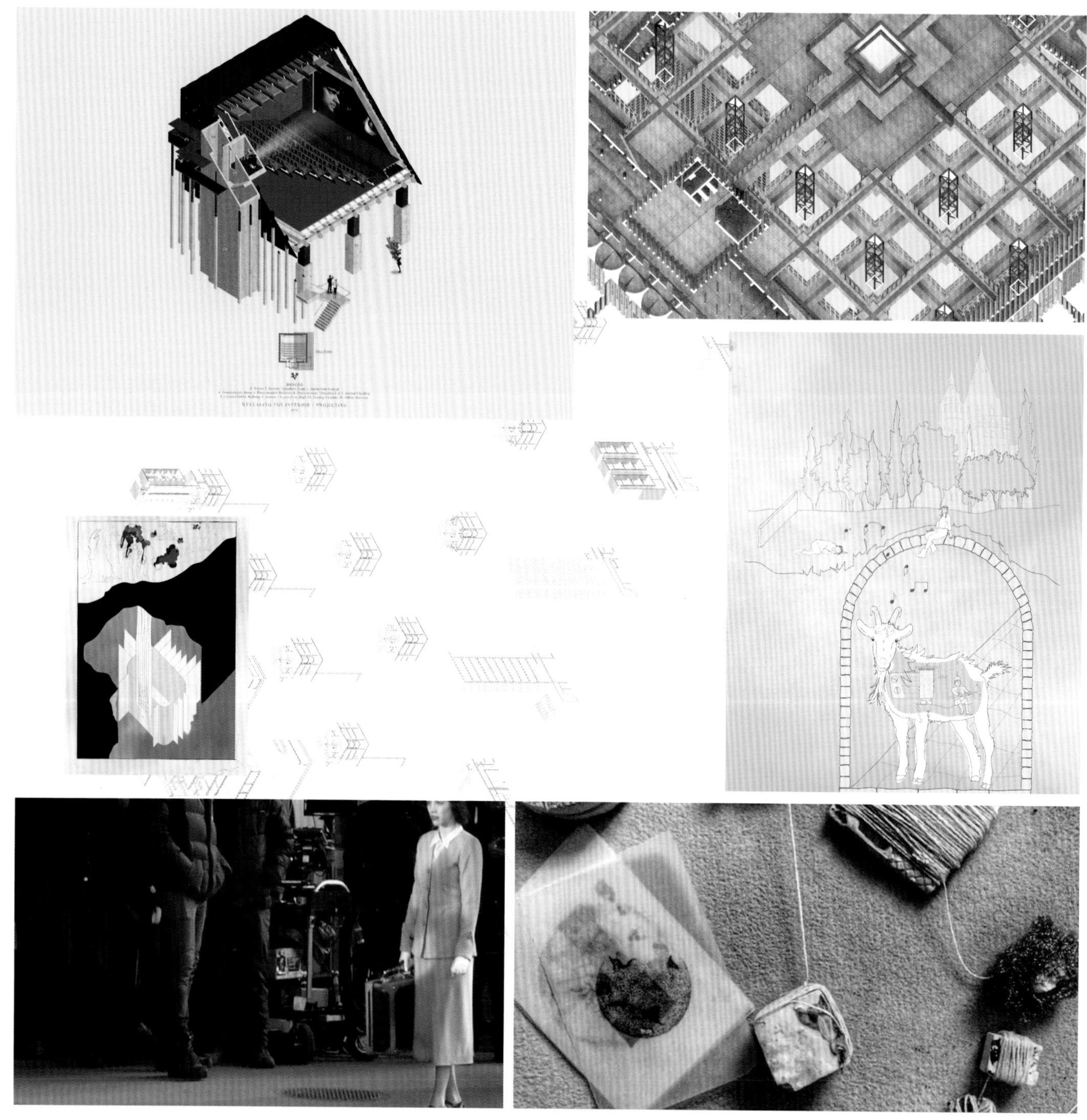

Ben Stringer, Peter Barber & Maria Kramer

Ben Stringer *teaches design and cultural context studies at the University of Westminster. Recently he has been publishing articles about architecture and rurality.*

Peter Barber *has a practice noted for its social housing and urban design projects, mostly around London. He also teaches design studio at the University of Westminster.*

Maria Kramer *is a practising architect who also teaches design studio and professional practice studies at the University of Westminster.*

DS12: Thames City Villages / Alterdomesticity 3.0 / India 2.0

Yr1: Samuel Clarry, Dorian Cortes, Phillip Forde, Nouha Hansen, Paresh Parmar, Mirabell Schmidt, Lela Sujani, Vincent Tsang, Filip Zielinski

Yr2: Henry Battey, Lukas Chung, Hayley Grace, Francesca Harding, Esther Heppolette, Jessica Humphrey, Denice Mann-Toyinbo, Chris Mannings, John Edmund Odametey, Tina Oladeji, Harriet Powell, Bradley Roast, Alexander Somerville, Dylan Warren, Thomas Wild

OUR BRIEF FOR the year was to imagine and design densely populated and 'publicly owned' city island villages in the Thames Estuary, a project that intersects issues of housing, industry, ecology and environment.

A key issue for our studio is London's ridiculous housing shortage, which has to be a catalyst for imagining new and better modes of existence and new ways of designing cities.

Another catalyst for us this year is the construction of the Thames Tideway 'super-sewer' which will stop London's sewage from flowing into the river and bring new life to the estuary ecology.

We worked with ideas of 'public ownership' and 'public funding' and considered alternative socio-economic possibilities for the production of affordable homes and sustainable neighbourhoods. What might architects' roles be in an evolutionary urbanism that tried to address London's inequalities and environmental problems on a large scale?

In semester one, we learnt about the Thames estuary, its economy and ecology, the threat of rising water levels, how it has been represented in fiction, about the idealistic settlements that have been built alongside it in the past and about its current demographics. Everyone chose their own site and developed their own variations on the brief and began designing island cities, towns and villages.

In semester two we shifted down scales and paid more attention to the domestic and cultural life of the islands and their relationships with their sites.

Field Trip

Early in semester two we went to the big cities of Delhi, Ahmedabad and Mumbai and learnt from different types of planned, informal and historic urban settlement and housing forms. We also travelled deep into the Maharashtra countryside for an inspiring couple of days at the Jetavan centre in Sakarwadi village. We also went to Tilonia village in Rajashtan to visit the brilliant Barefoot College.

Guest Critics:
Roudaina Alkhani, Pierre d'Avoine, Toby Burgess, Nat Chard, Sandra Denicke-Polcher, Antony Engi-Meacock, Susannah Hagan, Nabeel Hamdi, Frances Holliss, Jane McAllister, Michael Newman, Alicia Pivaro, Kester Rattenbury, Peg Rawes, Yara Sharif, Igea Troiani

Special Thanks:
Everyone at Jetavan, Maharashtra, especially Supriya Rai and Nandini Janardhanan; The whole village of Sakarwadi, especially the children who are fantastic; Sameep Padora in Mumbai; Vanita Verma in Delhi; Swati Janu at MHS CITYLAB, Delhi; Everyone at the wonderful Barefoot College, Tilonia; The Thames Tideway team; The Architecture Foundation for setting up the Megacrits; Petra Cox and everyone at Crossness Pumping station

Alex Somervillle

(top) Harriett Powell; *(bottom)* Jessica Harding

(top) Henry Battey; *(bottom)* Vincent Tsang

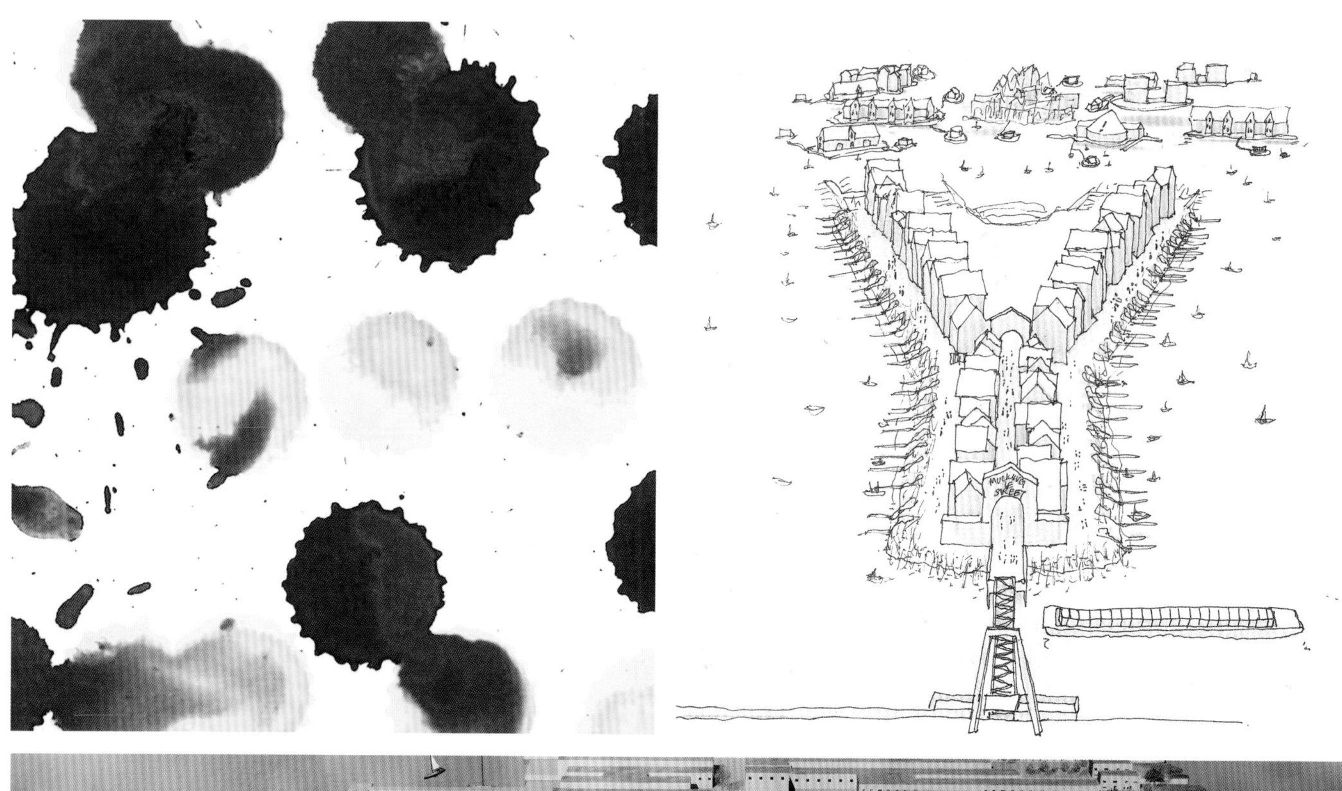

(top left) Paresh Parmar; *(top right)* Tina Oladeji; *(bottom)* Sam Clarry

(top) Chris Manning; *(bottom)* Alex Somerville

Andrew Yau & Andrei Martin

Andrei Martin - *Partner at Architecture, Andrei is a designer, researcher and academic, interested in the potential of new architectural typologies to transform urban experience and reshape contemporary culture. He has published, lectured and exhibited internationally.*

Andrew Yau - *Co-Founder, Co-Director (London) and International Project Director of Urban Future Organisation, Andrew seeks design innovation & ecological novelty with cultural sensibility and practical inventiveness. He is the design lead behind various award-winning projects.*

DS13: Allure and Illusion

Yr1: Marco Catena, Ramone Dixon, Elliot Benjamin Hill, Lazaros Elias Kyratsous, Mingyang Li, Mohammed Shah Abdul Muhaymin, Neil Antony Qunn, Larisa Tsydenova, Reihaneh Yaghoubi, Kriss Zilgalvis, Dagmar Zvonickova

Yr2: Calum Cole Campell, Kathryn Chung, Raluca Irina Ciorbaru, Kent Gin, Laurens Henry Jacobs, Natasa Kitiri, Cindy Mehdi, Richard Vuk Perry, Romaneek Rattu, Migle Surdokaite, Jean Paul Tugirimana

DS13 OPERATES AS an applied think-tank, performing cultural analysis and design research. This year, through the context of Hong Kong's urban transformation, we looked at the role, relevance and political agency of architecture in a contemporary cultural landscape defined by affect, mood, atmosphere and sensation.

At DS13, we are fascinated by the wonder, suspense and surprise of objects. Ensnared by the incredible sway their forms hold over us, we allowed ourselves to surrender to their allure and illusion.

Moving beyond the limitations of Deleuzian becoming, smooth manifolds, intensive flows and continuous variation that have defined disciplinary discourse for the past two decades, we seek to explore new forms of architectural coherence through objects and their relationships.

Our work aims to make inroads into a new territory of architectural imagination that is concerned with boundaries, edges, volumetric primitives and relations not of continuous flows and fields but of separation and difference. Instead of the hyper-indexicality of data-driven surfaces we are drawn to chunks, joints, niches, patchiness, inlaying, interiority, and the ambiguous experiential figuration of discrete entities. Instead of an architecture motivated by external forces, false scientism and data-processes, we are drawn to an architecture that is procedural yet irreducible – an architecture whose most important quality lies in its resistance to a rational decipherability.

Guest Critics:
Christian Parent (Oslo School of Architecture and Design),
Jason Antony Sam (Hunters), Francesco Montaguti (Hawkins\Brown),
Alex Sun (PLP Architecture), Andrew Watts (Grimshaw Architects),
Nicholas Strachan (Leslie Jones Architects), Anat Stern (Zaha Hadid Architects)

Special Thanks:
Holger Kehne & Hong Kong University, Tobias Klein & Hong Kong City University Ran Ran Shaw Media Centre; Dorothy Fong & Hong Kong Polytechnic University; Kenny Kinugasa-Tsui & Bean Buro & Workplace HK; David Clayton, William So & Aedas HK; Amarindra Rana, Francesco Sacconi & Wood Bagot Asia; Tean Chee Ko, Doyeon Cho & RMJM HK; Shuyan Chan, Iker Mugarra & UN Studio HK; Adelina Chan - Macau Architectural Historian; Hong Kong City Gallery; Hong Kong Housing Authority & Exhibition Centre

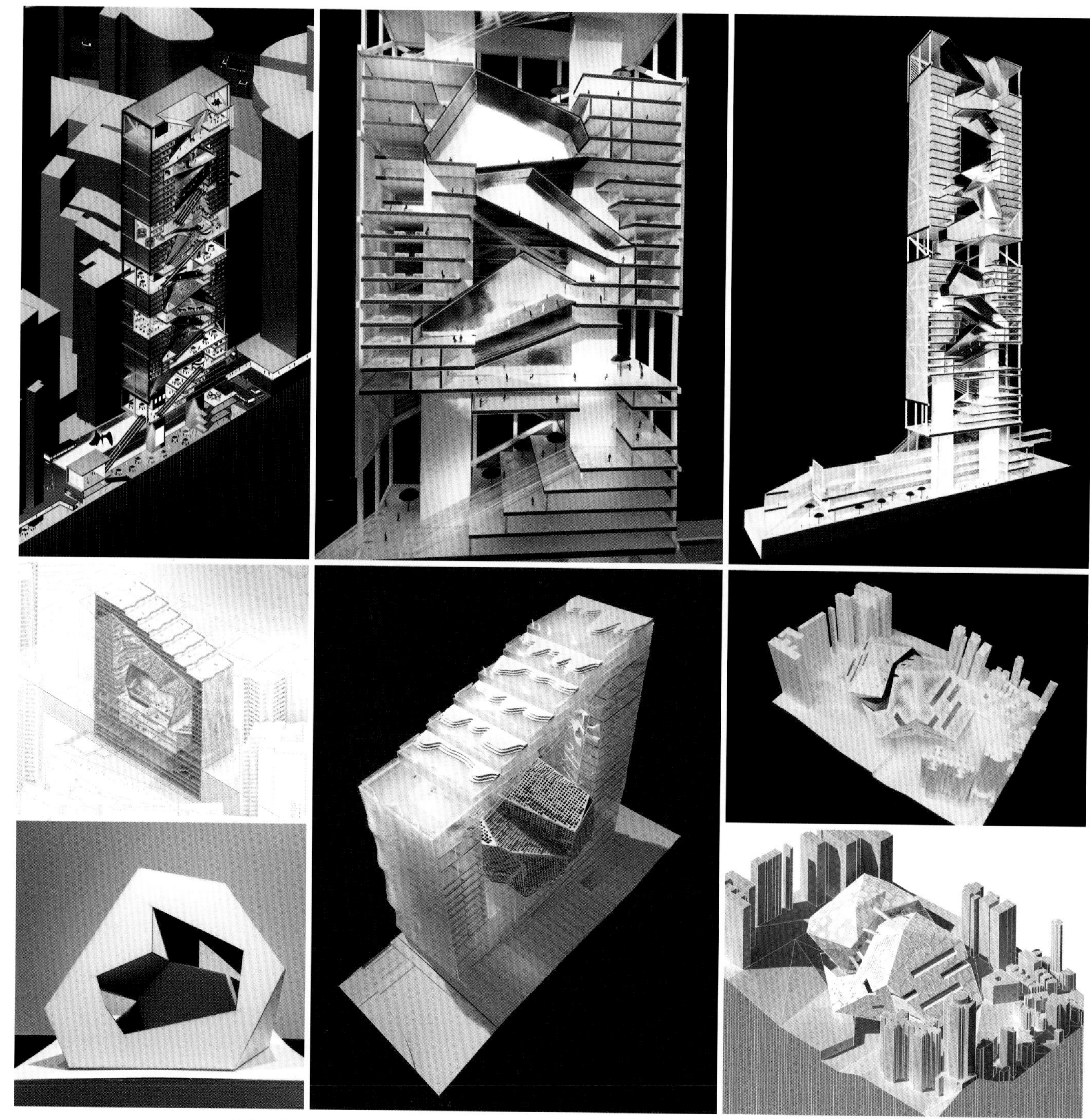

(clockwise from top left) Dagmar Zvonickova; Kent Gin and Mohammed Muhaymin; Elliot Hill; Natasa Kitiri and Mingyang Li; Elliot Hill

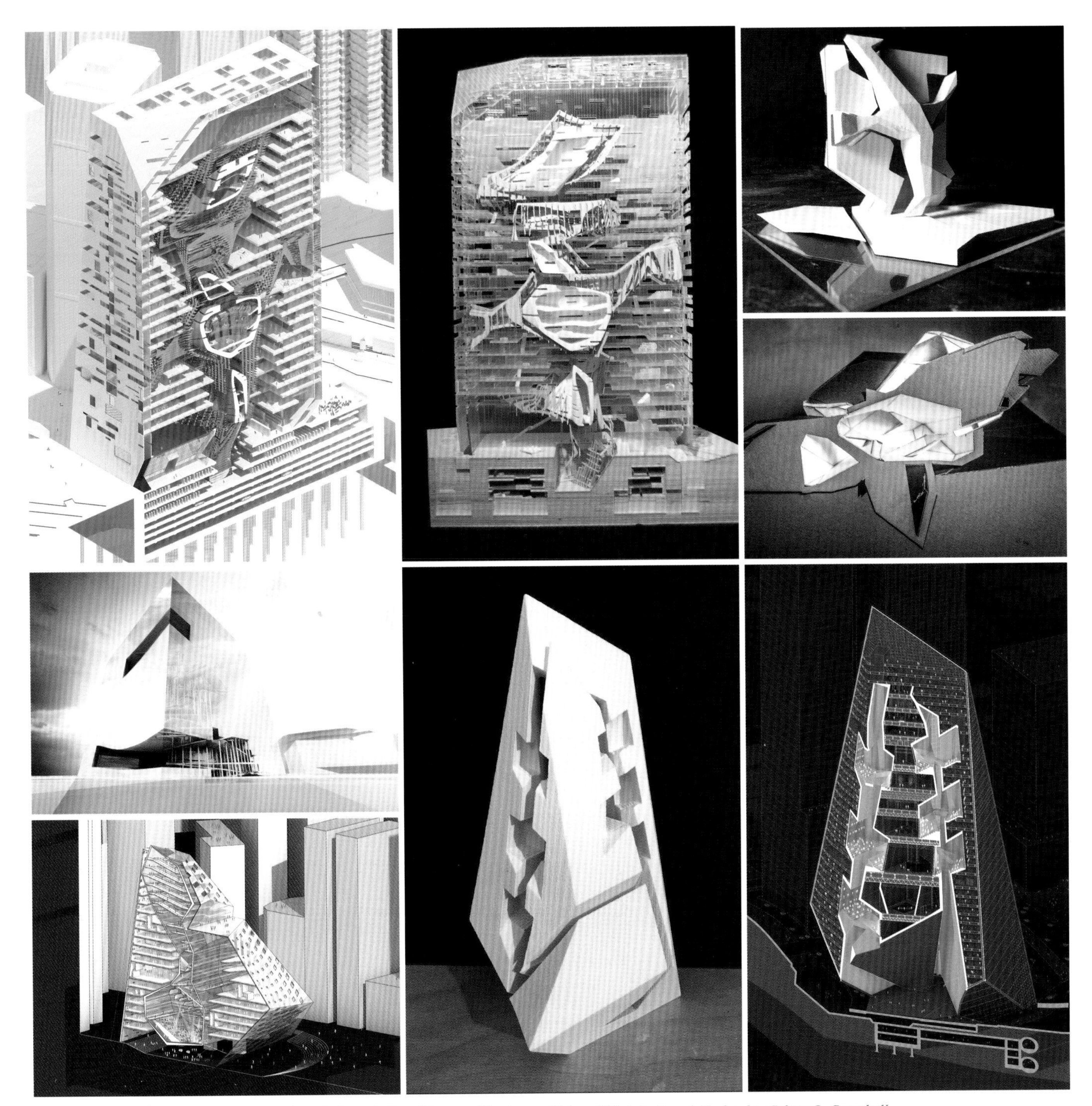

(clockwise from top left) Larisa Tsydenova; Calum C. Campbell and Lazaros Kyratsous; Natasa Kitiri; Reihaneh Yaghoubi; Calum C. Campbell

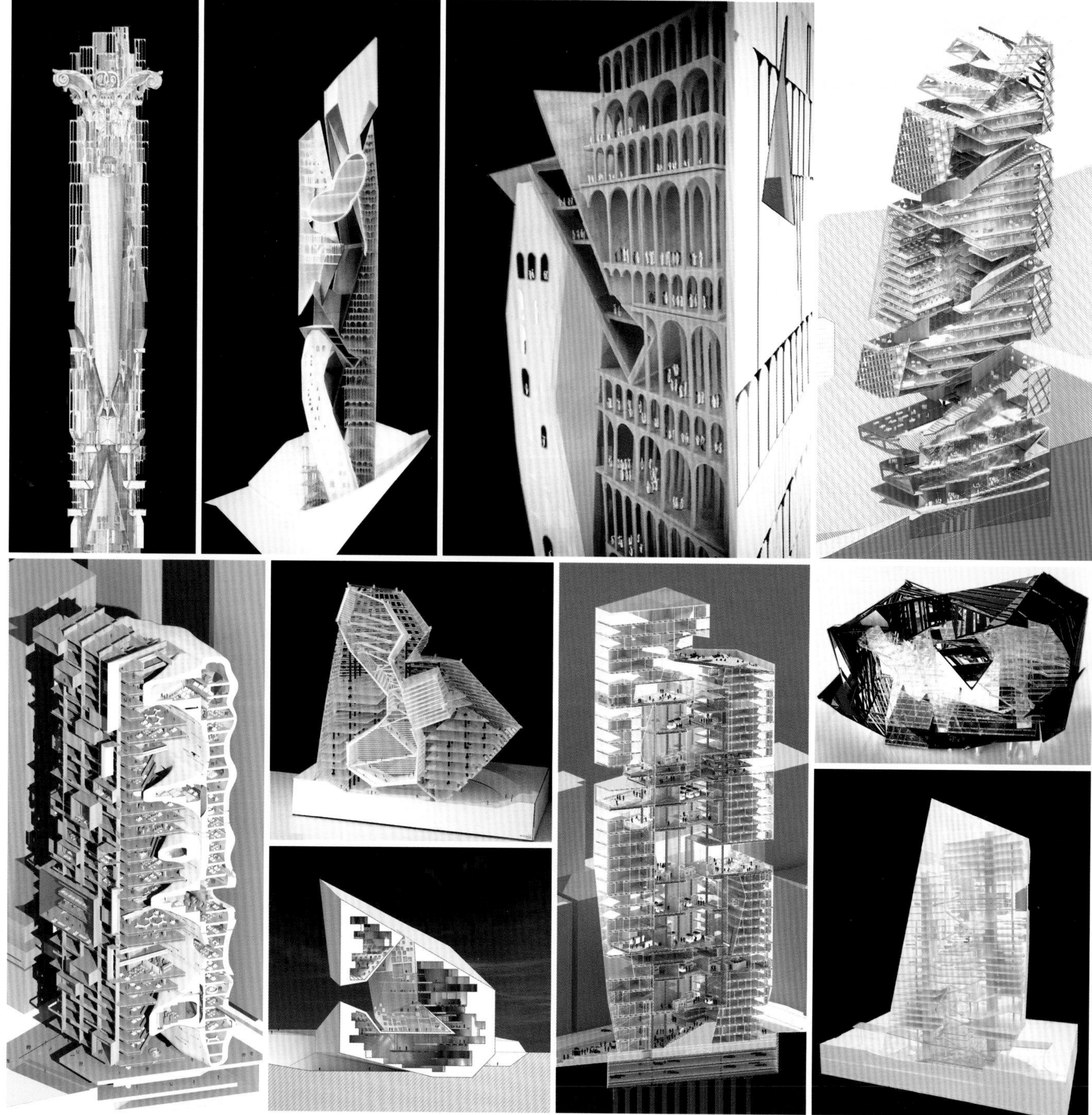

(clockwise from top left) Raluca Ciorbaru; Marco Catena; Kriss Zilgalvis; Mingyang Li; Romaneek Rattu; Kathryn Chung and Reihaneh Yaghoubi; Reihaneh Yaghoubi; Jean-Paul Tugirimana

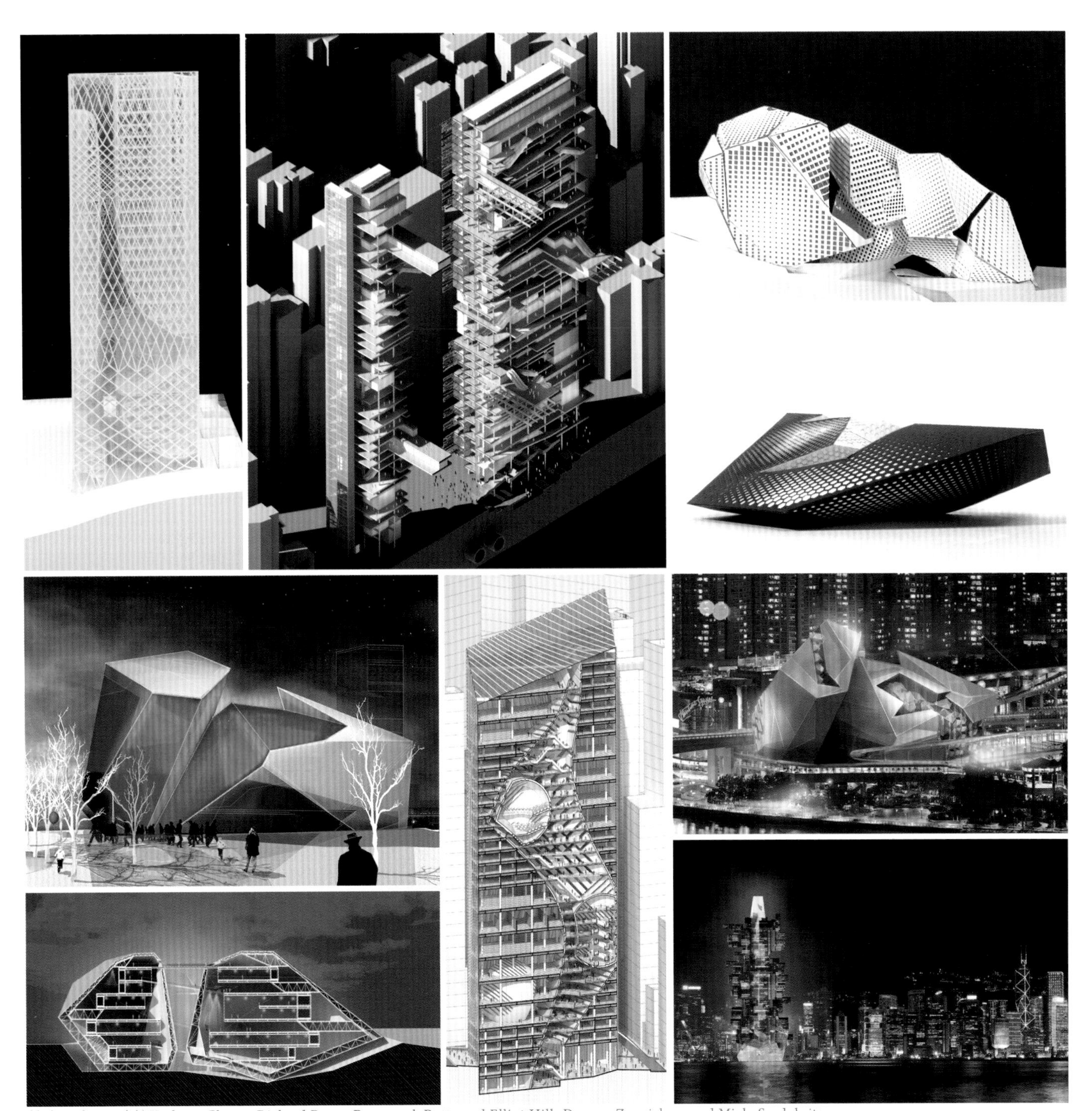

(clockwise from top left) Kathryn Chung; Richard Perry; Romaneek Rattu and Elliot Hill; Dagmar Zvonickova and Migle Surdokaite; Raluca Ciorbaru and Marco Catena; Lazaros Kyratsous; Migle Surdokaite, Kent Gin and Mohammed Muhaymin; Raluca Ciorbaru and Marco Catena

Sean Griffiths & Kester Rattenbury with Ruby Ray Penny

Sean Griffiths *is an artist and architect. He was a founder and director of the practice FAT, and now practices as Modern Architect, undertaking gallery-based installations, public art works and architectural projects.*

Kester Rattenbury *is an architect and writer. She is the author of* This Is Not Architecture, *the* Supercrit Series *(with Samantha Hardingham), she led the Archigram Archival Project, and her new book* The Wessex Project, Thomas Hardy Architect *is due out in November 2017.*

Ruby Ray Penny *is an architect and former student of DS15.*

DS15: Lines of Occupation. Lines of Inhabitation

Yr1: Riccardo Fregoni, Paulina Huurkari, Agnieszka Kowalska, Alexandra McCluskey, Sean Morrison, Jennifer Nguyen, Dominic Norman, Angus Smith, Alexia Soteriou, Daniel Wu

Yr2: Elise Aldén, Rhiain Bower, Charles Cullen, Matthew Deeming, Benjamin Ellis, Pippa Hale-Lynch, Ciaran Linane, Max Martin, Alex Nqai, Dan Rymer-Trenholme, Conor Sheehan

DS15 STUDIES 'CHANCE' as a design method via the transposition into architectural design of the American composer, John Cage's aleatoric techniques for musical composition. The studio's approach encourages students to divest themselves of existing prejudices, tastes and preconceptions in the development of inventive design processes that challenge the underlying assumption that design is a rational, linear and preordained activity predicated on intentionality. In taking on Cage's conception of 'sounds existing for themselves and not as part of human invented structures', DS15 focuses not on architectural 'concepts' as embodied in the composition of plans, sections and elevations, but rather on the human encounter with actual things in the form of chance-derived components. These elements emerge out of purposeless play 'in accordance with nature in the manner of her operation' as Cage would have put it, rather than being consciously designed.

Instead of acting like cartographers, territorialising the world with gridded and predetermined 'lines of occupation', DS15 students follow 'lines of inhabitation' in the manner of the nomad. As such, they find their way as they go along without the comfort of knowing the final destination. This leads, in turn, to a wider environmental awareness with attention given to sounds, tactility and the performative qualities of space as well as the visual. It promotes an understanding of the limits of conventional drawings and encourages the invention of new kinds of drawing and modes of representation that can begin to convey this wider awareness.

This year, these methods have been applied to a mixed-use housing project sited in Japan. In discovering something of the particularities of the Japanese sensibility on their field trip to Tokyo and Kyoto, the students have learnt about the affinities between the philosophies of 'Chance' and the ideas embedded deeply within Japanese culture and its philosophies of Zen that profoundly influenced the ideas of John Cage.

Guest Critics:
Eddie Blake (Sam Jacob Studio), Tom Bower (All Design), Marie Coulon (Director, Betts Project), Molly De Courcy Wheeler (Modern Architect), Mel Dodd (Central Saint Martins), Professor Kate Heron (Director, Ambika P3), Owen Hopkins (Curator, John Soane Museum), Robin Klassnik (Director, Matts Gallery), Tomas Klassnik (The Klassnik Corporation), Joc Marchington (artist, JOCJONJOSCH), Kate McTiernan (The Shuffle Festival), Jo Melvin, Rowan Moore, Giles Smith (Assemble), Douglas Spencer, Yuki Sumner, Ellis Woodman (Architecture Foundation)

Special Thanks:
Ruby Ray Penny (Eric Parry Associates) for standing in during Kester's sabbatical;
Douglas Spencer for accompanying us on the field trip to Japan;
Yuki Sumner for being our guide in Tokyo and Kyoto, and in-house expert on all things Japanese

(left) Ciaran Linane: *Timber Column; (right)* Ciaran Linane: *A Patchwork Construction*

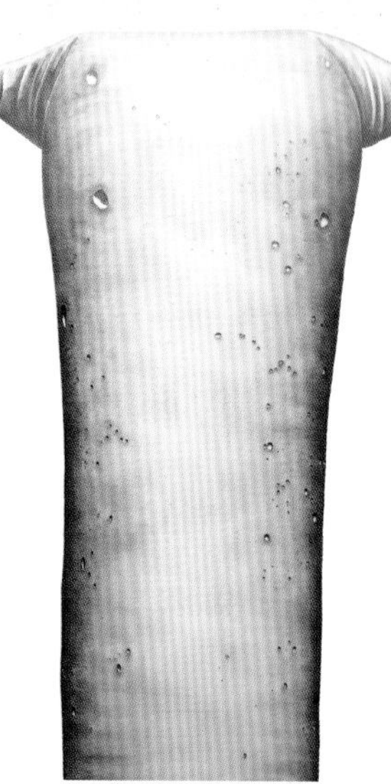

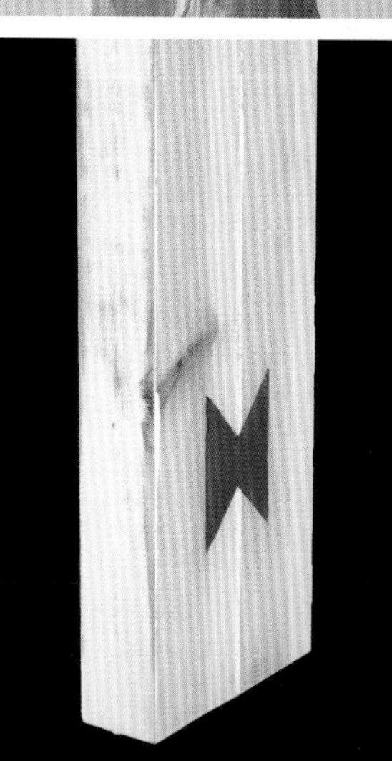

(top left) Charles Cullen; *(bottom left)* Max Martin;
(right top-bottom) Riccardo Fregoni, Alexia Soteriou, Matt Deeming

(left) **Rhiain Bower:** ***Brush Column;*** *(right)* **Conor Sheehan:** ***Bleach Plan;***

(top left) Max Martin: *Alleyway Proposal Drawing*; (centre left) Alex McCluskey, Alex Nqai, Dan: *Timber Screen*; (bottom left) Alex Nqai: *Paperroll Window*

(left) Elise Aldén: *Nori Ama: nOrinOri Screens*; *(right)* Benjamin Ellis: *Colonnade*

Anthony Boulanger, Stuart Piercy & Callum Perry

Anthony Boulanger *has an MArch from the Bartlett UCL and is co-founding partner of AY Architects, recognised for innovative design and research, winner of the Stephen Lawrence Prize in 2013.*

Stuart Piercy *is a Fellow of the Royal Society of Arts and founder of the acclaimed award-winning practice Piercy&Co.*

Callum Perry, *DS16's newest member, graduated from the studio in 2014 and has since been working at Grymsdyke Farm and at Piercy&Co. Together they offer students a platform for experimentation of architectural concepts instigated by a culture of making.*

DS16: Fire & Ground

Yr1: Nicola Charalambides, Jessica Clements, Yunxia Dai, Janan El-Musawi, Felicity Holmes, Hollie Muir, Haneen Shames, Samantha Wilson

Yr2: Katherine Baulch, Matthew Beaumont, Amy Bourne, Phoebe Burnett, Claire Humphreys, Chenyang Luo, Tim Matthews, Marianne Mehdizadeh, Marta Piasente, Danielle Purcell, Rista Shrestha, Claudia Turton

DS16 RETURNS FROM a year sabbatical to continue to build on an ethos that challenges students to create experimental spatial design projects that are informed by a critical response to social, cultural, political and economic contexts with an emphasis on an engagement with materials and an understanding of craft. We support students to explore specific interests in material processes by facilitating specialist fabrication input.

The process and techniques for the making of ceramics was the theme for an intense 5 weeks of creative collaboration at the start of term 1. In small groups, and with specialist help from ceramics expert Jessie Lee, students utilised the unique facilities at Grymsdyke Farm to interrogate, test, design and install a variety of ceramic pieces. The initial challenge was to consider the ceramic replication of an inspirational artefact of cultural significance. This was then re-interpreted and adapted as a site specific installation in the setting of the farm. The intrinsic process of forming, moulding, casting, firing and glazing, performed by both analogue and digital means, was as important as the final installations.

The investigations shifted to the scenic city of Porto as the base for the main individual design project, where students conceived their own briefs and carried out research to situate their interventions. We were initially attracted to the city by its UNESCO World Heritage status, a delightful history of ceramics and a culture of contemporary architectural vernacular. We ended up becoming engaged with a struggling, semi-abandoned, urban imperative, derelict by its heritage safeguards and the financial crisis and resulting in population decline through mass suburbanisation. This being curiously at odds with an on-going attempt of touristification to redefine the city's future.

Many enquiries evolved as bold reactions to this unusual urban, social, cultural and environmental accumulation. A variety of processes were encouraged to develop designs with an explicit civic initiative, operated by an engagement with the experience of making and the architect's place in the material world.

Guest Critics:
Alessandro Ayuso, Harry Bucknall (Piercy&Co), Melissa Clinch (Wilkinson Eyre), Sophie Cole (AY Architects), Murray Fraser (UCL), Luis Grilo (Piercy&Co), Alex Haggart (Piercy&Co), Yannis Halkiopolous (Piercy&Co), Guan Lee (UCL/RCA), Yeoryia Manolopoulou (UCL), Ben Newcomb (Hawkins\Brown), Simon Tonks (RSHP), St John Walsh (AY Architects), Victoria Watson (RCA)

Special Thanks:
Guan Lee for his generosity with Grymsdyke Farm
Jessie Lee for all her expert support with ceramics
Pedro from 'The Worst Tours', Porto

(top) **Rista Shrestha, Tim Matthews, Emylia Kalyvides:** ***Coded Landscapes;*** *(bottom)* **Katherine Baulch, Claire Humphreys, Yunxia Dai:** ***Lamella***

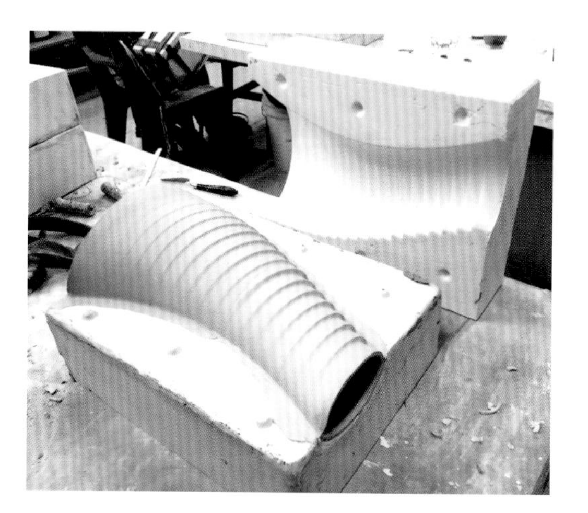

(left) Katherine Baulch: *Civility Hill - Quarried Chamber; (top right)* Rista Shrestha, Tim Matthews, Emylia Kalyvides: *Coded Landscapes;* *(centre right)* Marianne Mehdizadeh, Marta Piasente, Nicola Charalambides: *Pronto; (bottom right)* Matthew Beaumont, Samantha Wilson, Jessica Clements: *Poppy Tears*

Matthew Beaumont: *Fontainhas Escarpment - Housing and Festival Landscape*

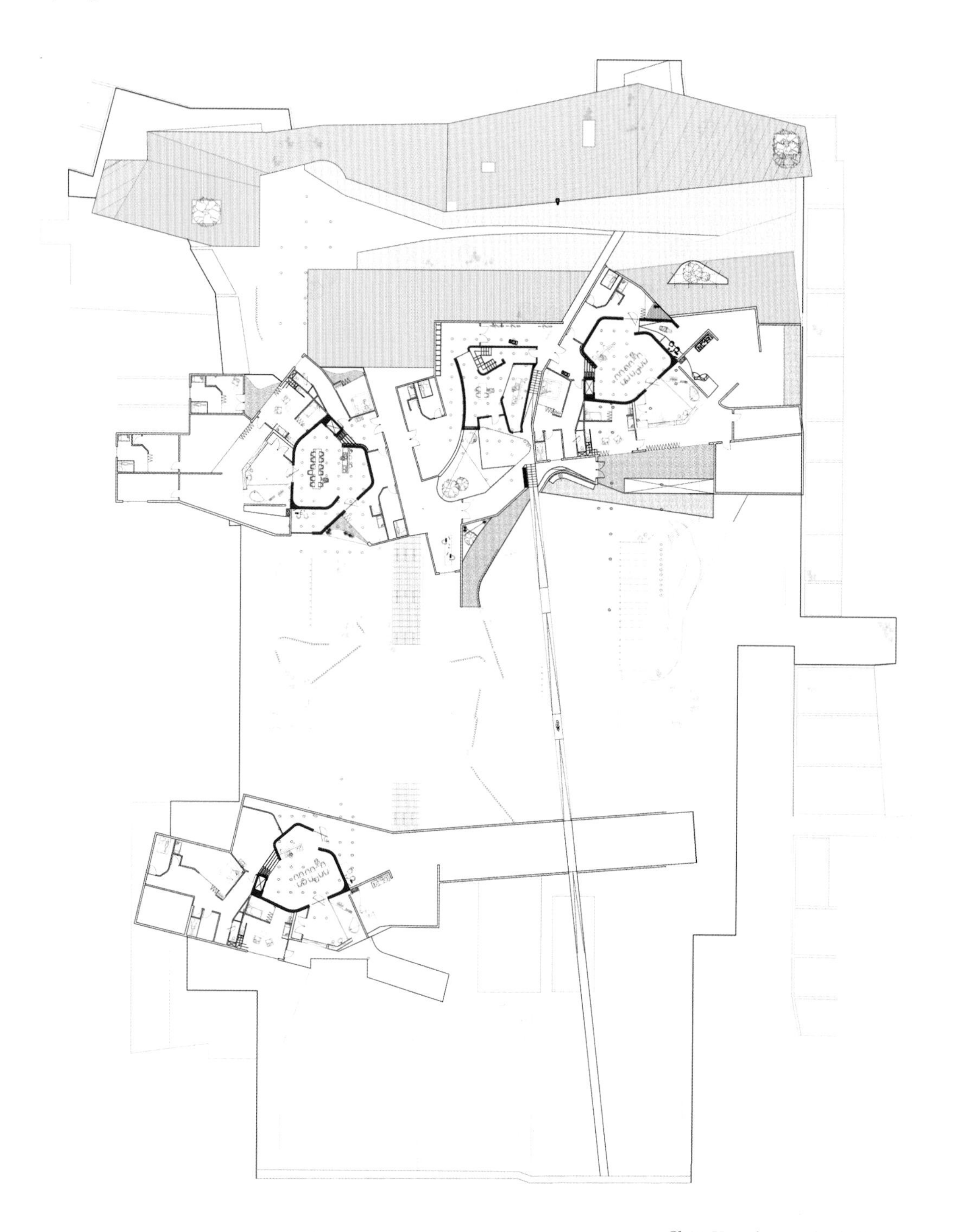

Claire Humphreys: *Island - The New Ilha, 1st Floor Plan*

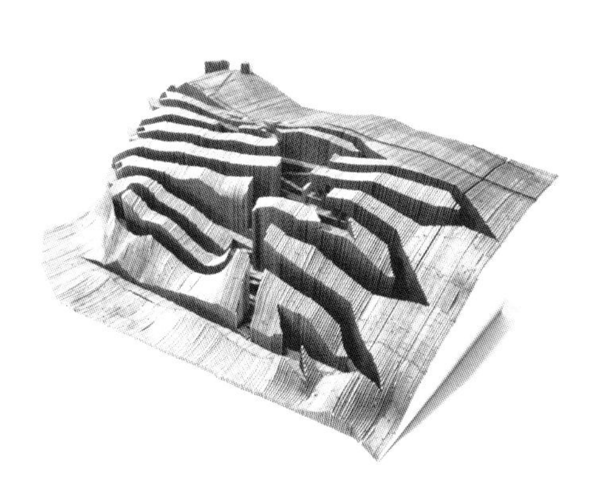

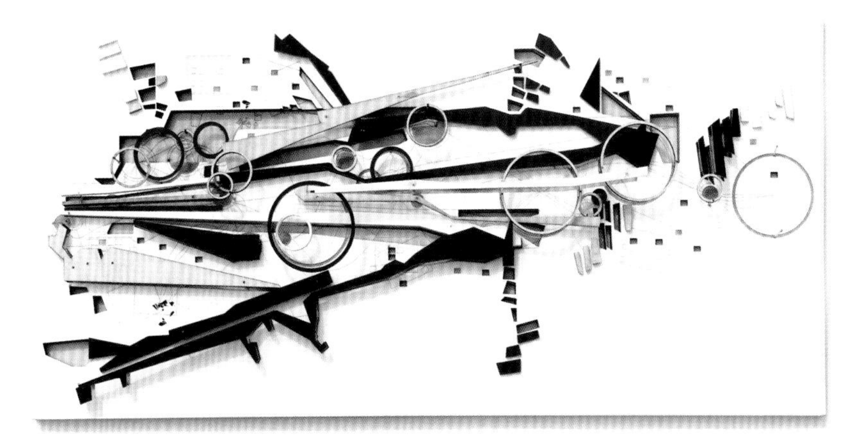

(top & bottom left) Yunxia Dai: *Duoro Cliff Cemetary and Crematorium;* *(bottom right)* Pheobe Burnett: *'Amor de Perdicao' (Doomed Love) Concept Model III*

Lindsay Bremner & Roberto Bottazzi

Lindsay Bremner *is an architect and Director of Architecture Research in the Faculty of Architecture and the Built Environment at the University of Westminster. She is Principal Investigator of the Monsoon Assemblages project.*

Roberto Bottazzi *is an architect, researcher, and educator based in London. He is a Senior Lecturer at University of Westminster and a Teaching Fellow at the Bartlett, UCL, where he teaches RC14 in the Master of Urban Design Programme.*

DS18: Monsoon Assemblages Chennai

Yr1: Constantina Avraamides, Sarah Bass, Charlotte Birch, Rob Fernandes-Dwyer, Rosanna Rolfe, Ben Street, Nora Szosznyak, Georgia Trower

Yr2: Tom Benson, Monica Cristu, Seetul Ghattaora, Jeronimo Garcia, Emma Hilton-Grange, Sebastien Monceaux, Andreea-Laura Nica, Connor Page, Cid Schuler, Calvin Sin, Charles Weston-Smith

BETWEEN 2016 AND 2019, DS18 is participating in the research agenda of Monsoon Assemblages, a five-year ERC funded research project working in three cities in South Asia: Chennai, Dhaka and Delhi. These cities are places where neo-liberal development is conspiring with changing monsoon patterns to produce floods, heatwaves, outbreaks of disease or water shortages and making urban life increasingly vulnerable. By exploring the multiple ways in which the monsoon has historically been woven into the fabric of urban life and the forms of knowledge that have been formulated around it (scientific, cultural, everyday), the project aims to explicate experimental approaches to architecture and urban planning to challenge neo-liberal protocols and better co-habit with monsoonal excesses. It is this agenda that DS18 is advancing.

'In the context of urban and architectural processes driven almost exclusively by economic and political interests and concerns, what might it mean to develop urban and architectural strategies for and with the monsoon, a global system massively dispersed in space and time, yet with profoundly local consequences and cultures?'

In 2016/17, the studio began by simulating monsoon rain as a way to develop its programme and aesthetic. Students visited Chennai where they were hosted by the School of Architecture and Planning at Anna University. They undertook field work along a 9km transect through the Pallikaranai Marsh, a large water body in South Chennai encroached on by an IT corridor, and identified a site on this transect to engage with the studio's research questions and methods. In 2017/2018, the studio will explore this agenda further in Dhaka and in 2018/19 in Delhi.

Guest Critics:
Laura Allen (Smout Allen Architects), Karl Beelen (University of Karlsruhe), Harshavardhan Bhat, Nerea Calvillo (University of Warwick), Beth Cullen, Richard Difford, François Girardin, Susannah Hagan, Jane MacAllister (London Metropolitan University), Oscar McDonald (Wilkinson Eyre Architects), Michael O'Hanlon (DSDHA Architects), Sowmya Parthasarathy (ARUP), Ben Pollock (Fletcher Priest Architects), Anthony Powis, Alfredo Ramirez (AA), Alice Thompson (Dan Marks Studio), Alex Watts (Eric Perry Architects)

Special Thanks:
Pushpa Arabindoo, Beth Cullen, Cath Hassell, Priti Narayan, Sekar Raghavan, Rajeswari Ravi, Ranee Vedamuthu, Jayshree Venkatesan and Michele Vianello for studio inputs in London and Chennai.

Laura Nica: *Hybrid Hydrology & Other Wet Social Aggregates, Section & Masterplan*

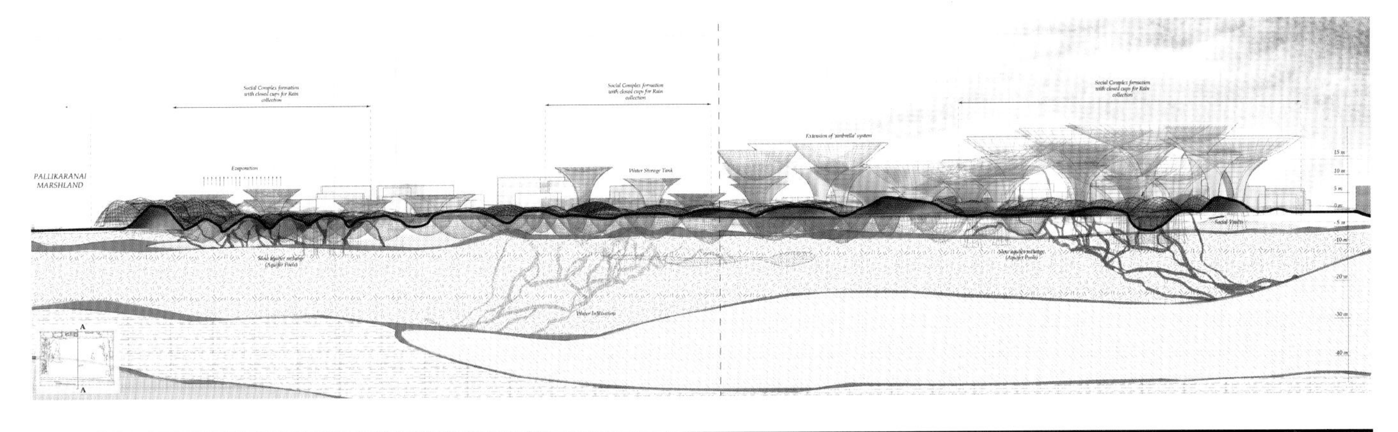
PALLIKARANAI MARSHLAND
Social Complex formation with closed cups for Rain collection
Evaporation
Social Complex formation with closed cups for Rain collection
Water Storage Tank
Extension of 'umbrella' system
Social Complex formation with closed cups for Rain collection
Social Vaults
Slow aquifer recharge (Aquifer Pools)
Water Infiltration
A
A
15 m
10 m
5 m
0 m
-5 m
-10 m
-20 m
-30 m
-40 m

(left) Cid Schuler: ***Monsoon Bio-doppler***; *(top centre)* Jeronimo Garcia: ***LEGO-LACUS Water Harvester***; *(top right)* Seetul Ghattaora, Neelankarai Monsoonal Refuge; *(bottom right)* Emma Hilton Grange, The Link: ***SMME and Cottage Industry Hub***

(top) Tom Benson: *Datascape: Instrumental Marshland;* *(bottom)* Monica Cristu: *Inhabited Peri-marsh Landscape*

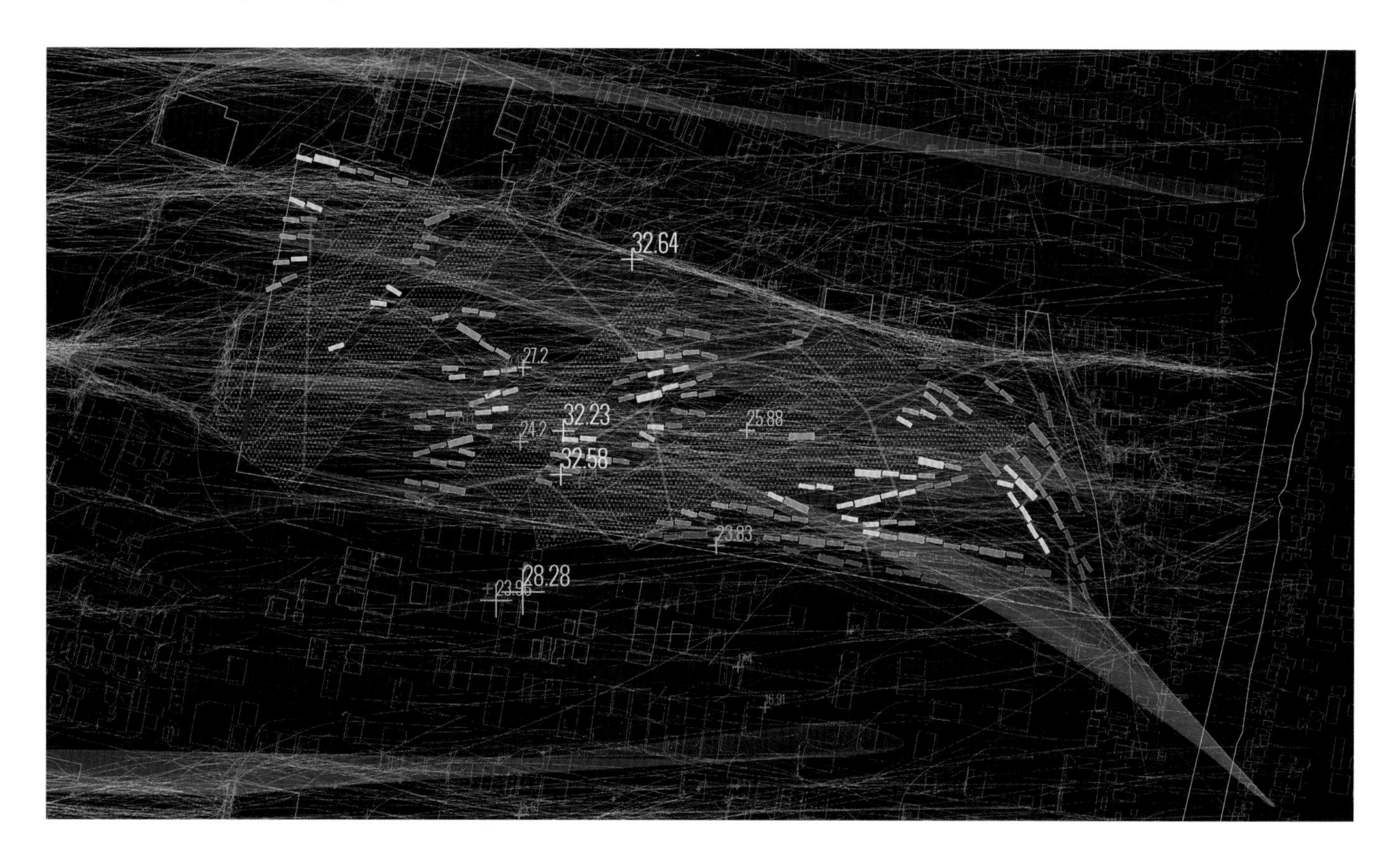

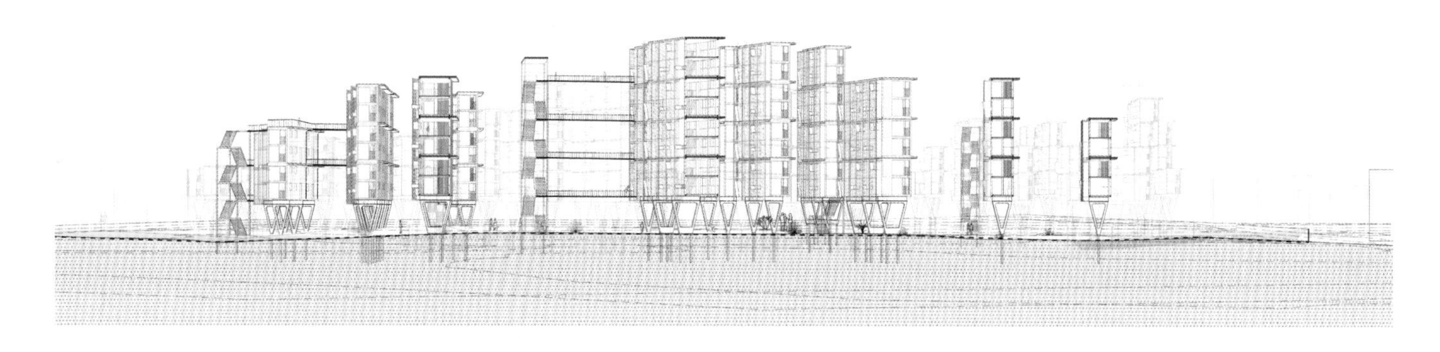

Calvin Sin: *Chalikundu Marsh Housing, Masterplan*

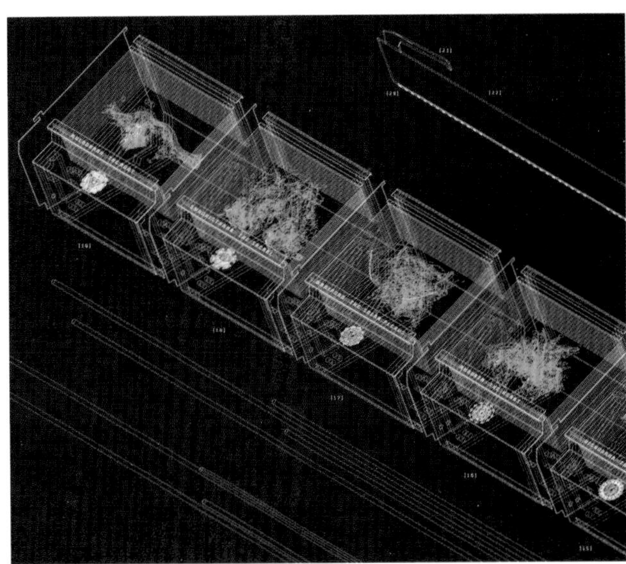

(top) Sebastien Monceaux: *Amphibious Bridge;* *(bottom)* Charles Weston Smith: *The Physicality of Dreams, Construction Drawing*

Gabby Shawcross & Stephen Harty

Gabby Shawcross *is an architect and artist and director of Studio Of Cinematic Architecture (SOCA).*

Stephen Harty *is an architect and director of Harty and Harty.*

DS20: Still-Frame / Short-Cut / Long-Shot

Yr1: James Butler, Saffa Dehghani, Lucy Dunn, Tom Gorringe, Yannis Hajigeorgis, Fred Howarth, Tom Kendrew, Josh McDermott, Nat Reading, Adam Todhunter, Wang Juei-Ching, Chris Waters, Amy Wong

Yr2: Thameenah Ahmad, Abigail Connor, Viviana Fulfuc, Jason Palmer, Hristina Stoyanova, Sia Szihang

WE USE FILM to design and represent architecture.

We explore animated relationships between architecture and occupants, simulate moving experiences of space, describe dynamic events and speculate on future scenarios.

Our techniques include storyboards, motion-matching, time-based drawing and interactive mock-ups. Our films synthesise real-world situations with inventive propositions, responding to critical observations and anticipating cultural shifts or technological advances.

We adopt conceptual art practices to add complexity and meaning to each frame, to challenge and disrupt conventions of subject and object and find new ways of seeing.

This year we looked at motion in architecture and architecture in motion. We made journeys through space (quick direct routes and choreographed spatial sequences) in search of architecture that permits encounter and elicits delight.

STILL-IMAGE We started the year making large-scale still images to capture the spirit and complexity of our age.

SHORT-CUT We then expanded on the meaning in a single frame to create sixty-second spatial sequences, real-world, real-time points of view, composited with virtual and physical models.

LONG-SHOT These studies were developed into bold ideas for complex, time-based building proposals around Spaghetti Junction in Birmingham. Real-time experiences, daily transitions and seasonal changes are layered with long-term strategies and speculations for dynamic and evolving architecture, including a mobile office tower, a drive-thru parliament, a hydro-electric spa and a residential mega-structure.

TURIN In November we travelled to Turin for the 34th Torino Film Festival. By day we visited the rooftop race-track of the Fiat factory and Nervi's concrete cathedrals, by night we watched experimental films and animations.

Guest Critics:
David Bussell, Christina Christodoulidou, Joseph Frame, James Kirk, Cordula Weisser

Special Thanks:
Roberto Bottazzi, Dusan Decermic, Darren Deane, Richard Difford, Adam Heslop, Jason Bruges Studio, Will McLean, The Workers

FILM FORMAT / STRUCTURE

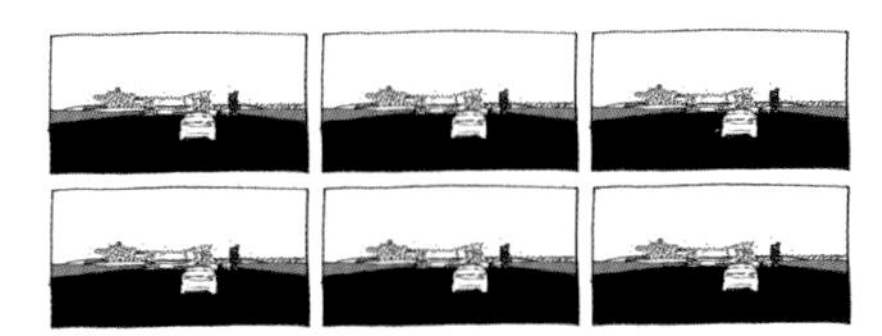

FILM FORMAT - Six screens, each depicting one of the six sequential journeys through the proposal from the approach to the site to the end of the sequence.

SITE APPROACH - Solid roads with hints of space in the background

EXIT FROM THE ROAD

KEY SCENE - S2 -Warm up sequence
CAMERA TECHNIQUE - Handheld, POV, Running
LIGHTING - Natural Lighting, Apertures
AUDIO - Running footsteps

KEY SCENE - S1 - Ground floor Casino
CAMERA TECHNIQUE - Handheld, POV
LIGHTING - Artifical, Bright, Colourful
AUDIO - Slot machines, music

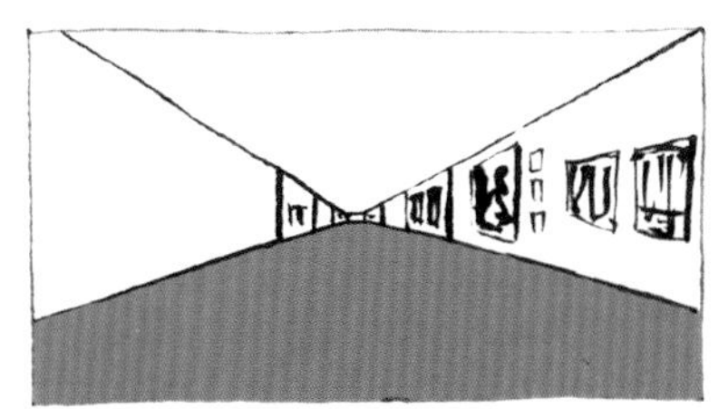

KEY SCENE - S6 - Long walkway - Internal activity
CAMERA TECHNIQUE - Handheld, POV, Walking
LIGHTING - Artifical, Clean lighting, Gallery
AUDIO - Footsteps, whisper

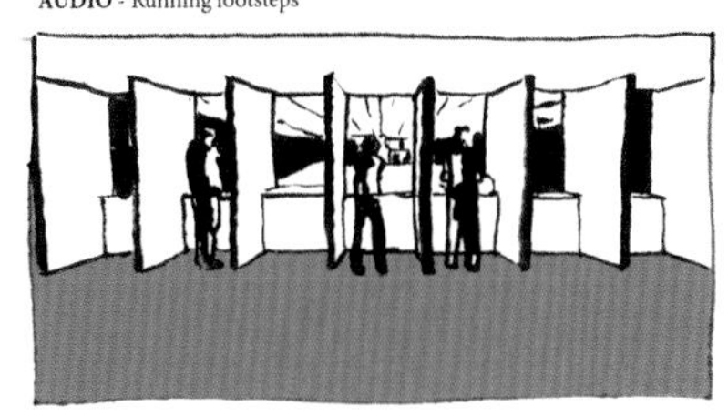

KEY SCENE - S3 - Shooting Range
CAMERA TECHNIQUE - POV, follow bullet
LIGHTING - Artificial, White light
AUDIO - Gunshots

KEY SCENE - S6 - Progression through Long walkway
CAMERA TECHNIQUE - POV, External and internal
LIGHTING - Artifical, Clean even lighting, Gallery, Natural
AUDIO - **Footsteps, whisper**

KEY SCENE - S5 - Restaurant Cafe spaces - key qualities
CAMERA TECHNIQUE - POV, slow movement
LIGHTING - Variable, Exagerate natural lighting
AUDIO - chatting, Music

KEY SCENE - S3 - Virtual Shooting Range
CAMERA TECHNIQUE - POV, between realistic and line render
LIGHTING - Artificial, projection
AUDIO - **mititary speak**

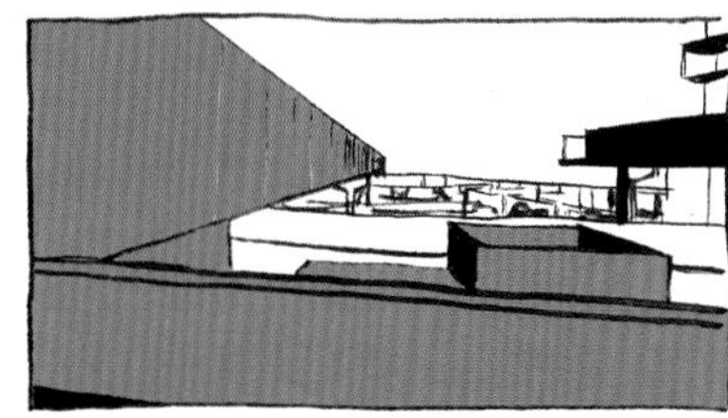

KEY SCENE - S6 - Long walkway Look back, contextualise proposal
CAMERA TECHNIQUE - POV, Stationary
LIGHTING - Natural
AUDIO - **windy, Cars**

KEY SCENE - S1 - Top floor Casino
CAMERA TECHNIQUE - Handheld, POV
LIGHTING - Artifical, Bright, Colourful
AUDIO - Slot machines, music

KEY SCENE - S4 - Exit from sleep
CAMERA TECHNIQUE - POV, slow movement, out of focus
LIGHTING - Overexposed natural lighting
AUDIO - **Windy, Cars**

KEY SCENE - S2 - End of sequence
CAMERA TECHNIQUE - Handheld, POV
LIGHTING - Artificial to natural
AUDIO - **Muffled wind**

KEY SCENE - S2 - Moving onto S6
CAMERA TECHNIQUE - Handheld, POV
LIGHTING - natural
AUDIO - **Windy, Cars**

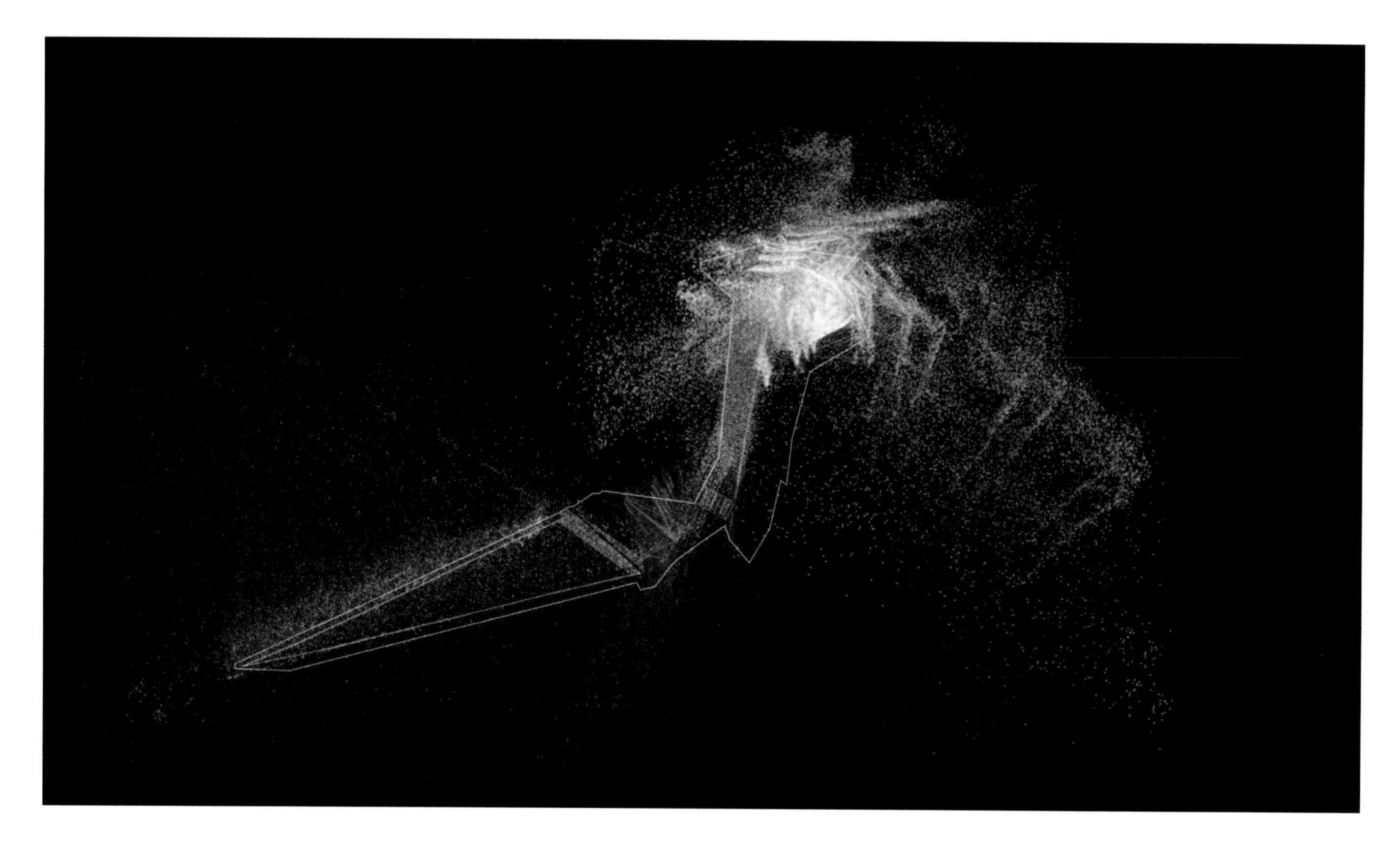

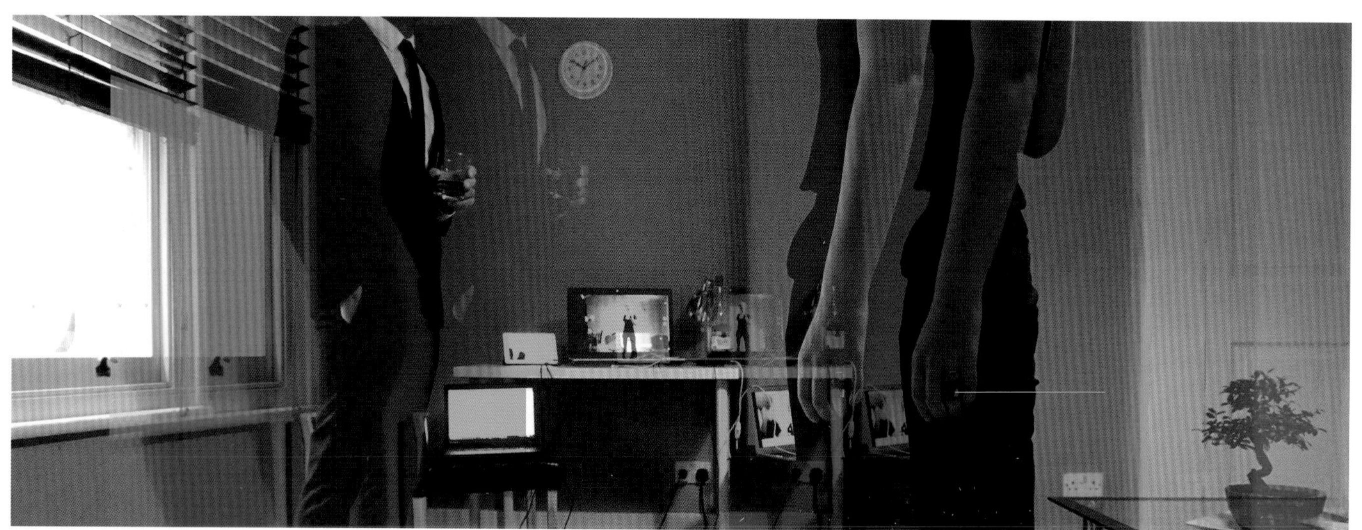

(top) Viviana Fulfuc: *Hydro-Electric Spa*; *(bottom)* Hristina Stoyana: *Mobile Office*

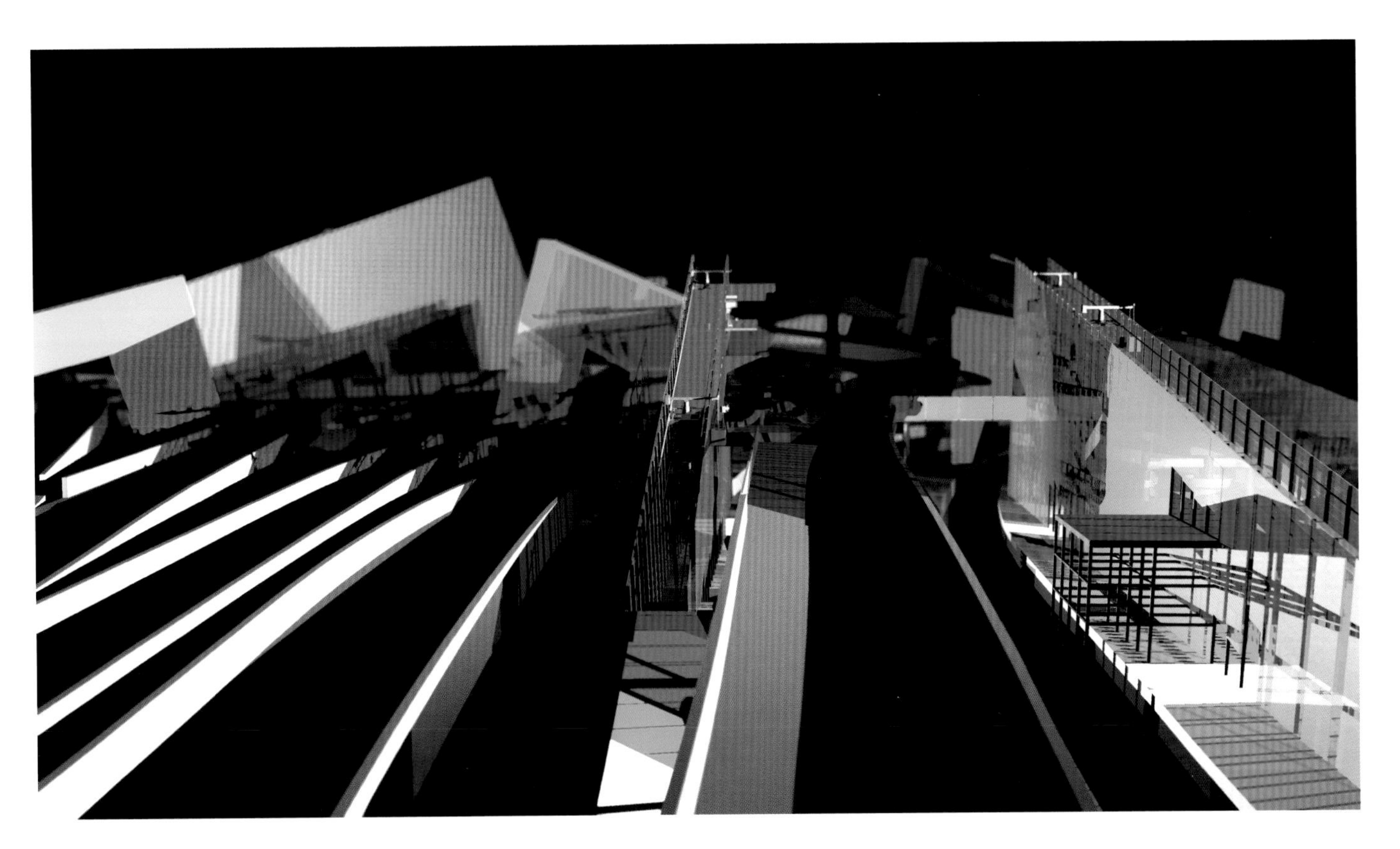

(top) Nathaniel Reading: *Overdrive Festival;* *(bottom)* Tom Kendrew: *Refuge City*

(top) Thameenah Ahmad: *3-Speed Theatre;* *(bottom)* Tom Gorringe: *Leisure Factory*

(top) Saffa Denghani: *Mill*; *(bottom left)* Yannis Hajigeorgis: *Motion Matching*

Clare Carter, Gill Lambert & Nick Wood

The studio *is interested in edgelands. We operate in challenging environments and places of disruption and discontinuity. Working from the everyday, we build a narrative based on local investigations; contextual, historical and spatial. Our approach is about re-invention and re-imagining at these interface conditions, envisaging brighter futures. The post-industrial condition has been our focus this year.*

We also operate in practice: **Gill Lambert** *is Associate at AOC Architecture;* **Nick Wood** *is Founder of How About Studio; and* **Clare Carter** *ran her own practice for over ten years specialising in housing and health.*

DS21: The Great North Way

Yr1: Ruchita Dhokia, Yasmin Elsadig, Alex Fell, Jack Guerrier, Ryan Hinson, Richard Morrison, Gordon O'Connor Read, Martina Staneva, Alexandra Sonechkina

Yr2: Kim Assemat, Mihai Chiriac, Ricky Glover, Roan Howard-Jones, Keaton Howes, Andre Kelly, Simon Nicholls, Edward Rawle, William Swales, Oscar Wilson, Ruby Wilson

WORKING WITHIN A post-industrial landscape, we made propositions for revitalising and re-imagining the town of Doncaster and its former coal mining communities.

The last three deep-pit coal mines closed in December 2015 and the mining industry of Yorkshire came to an end after decades of coal extraction, with consequences for the local economy and community. Doncaster's central location in the UK means it has now become an important distribution centre for companies like Amazon. The recent Brexit vote has exposed a strong division between London and the rest of the country. Doncaster voted Leave.

Within this given context, we began with a forensic study of the land, making richly illustrated mappings. Then working with the material culture of local communities, we made artefacts or tokens inspired by this folk art:

A boiler suit embroidered with poignant moments from the miners' past.

A donkey jacket celebrating the Yorkshire Rose made for wearing as a disobedient object.

A kettle carefully crafted from home-made off-casts.

Themes established in the artefact-making followed through into the major design project, Doncaster Works. Speculating on the idea of a resurgent Doncaster, students considered whether to make a new civic space, repurpose an existing structure or suggest a new industrial infrastructure for Doncaster and its environs.

VIA DONCASTER reinvents the warehouses of the mega distribution centre by creating a craft co-operative creating sustainable products as part of a rich community of makers.

THE PIT CLUB creates a series of carefully located 'golden' interventions in the post-mining landscape; the visitor is given the opportunity to remember the local mining heroes.

RAISE THE ROOF proposes homes for a new community of distribution centre workers spanning over the existing warehouse; the inhabited truss providing spaces to foster the communal spirit which has been lost from the hyper-controlled lives of warehouse workers.

Guest Critics:
Nimi Attanayake (nimtim architects), Robert Brown, Kenzaf Chung, Dominic Cullinan (SCABAL), James Dunn (Weston Williamson), Anthony Engi Meacock (Assemble), Alice Fung (Architecture 00), Will McLean, David Rieser, Heather Ring (Wayward Architects), Fergus Seccombe (Hopkins Architects), Giles Smith (Assemble), Jamie Wakeford (Hayhurst and Co)

Andre Kelly: *Via Doncaster*

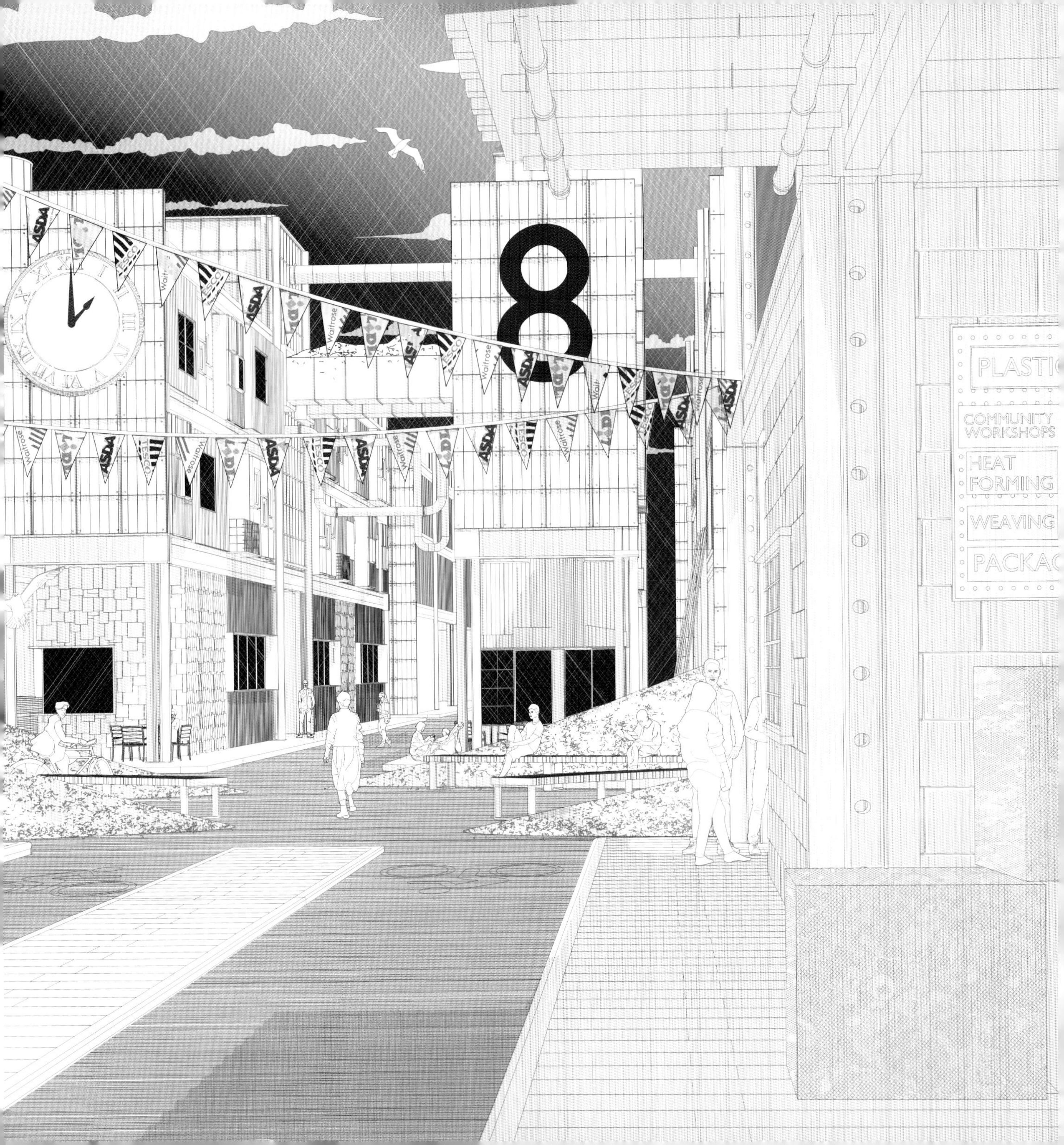
8
ASDA
TESCO
Waitrose
COMMUNITY WORKSHOPS
HEAT FORMING
WEAVING

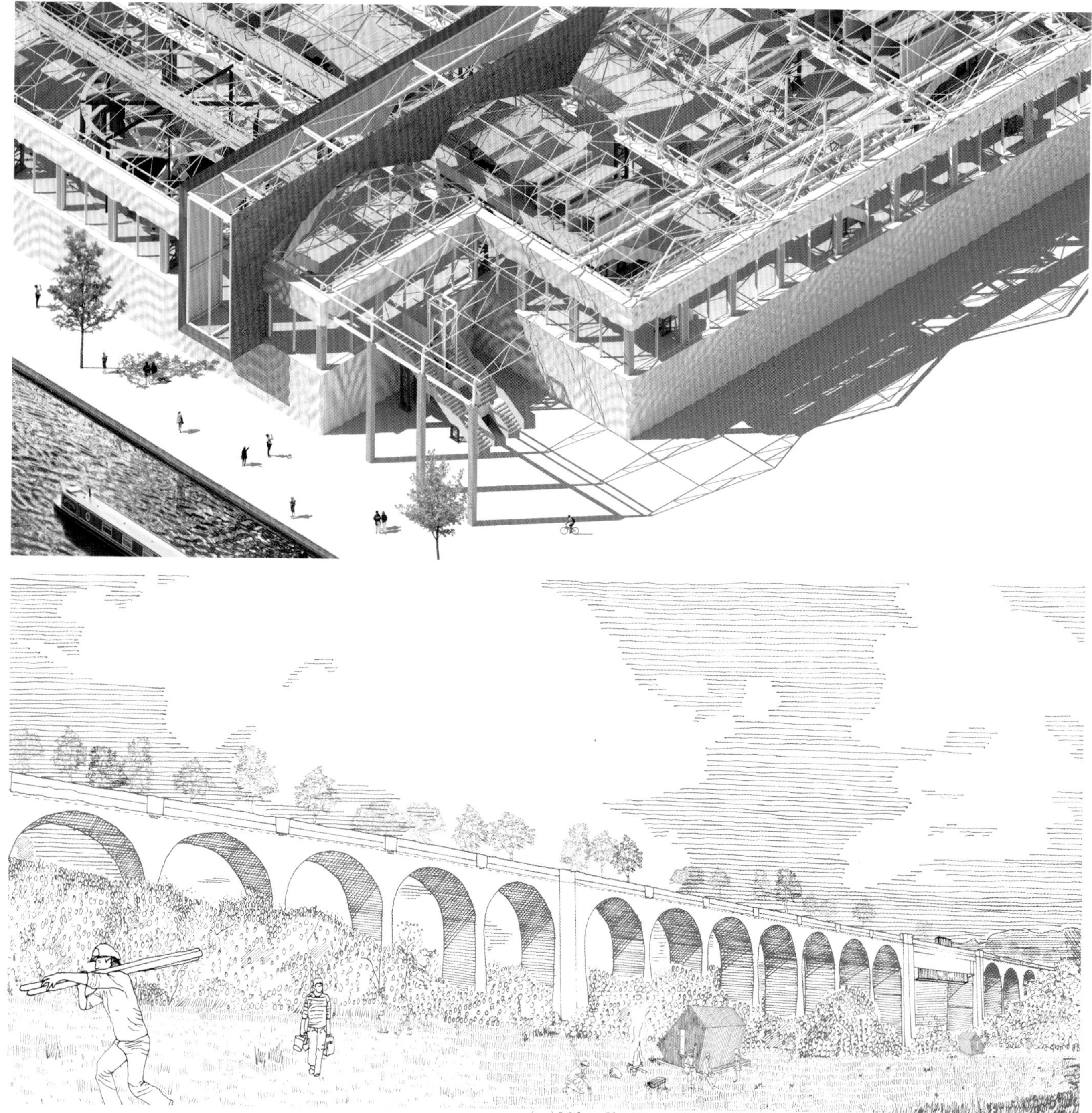

(top) Mihai Chiraic: *Cathedral of Fabrication;* *(bottom)* Ryan Hinson: *Roamers' Retreat;* *(opposite)* Ruby Wilson: *Disobedient Buildings*

(left) Alexander Fell: *Memories of Mining*; *(right)* Keaton Howes: *Monuments of a Colliery: The Pit Club*

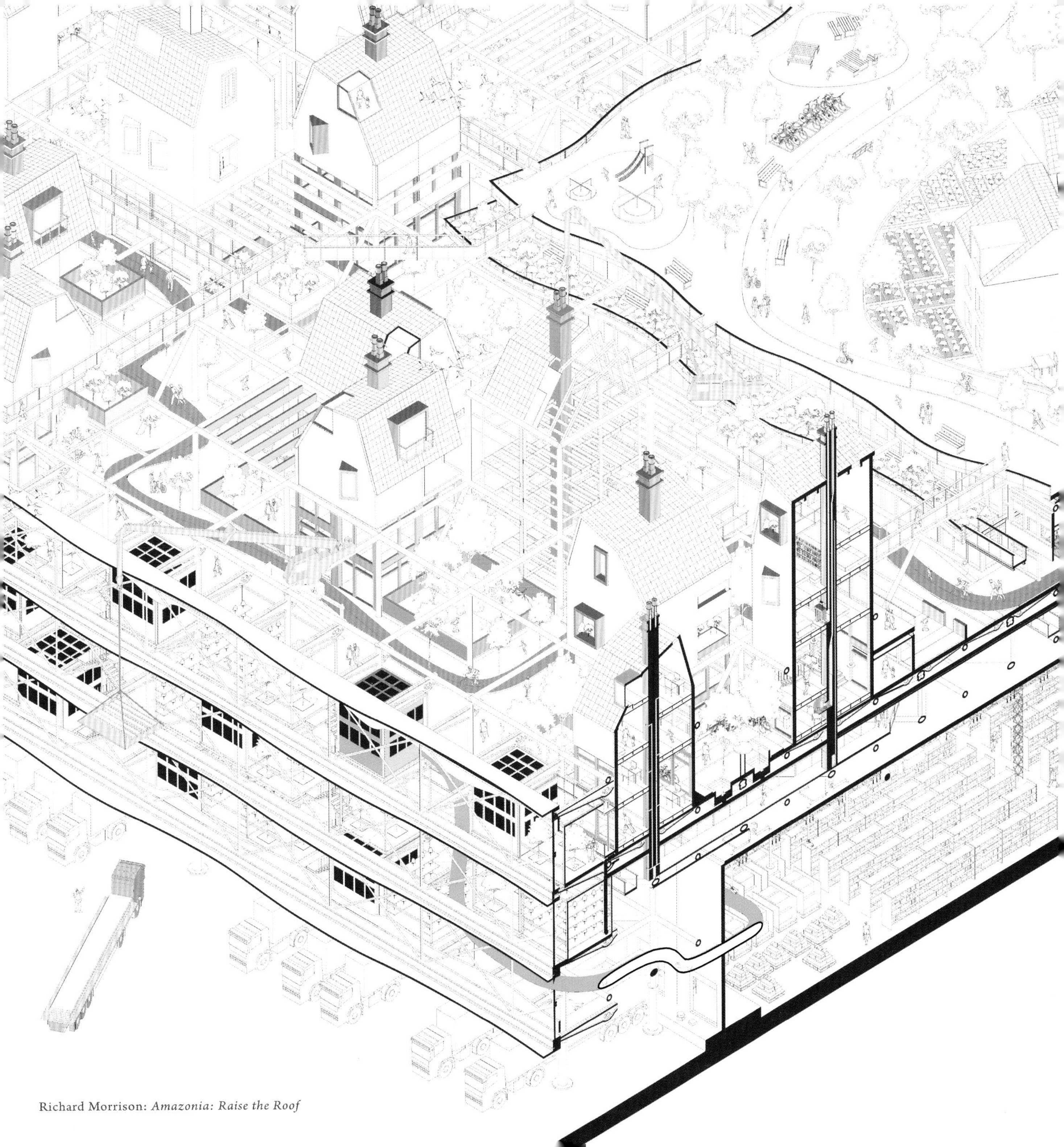

Richard Morrison: *Amazonia: Raise the Roof*

Nasser Golzari & Yara Sharif

Nasser Golzari and Yara Sharif *are practicing architects and academics with an interest in design as a mean to facilitate and create resilient communities within contested geography. Combining research with design, their work runs parallel between their architecture practice NG Architects, London, and Design Studio 22 at the University of Westminster. They co-founded Palestine Regeneration Team (PART), a design-led research group that aims through speculative and live design projects to search for creative and responsive spatial possibilities. Golzari and Sharif's collaborative live projects have won a number of awards including the 2013 Agha Khan Award, 2014 Holcim Award for Sustainable Construction, and recently RIBA President's Award for Research 2016 on Cities and Communities Category (Commendation).*

DS22: This Sea is Mine

Yr1: Alistair Backhouse, Rafaella Christodoulidi, Clarissa Evans, Sophia Gravina, Hussein Houta, Anna Malicka, Iza Sasaran, Pippa Skingsley, Xin Swift, John Wildsmith, Costas Xenophontos

Yr2: Chirag Desai, Lisa Gustavsson, Konstantina Loli David, Asif Mubarak Khan, Tulshi Patel, Zhini Poh, Esme Rothwell, Aurelija Virsilaite

WE AIM TO create a strong link between practice, research and academia. Our way of working as a design-led studio is close to how projects develop in our practice with a continuous process of testing, experimenting and making, combining research with design. This triangular relationship adds richness to the experience of the students as they get involved in speculative as well as live projects.

In this academic year, we continued our 'research by design' journey across 'absent' and uncertain landscapes where time and mobility have become irrelevant. This time, however, we started the journey from the sea, and more specifically the Mediterranean Sea – which is becoming a prototype for the hyper-connected and enduringly fragile world of the present. Leading to the edges of the Red Sea, Dead Sea and the Perisan Gulf, we tried to unpack and expose the hidden layers and dynamic potentials of coastal cities.

The Sea, which is becoming a 'theatre of the absurd', has been omitted from the common narratives. Subsequently, it has been transformed into another component of escape and entrapment for those fleeing uncertainty today. Yet, this same sea can be re-claimed to include, stitch, empower and position the excluded absent cities and communities back on the map.

Stemming from the need for an alternative discourse and a critical form of architectural practice that engage with spatial, social and environmental realities, the studio reconstructed new architectural narratives on the sea and at its coastal edge to create responsive proposals that can nourish a space of possibility and imagination.

The studio started its journey from the water edges of the Persian Gulf and the Mediterranean, designing series' of interactive devices that can feel the invisible coastal cities, or interact with the human movement on the surface of the land, or map those trapped at the edges, or within the sea with their absent narratives. These later lead to the main design projects exploring how architecture can provoke, subvert and awaken the coastal cities of Haifa, Jaffa, Gaza, Abadan, and Qeshm, some of which have been trapped at the edge of the sea and left with their architecture to be 'arrested' and frozen in time.

Guest Critics:
Salem Al Qudwa, Pierre d'Avoine, Hannah Bauhman, Anthony Boulanger, Lindsay Bremner, Harry Charrington, Alia Daoud, Darren Dean, Davide Deriu, Richard Difford, Maria Jose Arenas Escobar, Alejandro Gutierrez Fabregat, Ron Kenley, Charlotte Khatso, Benson Lau, Andrei Martin, Jane Mcallister, Robert Mull, Ciaran O'Brian, Samir Pandya, Andrew Peckham, Mirna Pedalo, Chris Pierce, Dean Robson, Gabby Shawcross, Victoria Thong, Filip Visnjic

Special Thanks:
Andreas Christodoulou, Robert Mull and Christopher Pierce for their support

Esme Rothwell: *Predictive Analytics Paradise*

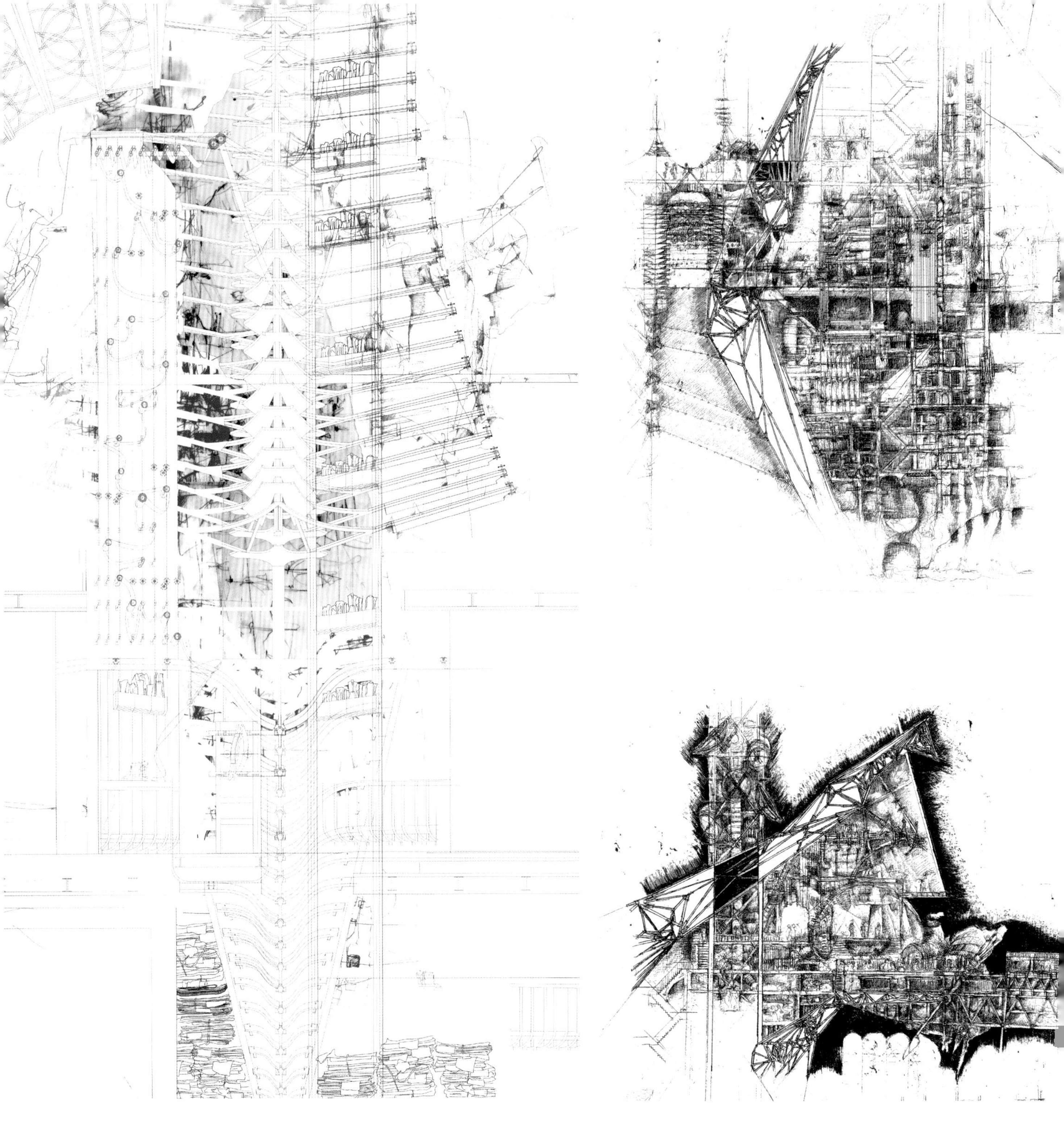

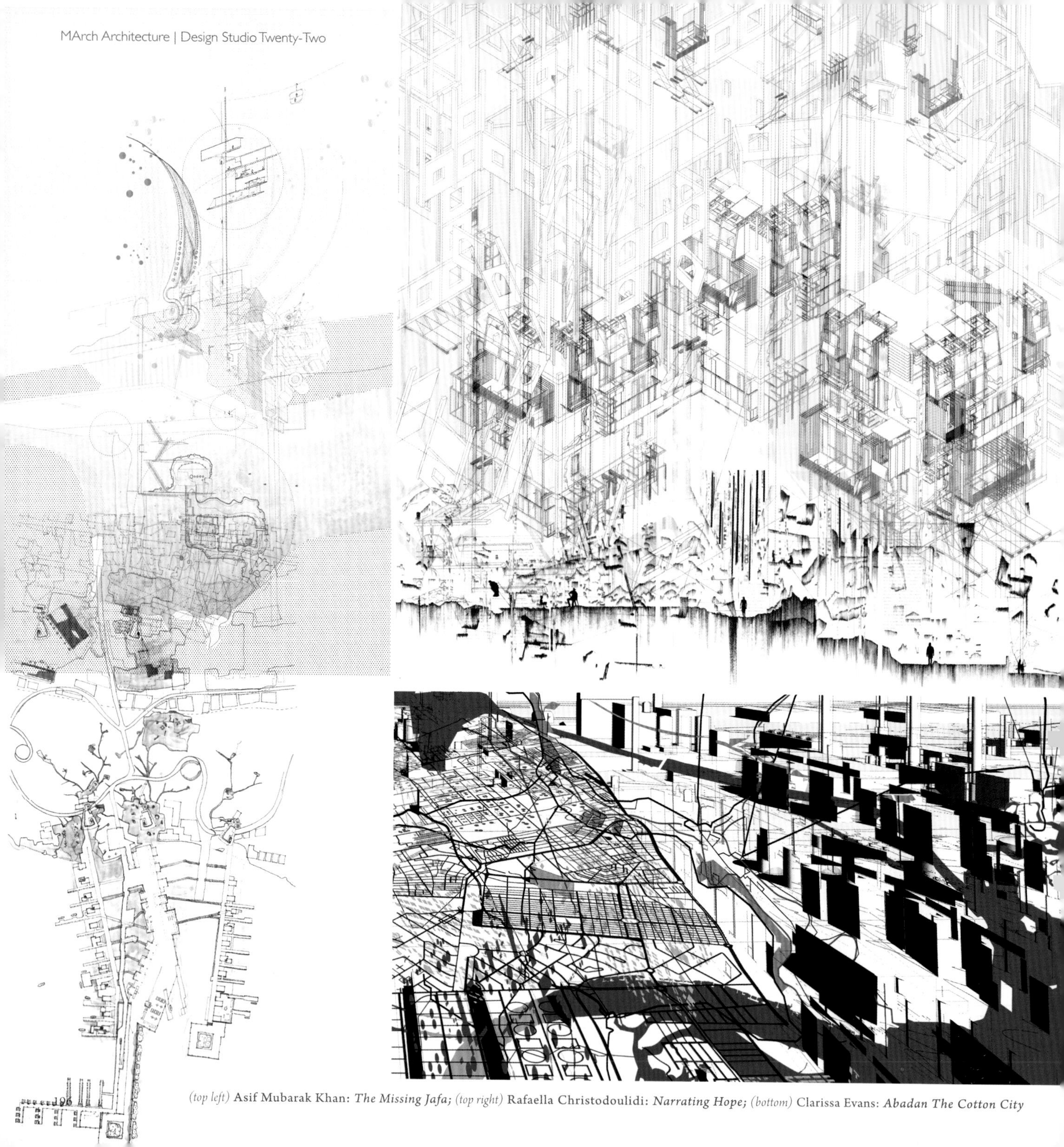

(top left) Asif Mubarak Khan: *The Missing Jafa;* *(top right)* Rafaella Christodoulidi: *Narrating Hope;* *(bottom)* Clarissa Evans: *Abadan The Cotton City*

(top) Zhini Poh: *The Breathing Port of Suza;* *(bottom)* Tulshi Patel: *Allegory of Sand*

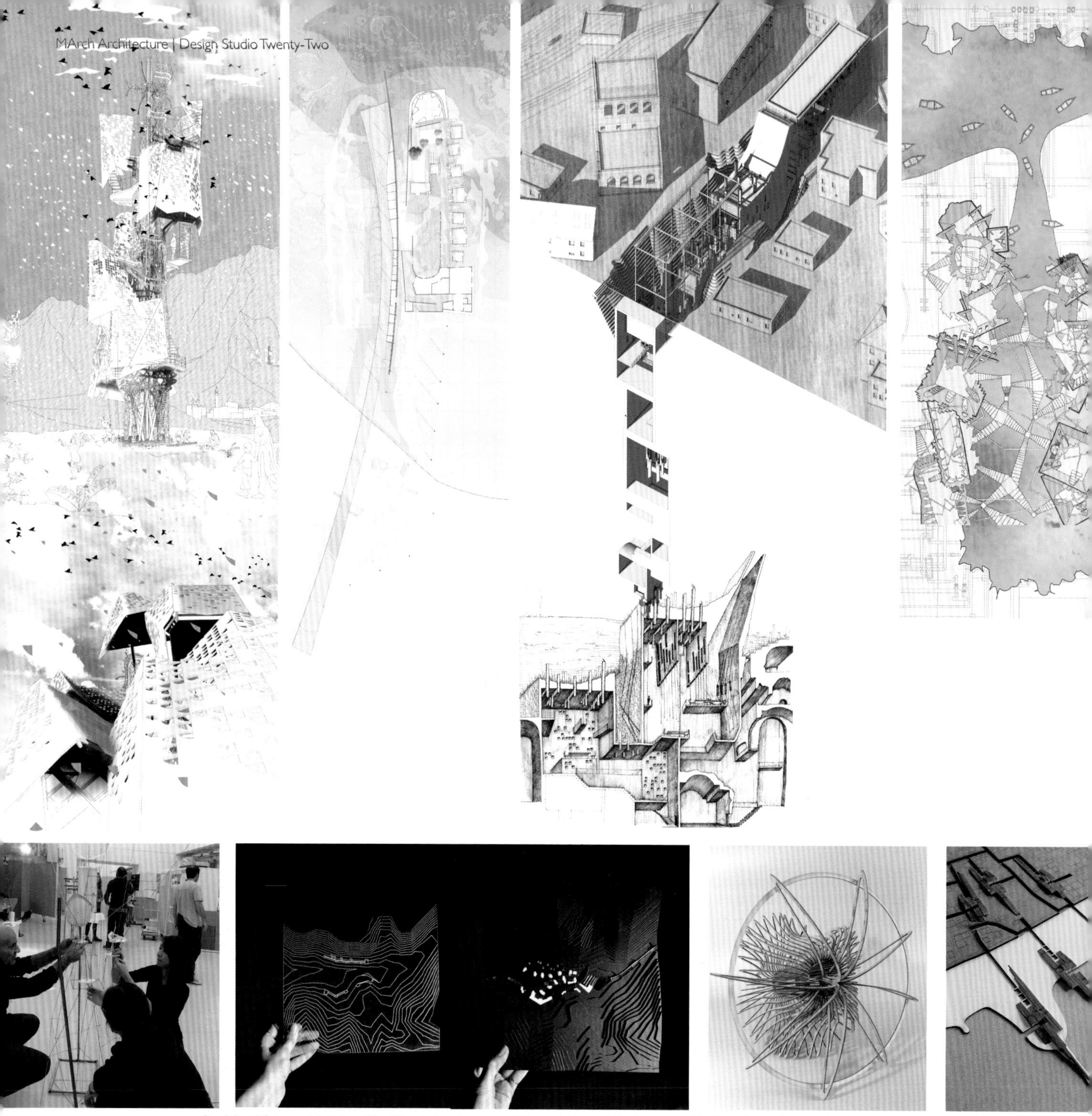

(top left-right) Anna Malicka: *The Cloud;* Iza Sassaran: *Women's Port of Qeshm;* Aurelija Virsilaite: *Slim Archeolog;* Xin Swift: *The Collaged City;*
(bottom left to right) Zhini Poh and Xin Swift: *The Pearls Device;* Philippa Skingsley: *Model;* Lisa Gustavsson: *Fishing without Water, Farming without Land*

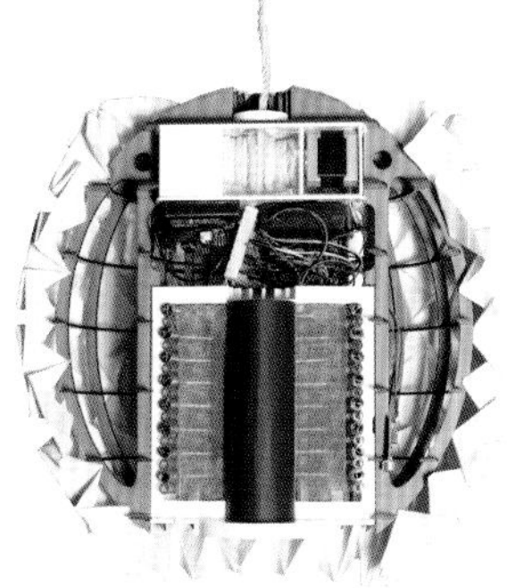

(top) John Wildsmith: *Stitching Corridors; (bottom left)* Alistair Backhouse: *Fishing Light; (bottom right)* Costas Xenophontos: *The Time Device*

How do we talk about architecture when what constitutes architecture is not architectural?

Jean Nouvel 1997

ARCHITECTURE IS ALWAYS a renovation, a remaking of places. Architects design relationships not objects, and an architectural project is a fragment of a network; always connected to, and always part of, something else: individuals, society, history, landscape, physical and social ecologies, climate, materials, and technology.

The Department therefore offers students, alongside the synthetic design studio, opportunities to develop their design capability within a context of continually extending theoretical and critical knowledge – broadly ethical and professional studies, history and theory, environmental and technical studies.

Harry Charrington
Head of the Department of Architecture

BEYOND THE STUDIO

A History of Architecture

Module leaders: Sarah Milne, Richard Watson, Victoria Watson

with contributions from: Nicola Allett, Eva Branscome, Claire Brunnen, Harry Charrington, Corinna Dean, Elantha Evans, Kate Jordan, Gwyn Lloyd Jones, Mike Rose, Shahed Saleem, Kate Squire

PALs: Duncan Catterall, Nouha Hansen, Roan Howard-Jones, Min Kang, Chris Mannings, Cristina Poescu, Iza Sasaran, Mirabell Schmidt, Will Swales, Alexandra Wojciak

The History and Theory courses at the PCL are essential in the development of both critical ability and creativity. The object is to give the student an understanding of 'the language of architecture' in relation to ideology, through the study of whole cultural complexes. It should also enable the student to recognise certain architectural themes which persist through technical and social change and to understand their transformations.

Alan Colquhoun, Architecture Unit, Polytechnic of Central London, History & Theory, *AD 46*, July 1976

THIS YEAR WE launched the new Undergraduate History and Theory programme into the Learning Future, beginning with CC1: A History of Architecture. The module is shared by the first year BA Architecture and BA Interior Architecture courses, to be joined in the coming academic year by BSc Architecture & Environmental Design. CC1 explores spatial principles and key movements in Western architectural history from the classical period to postmodernism in the late twentieth century. It introduces reading, writing and research skills, equipping students to closely observe and participate in architectural culture. Taking advantage of Westminster's location, there is a particular emphasis on London's buildings. The module is taught by means of slideshow lectures, interactive workshops, and invited presentations from librarians and archivists. It includes building visits and walks to a diverse range of locations and places in London. The accompanying photograph captures a small group of students preparing themselves to enter Ernő Goldfinger's controversial modernist intervention at 2 Willow Road, Hampstead.

This year's pioneer cohort rose well to Alan Colquhoun's challenge; perhaps a little bemused at the start, they proved to be highly receptive to the novelty of engaging with 'architectural language.' Some excellent workbook pages were produced, samples of which are shown on the page opposite, and competent essays were written. Both workbook and essay test and demonstrate criticality and creativity, requiring understanding and control of architectural media including words, buildings, drawings and the relationships between them.

One important feature of CC1 is the contribution made by the MArch teaching PALs, who formally act as guides on the building visits and walks and informally as mentors to the students.

(above) ***visit to Goldfinger's Willow Road, Hampstead;*** *(opposite - clockwise from top left)* **Maciej Worosilak, Sabreh Islam, Larisa Manga, Ella Daley, Eylem Bekem**

THE REGENTS PARK MOSQUE

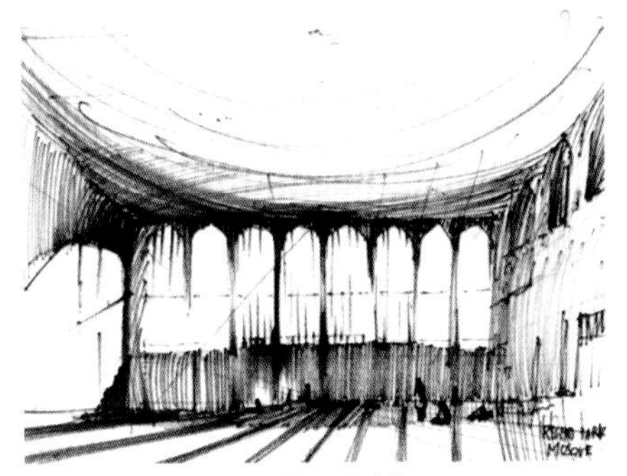

view of the praying hall

An international competition was held in 1969 to find a suitable design and was won by Sir Frederick Gibberd, one of the first generation of British Modernist architects and very much a member of the architectural establishment at the time.

Imposing Freemasonary Entrance

were prepared in accordance with ancient custom, so that you could be recieved at the door of the lodge, admitted into the presence of Brethren, intergrogated, obugated, brought to life, instructed, entrusted, proved and invested, as Freemasons have been from time immemorial '(1)

Part of the University of the Arts London colleges, Central St Martins is an art school located in the midst of kings cross's current large scale re generation project. The regeneration is seeing the re use of de indus trialised buildings, Cen tral St Martins being an example of this. Once a granary building designed by Lewis Cubitt (the same architect who did the station), it was restored for its current use as a place of higher educa tion. The spatial princi ple of the atrium can be applied to restored gra nary warehouse due to the large elongated skylights stretching over the roof of 'The Street' (An area inside the campus that is used for recreation al activities and eat ing etc.). The skylights give the impression that the space is exterior, furthering the 'street' characteristics that have intentionally been opti mized.

Rough plan conducted on site.

Personally, I was engrossed by the huge scale development swallowing the whole area around Central St Martins. The restoration of neigh bouring warehouses have the difficult task of preserving the historical content of the area, while paving the way for modern innovation and meeting the new demands of people.

The Royal College of Physicians

The Royal College of Physicians is a British professional body dedicated to improving the practice of medicine, chiefly through the accreditation of physicians by examination. Founded in 1518, it set the first international standard in the classification of diseases, and its library contains medical texts of great historical interest.

The current headquarters of the Royal College of Physicians (RCP) is a Grade I listed building designed by renowned architect Sir Denys Lasdun (1914-2001). Opened in 1964 next to Regent's Park, it is widely considered a modernist masterpiece and one of London's most important post-war buildings.

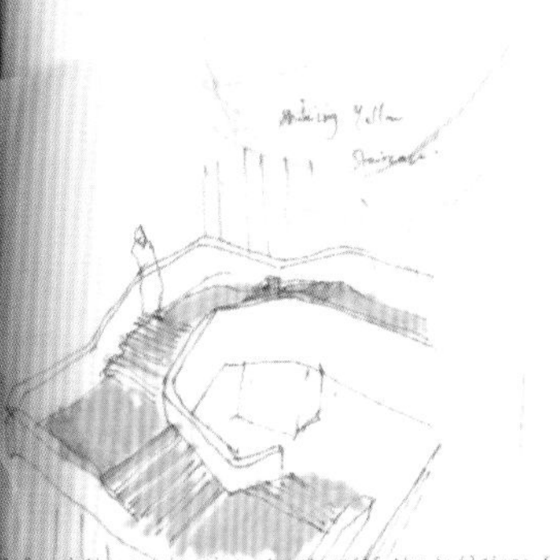

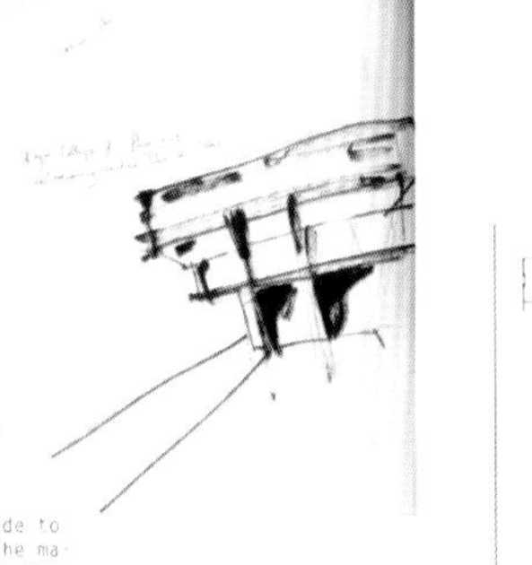

I found the overhanging structure of the buildings facade to be striking, but the yellow stairs were even more so. The materiality of the building was intricate with handmade marble and porcelain tiling covering the entirety of the facade. The entire building is a gian cantilever mwhich was intended to look as though it were floating. However, this is obstructed by the two pillars at the entrance which was a necessity.

The RCP follows four of the Spatial principles such as the Atriam, Stoa, Temple, and Megaron.

The Atrium - Walk

A System of Spatial Principles

In the global age the atrium principle continues to appear in the design of houses, department stores, hotels, club. But it also begins to appear in the design of what is sometimes called public space

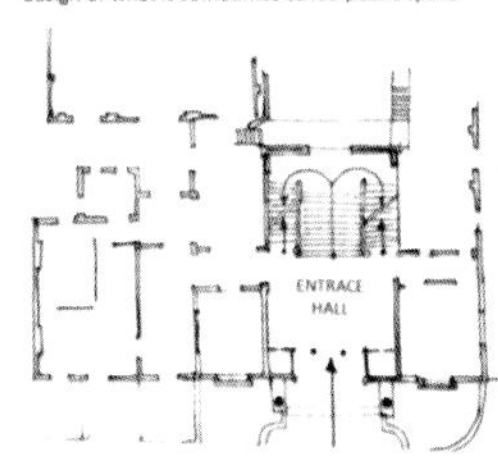

The Royal Institute of British Architects expresses the atrium principle. Once we enter the building, we can see the enclosed space, a large interior hall preceded by a court yard

In my sketches I tried to show the spatial principle of the atrium and how every space is linked to one another

In this sketch I tried to represent to front facade of the building with the entrace

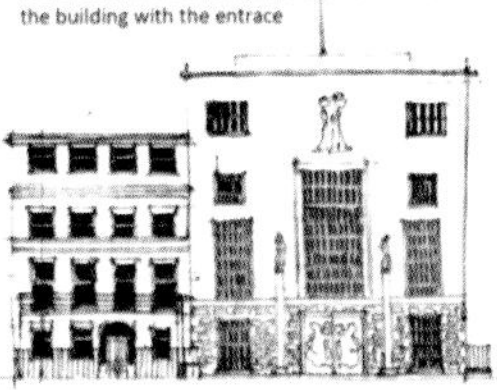

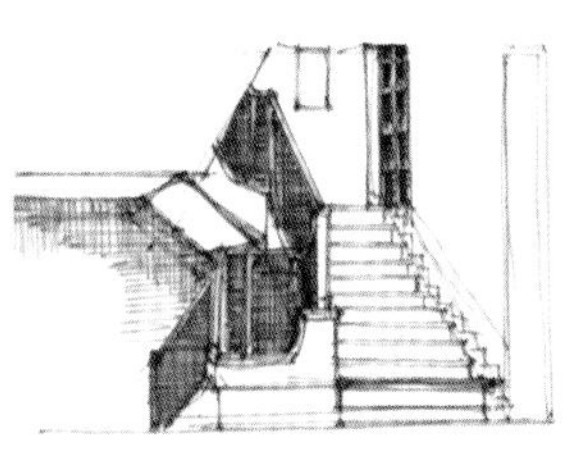

Once we enter the building we can see a large hall, with wide stairs that lead you to the first floor of the building. From the outside the building seems really small, but once we enter, the space is bigger than we can imagine. The ceiling is really high and has big brown columns

As I said, The Royal Institute of British Architects expresses the atrium principle because the persons gathered in the atrium are unknown to one another and they all have something in common because they share the same space

RIBA Atrium and main staircase sketch

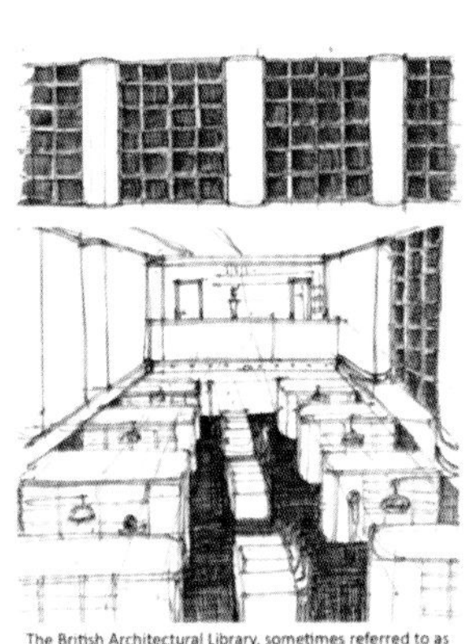

The British Architectural Library, sometimes referred to as the RIBA Library, was established in 1834 upon the founding of the institute with donations from members. Now, with over four million items, it is one of the three largest architectural libraries in the world and the largest in Europe

Cultural Context Extended Essay

Darren Deane, François Girardin, Jon Goodbun, Platon Issaias, Gwyn Jones, Kate Jordan, Constance Lau, Sarah Milne, Mike Rose, Shahed Saleem, Rachel Stevenson, Ben Stringer (module leader) & John Zhang

IN THEIR FINAL YEAR, BA Architecture and BA Interior Architecture students devise their own research topics for an extended essay and are tutored through their research and writing by a diverse group of academics. 2016/17 was another very good year, with an extremely varied array of subjects studied and written about and high numbers of students achieving distinction level grades.

Students typically put a lot of energy and critical thinking into their research and writing on this course. Although there was a very wide range of subjects under investigation this year, one can discern some ongoing trends: social housing and gentrification continues to attract quite a lot of (much needed) attention, as do case studies of particular issues of urban politics and sociology in cities around the world, which reflects the international nature of our student body. This year, a significant number of students also took on more architectural historical subjects, particularly from the mid-twentieth century and sometimes as a means to learn about architecture's relationships with philosophies and ideas from other disciplines.

Some of the many notable examples from the year include: Chris McManigan's study of Robin Hood Gardens; Abigail Hinchley's investigation into the meaning of home; Muhammad Hussain's study of modular construction; Katie Haigh's study of post-war prefabricated housing in the UK; Maciej Jungerman's study of Warsaw's cross city line stations; Myungin Li's re-reading of of the Trans-Siberian Railway as heterotopia; and Ola Hjelen's study of the role of architecture in the re-building of the Norwegian community of Åndalsnes.

(t l) Chris McManigan: ***Robin Hood Graffiti***
(b l) Abigail Haigh: ***Saenredam: Interieur van de Nieuwe Kerk te Haarlem, 1652*** *(Pieter Jansz Saenredam)*

(t r) Katie Haigh: ***Grade II listed prefab house, Wake Green Road Estate***
(c r) Maciej Jungerman: ***Warszawa Powisle Station*** *(© Piotr Mamnaimie)*
(b l) Ola Hjelen: ***Drawing of Åndalsnes, 1918, by Sverre Pedersen*** *(courtesy Norwegian National Library)*

Robin Hood

SZAWA POWIŚLE
LUSTRA

Technical Studies

Pete Silver, Will McLean, Scott Batty, Chris Leung & Andrew Whiting

THE TECHNICAL STUDIES teaching in the Department of Architecture at the University of Westminster has been designed as a linear progression from first year Undergraduate through to final year MArch. For each year of study, a lecture series underpins the structure of the teaching. In first year undergraduate, a fourteen-week lecture series is delivered by Pete Silver that sets out an approach to the structure, form, material and environmental principles that constitute the technology of the built environment. In second year undergraduate, Scott Batty runs the Site Diary project giving students their first experience of a construction site. During the first semester, Will McLean organises the Thursday evening 'open' lecture series to highlight new developments in the fields of architecture, engineering and environmental design.

We have embedded different types of teaching input and feedback throughout the BA and MArch courses and we regularly invite architects, engineers and other specialists to act as informal 'technical' tutors to the students during their final design projects. We host regular Friday afternoon tutorial sessions where visiting specialists act as consultants to our final year BA Architecture and MArch students in a relaxed 'studio' atmosphere. This specialist input (as in practice) helps to focus the work of the student in regards to structural clarity, visual comprehension and environmental sustainability.

http://technicalstudies.tumblr.com

Guest Lecturers and Visiting Consultants:
Simon Allford (AHMM), Matt Barnett-Howland (MPH), Roz Barr (Roz Barr Architects), Paul Bavister (Audialsense/UCL), Giovanni Beggio (RPP), Jago Boase (StructureMode), Christine Cambrook (Buro Happold), Christina Christodolou, Conrad Cherniavsky (Waind Gohil Potter), Joseph Conteh (JU:KO), Rachel Eccles (Hût Architecture), Christophe Egret (Studio Egret West), Nick Emmony (Laing O'Rourke), Julie Fleck (Construction Industry Council), Emma Flynn (AStudio), Allan Haines (EDICCT), Cath Hassell (ech2o), Dave Heeley (Morph Structures), Ed Hollis (Structuremode), Oliver Houchell (Houchell Studio), Rob Garvey (UoW), Jacques Gaudin (StructureMode), Katy Ghahremani (Make), John Griffiths (Ooma Design), Rowland Keable (Rammed Earth Consulting), Yashin Kemal (RPP), David Kendall (Optima Projects), Christian Kerrigan (AStudio), Benson Lau (UoW), Paul Maddock (HTA), Geoff Morrow (Structuremode), Robin Partington (Robin Partington and Partners), David Rayment (Morph Structures), Rosa Schiano-Phan (UoW), Esther Rivas Adrover (University of Cambridge), Enric Ruiz-Geli (Cloud 9), John Spittle (Wiehag), Phil Waind, (Waind Gohil Potter), Andrew Watts (Newtecnic), Graham West (West Architecture)

hnical studies TS6A
eoff Morrow
uremode
neering Humanitarian Projects
Oct 6pm Room M416
technical studies TS2A
Graham West
West Architecture
Fitzrovia House
3rd Oct 4pm Room M416
technical studies TS6A
Emma Flynn + Christian Kerrigan
AStudio
Living Architecture
3rd Nov 6pm Room M416
technical studies TS6A
Christophe Egret
Studio Egret West
Recent Projects
10th Nov 6pm Room M416
technical studies TS3A
Chris Leung
BiotA Lab Bartlett / UCL
Bio-Receptivity
7th Oct 2pm Room Cayley
technical studies TS3A
Rowland Keable
Rammed Earth Consulting
Rammed Earth
14th Oct 2pm Room Cayley
hnical studies TSIP
avid Kendall
ma Projects
re Reinforced Polymers
h Feb 2pm Room M416
technical studies TS2A
Rosa Schiano-Phan
Environmental Design
31st Oct 4pm Room M416
technical studies TS6A
Robin Partington
Robin Partington & Partners
...two nails and a piece of string....
13th Oct 6pm Room M416
technical studies TS6A
Enric Ruiz-Geli
Cloud 9
20th Oct 6pm Room M416
technical studies TS3A
Cath Hassell
ech2o Consultants
Low Carbon Technologies
21st Oct 2pm Room Cayley
technical studies TS2A
Scott Batty
Making Architecture Briefing
24th Oct 4pm Room M416
chnical studies TS6A
aul Maddock
A Design
e Heartlands Project
h Oct 6pm Room M416
technical studies TS3A
Christine Cambrook
Burohappold
Health + Wellbeing
28th Oct 2pm Room Cayley
technical studies TS2A
Rachel Eccles
Hût Architecture
Greenwood Road
10th Oct 4pm Room M416
technical studies TS6A
Matt Barnett-Howland
MPH Architects
Building With Cork
8th Dec 6pm Room M416
technical studies TS2A
John Griffiths
Ooma Design
21st Nov 4pm Room M416
technical studies TS6A
Simon Allford
AHMM
Extra Ordinary + WCF
24th Nov 6pm Room M416
chnical studies TS3A
ther Rivas Adrover
rsity of Cambridge
eployable Structures
th Nov 2pm Room Cayley
technical studies TS2A
Scott Batty + Will McLean
Super Models
28th Nov 4pm Room M416
technical studies TS3A
Paul Bavister
Sound, Music, Acoustics +
Architecture
2nd Dec 2pm Room Cayley
technical studies TS2A
Roz Barr
Roz Barr Architects
14th Nov 4pm Room M416
technical studies TSIP
Pete Silver
Structural Stonework +
Reinforced Concrete
20th Jan 2pm Room M416
technical studies TSIP
Will McLean
Air Supported Structures
27th Jan 2pm Room M416

Dissertation

Douglas Spencer (module leader), John Bold, Harry Charrington, Davide Deriu, Richard Difford, Andrew Peckham, Jeanne Sillett, Ben Stringer

GROUNDED IN A History and Theory course, students choose their own subject to explore in the Dissertation, guided by tutors with a range of specialisms and methods. We encourage a wide range of topics and a plurality of approaches with the intention that the work produced will be distinguished by its high quality rather than by adherence to a rigid methodology or a School style.

Thameenah Ahmad

Disney-llusion explores the role of simulation, spectacle and the 'virtual' in architecture. Focused, in part, on older examples such as Disneyland and Disney World, the dissertation also considers more contemporary forms of spatially immersive media, such as video games and virtual reality. The implications of these simulated realities are explored in terms of how they impact upon and shape our experience of the designed environment.

Claire Humphreys

A collection of anthropological stories about the multi-cultural home, based on a familial history of domestic spaces, *Home: Adopted Britishness* reveals the 'home' as the main protagonist in challenging transnational belonging and shifting rituals. Focused on lived experience, this dissertation draws upon a post-colonial history that needs to be remembered, again, for an increasingly mobile population.

Elise Alden

Spaces of Places draws upon Doreen Massey's writings on space and the phenomenology of Christian Norberg Schulz in order to produce a mapping of the Swedish architect Sigurd Lewerentz's St Peter's Church. Also drawing upon site visits and archival research, the dissertation questions notions of space and place, and explores the tensions between localised and globalised perceptions of these though Lewerentz's architecture.

Benjamin Ellis

Blue, the Body and a Leap: Architecture of the Instant explores the work of French artist Yves Klein, who laid down one of the most intriguing and beguiling adventures in Modern art history, as he stepped beyond the canvas in response to the short-comings of his contemporaries to achieve the seemingly impossible feat of making the invisible visible through physical means.

(top left) Thameenah Ahmad: *Disneyland, Orlando*
(bottom) Claire Humphreys: *Adopted Britishness: Father's family, Mother's family*

(top right) Elise Alden: *Space of Places: Exterior/Interior of St. Peter's Church, designed by Sigurd Lewerentz*
(centre right) Benjamin Ellis: *The street where Klein produced his famous work* Leap into the Void

Raluca Ciorbaru

Architecture, Body and Motion in the Renaissance focuses upon Alberti's theories of pictorial composition and Michelangelo's transition from scuplture to architecture. Analysing drawings, paintings and scuplture, it speculates on how bodily motion was interpreted as a way of understanding and visualising movementm, and deployed as a unit of metric order, in the design process of Renaissance architecture

Arinola Abisola Oladeji

Building on Tradition, Appropriations of Local Histories in the Post-War Neighbourhoods of Italy focuses on the rehousing programme which took place in Matera, once known as the 'Shame of Italy', where designers fixated on vernacular motifs and the 'simple man' to produce hygienic and morally suitable homes for cave-dwellers in a new era of 'Neorealism' that swept Italy between the 1940-60s.

Rhiain Bower

Bariscio: The Slate Quarrymen's Barracks presents a study of the barrack dwelling slate quarrymen of north-west Wales. Out of sight and out of mind, these industrial dwellings have been overlooked since their construction 150 years ago, despite the important story they tell of the men who sacrificed their family lives to extract the slate that roofed the industrial world.

Rosemary Sonnenschein

Stonebridge: An Architectural Narrative of Life in Social Housing explores the impact the architecture of social housing in Stonebridge, London, had on people's lives in various forms throughout history. Each chapter contains a fictional, first person narrative. Based on extensive research, and with an emphasis on direct observations and interviews, these narratives are employed to unearth wider meanings from sources of personal experience.

(top left) Raluca Ciorbaru: *Architecture, Body and Motion in the Renaissance*
(bottom left) Rhiain Bower: *The Slate Quarrymen's Barracks*

(top right) Arinola Abisola Oladeji: *Matera (Sasso Caveoso)*
(bottom right) Rosemary Sonnenschein: *Stonebridge Collage*

Digital Representation

Richard Difford (module leader), Alessandro Ayuso, Miriam Dall'Igna, Jeg Dudley, Adam Holloway, Gabby Shawcross

UNDERTAKEN IN THE first semester of the first year on the MArch, the Digital Representation module provides the opportunity to learn some key computer skills and to reflect critically on the use of digital media in architecture. The module offers a choice of six different groups, each with a different focus and set of interests. The tutors for these groups are drawn from both practice and academia, providing critical reflection on the role of digital technology in architecture along with practical experience and technical expertise. Each group combines technical instruction with related theory and precedents. In this way everyone gets a chance to learn something new and to build on their existing knowledge and experience.

The six groups this year were as follows:

GROUP A: **Digital Craft**

Adam Holloway

Utilising digital fabrication and generative modelling tools, this group uses simulation and prototyping as part of a recursive cycle of testing and refinement in the design process.

GROUP B: **Performative Parametrics**

Jeg Dudley

Using evolutionary algorithms and project-specific analysis tools, this group sets out to construct and optimise parametric designs based on performative criteria.

GROUP C: **Computational Design**

Miriam Dall'Igna

Drawing on contemporary scripting and parametric modelling techniques, this group explores the potential for geometrically-driven computational design.

GROUP D: **Interactive Technologies**

Richard Difford

Focusing on the use of programmable graphics and physical computing, this group considers the way devices such as sensors, motors and lights can be used to construct responsive architectural features and environments.

GROUP E: **Film Making**

Gabby Shawcross

Concentrating on the creative opportunities presented by film-making, this group investigates the use of digital video editing and post-production tools.

GROUP F: **Body Agents**

Alessandro Ayuso

This group explores the relationship between design and bodies using modelling, animation, rigging and motion capture to create body agents – architectural meta inhabitants.

(top) Group A - Emilia Kalyvides; *(bottom)* Group B - Charlotte Birch

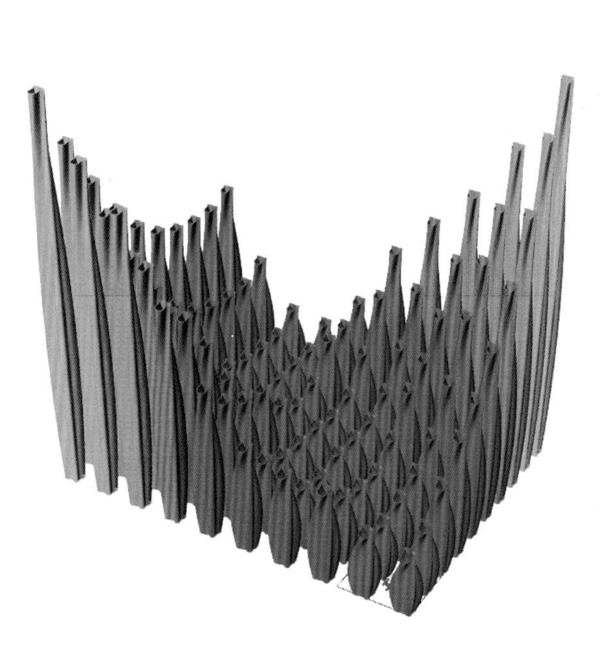

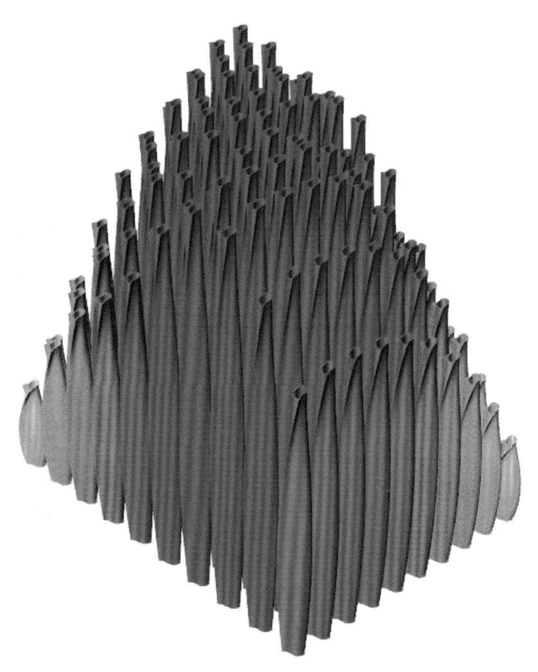

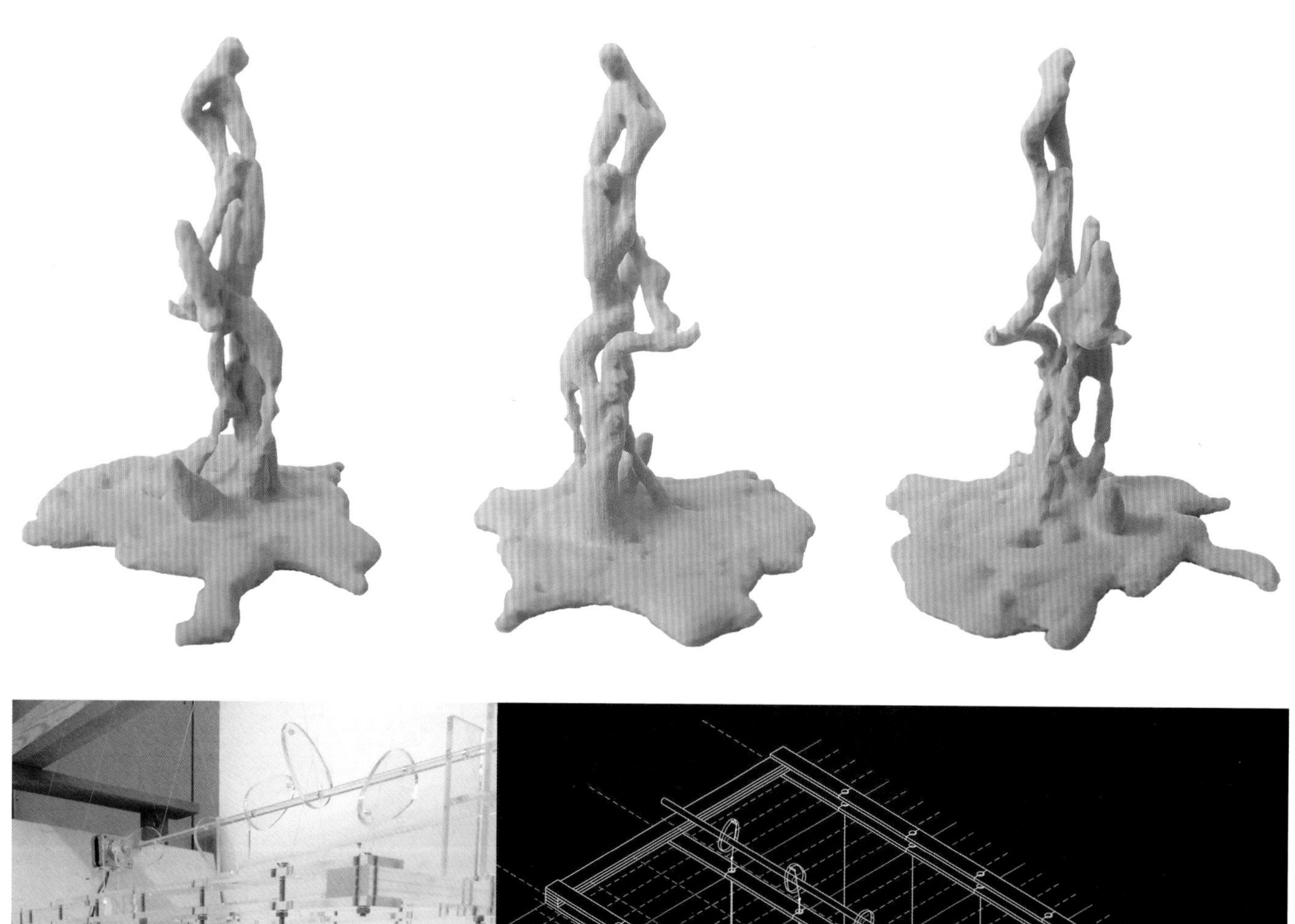

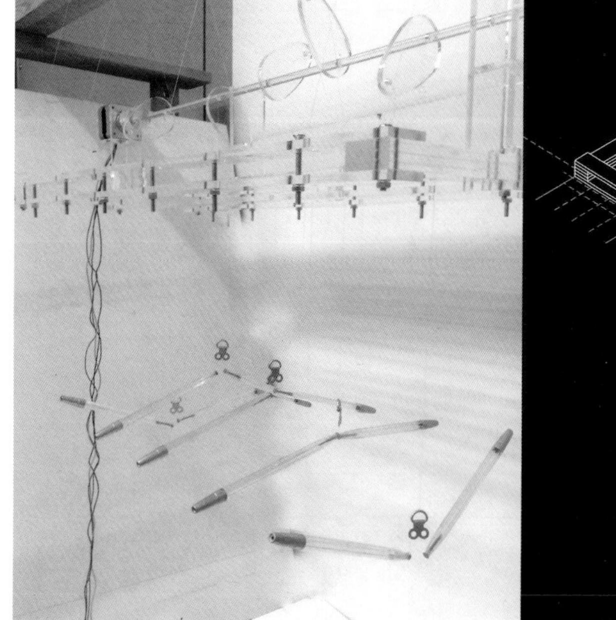

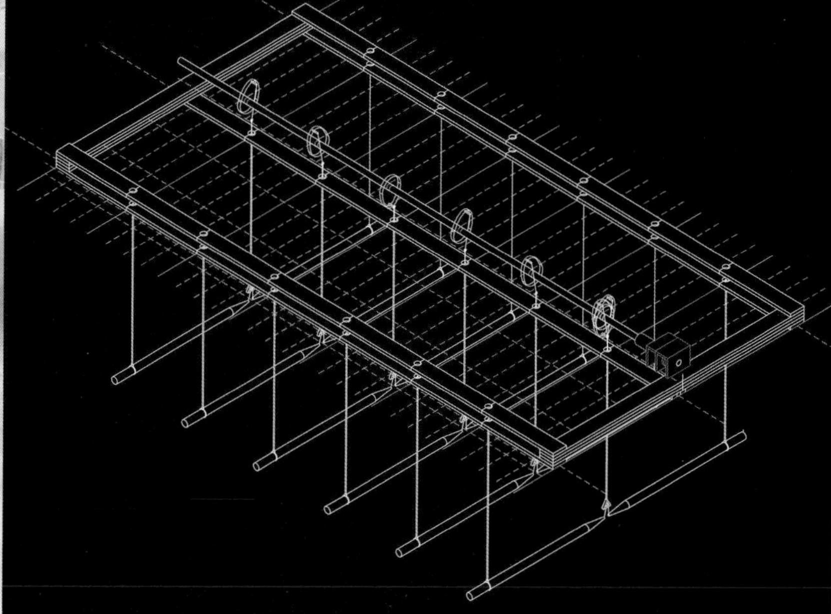

(top) Group C - Constantina Avraamides; *(bottom)* Group D - Anna Malicka

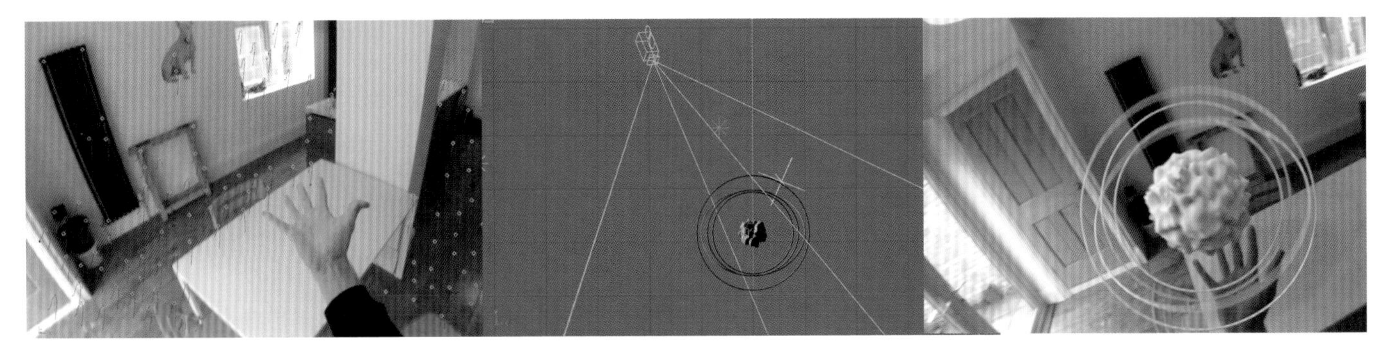

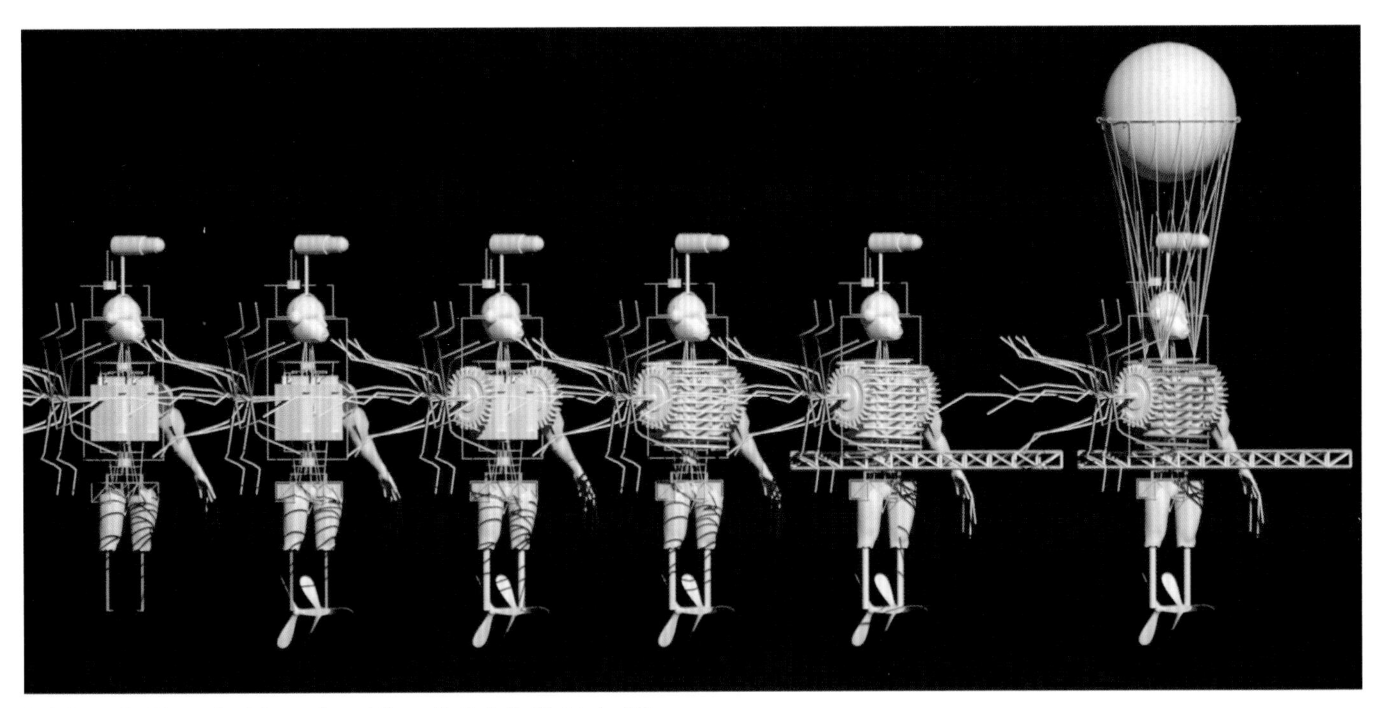

(top) Group E - Christopher Waters; *(bottom)* Group F - Rafaella Christodoulidi

Preparing for Practice: Professional Mentoring and Work Experience

THE UNDERGRADUATE THIRD YEAR work experience module, known as Preparing for Practice, continues to be an element of the course lauded by practices and the profession and highly valued by our students.

> *A privilege of the course at UoW is the work experience...I think we could all collectively agree that it gave us an incredible insight into the profession.*
>
> Anastasia Zabarsky, 3rd year

> *I found the practice placement incredibly rewarding. I was really pleased to be placed in a practice that specialises in conservation; the experience gave me insight into the realities of this area of the profession*
>
> Natalie Klak, 3rd year

> *Having completed the two weeks internship, I am now ready to start working in an architectural office and I feel I will be able to respond to what I am asked to do with confidence.*
>
> Marie Magnien, 3rd year

> *A two week placement in a well established practice with no previous experience was the perfect way to finish 3rd year! This opportunity is not given to other architecture students and that in itself made me really appreciate that such an opportunity was given to me.*
>
> Wilza Silva Mendes, 3rd year

Structured around two weeks of placement in practice, the module is designed to equip students with the skills necessary to apply for and secure a Year Out Part I position. Placements are organised by the Module Leader, Jane Tankard and the fABE placements team, and we have now reached a stage where we have more places than students!

The module works closely with the profession, many of whom contribute to the module, delivering practical and focused lectures on key aspects of the profession as well as honing the skills necessary to get a foothold in the industry.

The University's Career Development Centre also offers a Skills Academy to support the transition between academia and practice. Working with the Stephen Lawrence Trust, the scheme offers students profession-led workshops and practical help with job seeking.

In partnership with the RIBA, we also offer third years mentoring with a RIBA Chartered practice. Meanwhile, 2nd year students are offered the opportunity to gain practice-based internships over the summer break between 2nd and 3rd year.

Despite the course focusing on students gaining experience in architect-run practices, we have had students gaining experience in some unusual, but architecturally relevant contexts. In the past, a student worked with the Labour Party's Minister for the Arts formulating their strategy for Architecture and another student worked in a marble quarry in Italy.

Jane Tankard
Module Leader

RIBA Part 3

Wilfred Achille, Alastair Blyth, Stephen Brookhouse, Samir Pandya

THE UNIVERSITY OF WESTMINSTER runs the largest Part 3 course in the UK with over 400 students this year working in a broad range of architectural practices – more than 230 practices based in London and the south-east.

The students come from a wide variety of backgrounds including overseas schools of architecture. Often, architects who are registered but trained outside the UK attend the course to gain an in-depth understanding of the complexities of UK practice.

The course follows the requirements of the ARB/RIBA Professional Criteria and is structured as a series of building blocks with clear assessment points throughout the year.

The lecture courses are repeated twice a week to allow students to balance attendance with work commitments. Lectures are delivered by industry experts – including former students – and are recorded for easy future access.

Students' professional development in the workplace is supported by a team of 32 professional tutors – all architects in practice – who provide one-to-one tutorial guidance on project-based coursework. Professional examiners consistently comment on the high, critical standard of the coursework which we attribute to the structured tutoring system where students are challenged to think about practice differently.

The combination of the different student backgrounds, as well as the types and number of practices represented on the course, along with the tutors' and examiners' experience gives an unprecedented reach into the architectural profession. This enables the course to both draw from the breadth of practice experience as well as contribute to it.

One of our students, Tom Haworth, won the JCT Student Competition 2016, with his essay, 'Work Placements For The Student's Benefit, Not Their Employer's'.

This year, as in previous years, the course reached its target number of students in early May, an indication of the value that architectural practice attribute to it.

Alastair Blyth

Westminster Architecture Society

Team: Nouha Hansen, Crista Popescu and Zahra Mansoor. Special thanks to alumna Laylac Shahed

The society is created for students with the valuable and generous support of our tutors and faculty. We always welcome new ideas, members, and collaboration opportunities. Please get in touch:
architecture.soc@su.westminster.ac.uk

WESTMINSTER ARCHITECTURE SOCIETY is a student-led platform that complements the academic programme and allows for further, innovative exploration of architecture. The students have the opportunity to cultivate their curiosity and explore new concepts, and we believe in growing by sharing ideas and experiences. Through our activities and events, we aim to promote links between students, staff, and the wider architectural world.

We had an exciting year. In the first term, we teamed up with our Department of Architecture to organise PLAYWEEK 2016. A disruptive and creative event, the week offered a variety of short, intensive workshops that built on the diverse and interesting departmental teaching and allowed students to explore areas of architecture unfamiliar to them. From building a tensegrity pavilion, to big data analysis, making your own chairs, and even a popular life drawing workshop.

As students, we are continuously questioning and reflecting on how we see ourselves as part of a profession and what our contribution will be to its future. We held two engaging symposia this year, offering rich insight into diverse practices and approaches. In term 1, 'The Politics of Architecture', panelled by Ben Stringer, Harry Charrington, Roudaina Alkhani (Platforms), and Samir Pandya, looked into socially-aware architecture and activism in the profession.

In term 2, we discussed the future role of the architect in the construction industry in 'Negotiation in Architecture', panelled by Marion Brereton (BGS Architects), Harry Charrington and Eric Schrijver (Studio Memo).

We also had the great pleasure of hosting the wonderful lecture 'James Stirling: Inspiring Places and Spaces' given by Alan Berman (University of Liverpool and University of Oxford), which complemented the month-long events held by the RIBA to honour Stirling's contribution to modern architecture.

(left) WAS Symposium; (right) James Stirling Lecture Poster

OPEN Studio Westminster

Mirna Pedalo and Filip Visnic

OPEN STUDIO IS an interactive project run by the Department of Architecture at the University of Westminster to make its design, research and practice-based work available online while it is happening. The site acts as a real time teaching and learning environment in which the work of both students and staff is curated and documented – the work of its design studios, alongside its other teaching and research groups and workshops.

www.openstudiowestminster.org

Read more on our Blog:
www.openstudiowestminster.org/blog/

Follow us on Twitter:
twitter.com/openstudio_wm

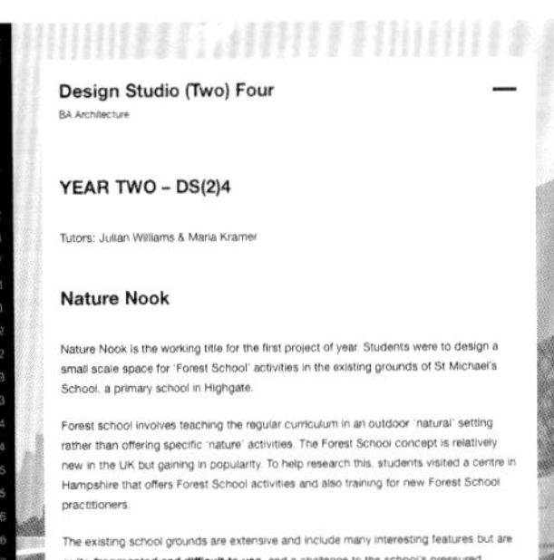

openstudio_wm Follow
25 posts 105 followers 137 following
Open Studio Westminster Project run by the Department of Architecture at the University of Westminster making its student work available while it is happening. **www.openstudiowestminster.org**

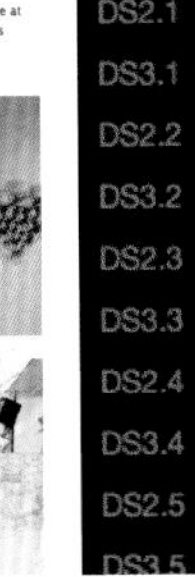

Mobile Home London project: DS3.6 venture into the Finnish woods

At the end of April, DS3.6 the wilderness of Finland. Finnish Forest Museum, s Helsinki. Under the guidar Sami Rintala and the DS3. Tom […]

Exhibition of Pavilion Designs

Design Studio [02] 05 have their Semester 1 design p

OPENStudio Web Platform

PLAYweek

the toil and labour of writing, day after day, without that magic lantern is immense

Charles Dickens

PLAYWEEK IS A disruptive, creative two-day event that – cutting across the 'normal business' of the Department's week-by-week teaching – suggests new and playful ways of working.

Jointly organised by the Department of Architecture and the Westminster Architecture Society, PLAYweek gives students and staff a moment in which to explore – anything. Any team of students and staff can make a proposal for an event – as long as it is open to all students from Year 1 to PhD – and they can bring external people as they wish.

This year saw intensive, productive, peripatetic, observational, and cross-disciplinary workshops and events taking places in the studios, the Fabrication Lab and across the city. Diverse and various, their commonality was their innovative wit; their serious-minded creative joy.

(clockwise from top left) **PLAYweek events:**
Drawing; Art Forms in Nature; Earth Building Workshop; Tensegrity Pavilion *(with thanks to Geoff Morrow & colleagues of StructureMode)*

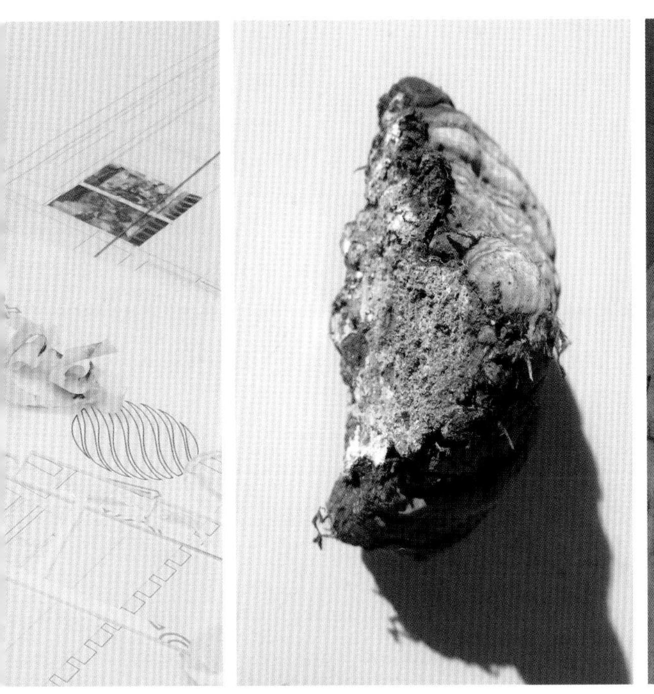
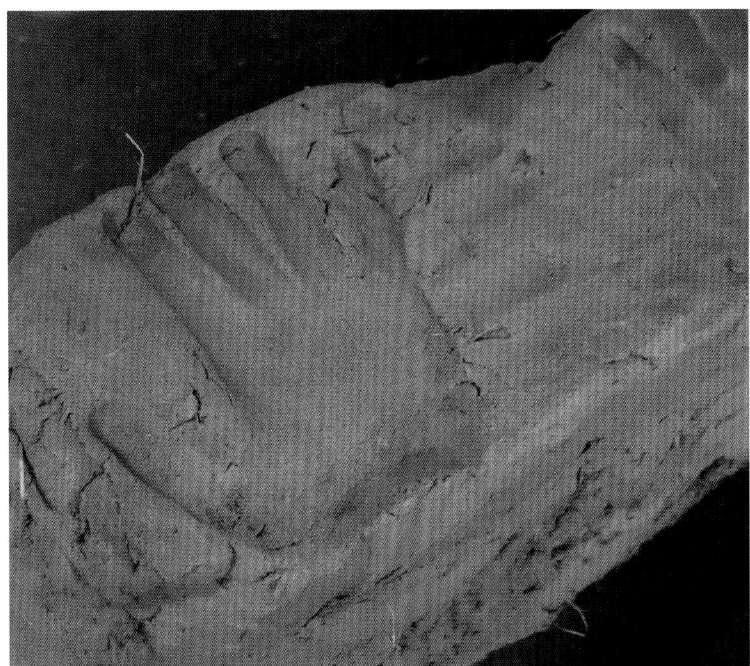

Fabrication Lab

THE FABRICATION LAB offers students and staff across the faculty the opportunity to work with the latest digital fabrication equipment as well as traditional craft processes for wood, metal and casting. Now combined with the Built Environment Lab, it also offers structural and environmental testing facilities.

It has been a busy year, beginning with a very successful first FAB FEST. This international fabrication festival produced almost 50 pavilions, with guest teams from eight countries. The creativity and variety of work it produced was extraordinary, as was the enthusiastic response from students, professionals from practice who mentored the teams, and from the many visitors who enjoyed the public events.

Following this success, we are hosting FAB FEST '17 this summer, opening out the festival to even more teams from around the world. We are expecting 25 teams from 16 countries, who will join more than 20 teams from the University of Westminster. The festival will be open to the public on 8th July for music, drinks and festivities and 9th July for an exhibition. See FABFEST.London for full details, and do please join us.

The festival also features the launch of the Lab's Architectural Robotics Theatre project. A.R.T. is a series of research projects exploring how industrial robots might be used to invent and develop new ways of creating innovative architecture. Each project develops through student workshops and speculative research, culminating in a week-long public performance in our unique robot cell overlooking Marylebone Road. The first of these events will be held during the week of FAB FEST.

Finally, we are delighted to announce the final stage of the refurbishment of the Lab. We won the funds this year to complete the renewal of the old workshops over the summer, modernising traditional making spaces and adding a new photography studio, Light Lab, and an extensive Materials Lab. We look forward to welcoming you to the new, greately enhanced Fabrication Lab in September 2017.

We want particularly to thank the Quintin Hogg Trust and DS Smith for their continued support with funding and materials for FAB FEST and A.R.T.

Dr David Scott
Director

(clockwise from top) ***FAB FEST featuring the Architectural Robotics Theatre, FAB FEST '17 poster; Fabrication Lab produce; Constructing***

ART

(top left) ***FAB FEST '16, Globe;*** *(top right)* ***FAB FEST '16 construction;*** *(bottom left)* ***Using the Fabrication Lab;*** *(bottom right)* ***Laser cutting***

(top) ***The Trans-Siberian March Band;*** *(bottom)* ***Constructing Pavilions***

STUDYING FOR A masters degree is a valuable opportunity. For some students, part way through their architectural education, it is a chance to specialise and develop their own design identity; for others, it is the first step towards a PhD and an academic career. But for all those engaged in masters level study in the Department of Architecture, a masters provides the context in which to reflect on their work as architects or designers and to enhance their design skills.

The Department of Architecture offers three masters programmes:

MA Architecture
MA Interior Design
MSc Architecture and Environmental Design

Each course has its own individual character and subject-specific content and is staffed by a team of specialist academics. Heading up these teams are the course leaders:

Dusan Decermic (course leader – MA Interior Design) is an architect who engages with both theoretical and design practices in architecture and interior design. He set up his own practice, arclab, in 1999 and in his professional career he has worked with numerous clients, large and small, including the Royal National Theatre and fashion designer Issey Miyake.

Dr Davide Deriu (course leader – MA Architecture) is an experienced lecturer and established researcher. His main interests lie in visual and spatial cultures, and he has published in leading journals and scholarly books, as well as magazines. In addition, he has edited works on architecture and landscape, and is a founding editor of the *Architectural Histories* journal.

Richard Difford (course leader – MA Architecture) is an academic with expertise both in creative technologies and architectural history. The primary focus for his work is the history of architectural representation and in the use of electronics and coding in architectural design. He has published numerous academic papers and supervised a number of award-winning dissertations.

Samir Pandya (course leader – MA Architecture) is an award-winning architect and academic. He is also Architecture Editor for the multidisciplinary journal *National Identities: Critical Inquiry into Nationhood, Politics & Culture* (Taylor & Francis) and an Editorial Board member for the architecture journal *FOLIO* (funded by the Graham Foundation for Advanced Studies in the Fine Arts).

Dr Rosa Schiano-Phan (course leader – MSc Architecture and Environmental Design) has extensive experience in the field of environmental design devoting most of her career to consultancy and research. She is co-director of Natural Cooling Limited and co-author of *The Architecture & Engineering of Downdraught Cooling*, published in 2010.

There are also many important contributors both from practice and the wider academic community at the University of Westminster and beyond. The following pages feature a small sample of the student work inspired and supervised by these dedicated scholars.

Richard Difford
Coordinator of Postgraduate Study

MASTERS

Davide Deriu, Richard Difford, Samir Pandya (Course Leaders)
Nasser Golzari, Krystallia Kamvasinou, Dirk Lellau, Clare Melhuish, Filip Visnjic

MA Architecture

Students: Elmira Afshar,Yaqoob Al Khaja, Maria Jose Arenas Escobar, Jevon Atmabrata, Behnaz Berengi,Ankur Chhabra,Alisa Elenevskaya, Linda Ferrari,Freddie Gee, Alejandro Gutierrez Fabregat, Danai Ilyadu, Basma Johar, Taraneh Joorabchian, Massimo Melloni, Giulia Merlo, Dana Nasser, Chinonso Surllivan Ohaneje, Al Shima Rehman, Zahraa Shamkhi, Maria Skiada,Nithila Subbaroyan, Karine Sylvestre Lorent Saenen.

THE MA ARCHITECTURE course offers a unique opportunity to pursue advanced postgraduate research combining high-level theoretical investigation with innovative design approaches. The programme is both wide ranging and flexible, facilitating alternative modes of study and a range of options, including the choice of either a written or design-based thesis.

The course also allows for specialism through its three designated pathways: Architecture (Cultural Identity and Globalisation); Architecture (Digital Media) and Architecture (History and Theory). Alternatively, students can also create their own pathway by selecting and combining relevant modules that meet their individual requirements. The range of optional and specialist modules offered allows students to develop their individual learning trajectories through the in-depth study of specific subject areas, involving theoretical components as well as practical applications. A series of theory-rich modules stimulate students to analyse current trends in architecture, design theory and practice on the basis of their research and critical judgement, and to use these insights to produce high-quality written work in a scholarly manner. In parallel, a set of design-oriented activities encourages students to develop their artistic, aesthetic and intellectual vision through the use of different media in order to produce individual proposals with a high level of spatial, material and formal resolution.

The course is taught within a dynamic learning environment that comprises seminar-based sessions along with studio-based activities, suitably integrated by a wide range of lectures, tutorials, site visits, research training sessions, and independent study periods. The primary emphasis, however, is on the thesis project or dissertation which is explored in the context of one of three tutor groups or 'research labs' aligned with each of the designated pathways.

Guest Lecturers & Critics:
Alessandro Ayuso, Amy Butt, Brad Carroll, Beth Cullen, Dusan Decermic, Mahsa Alami Fariman, François Girardin, Jon Goodbun, Reza Hakiminejad, Maja Jovic, Will McLean, Evangelia Magnisali, Sarah Milne, Mark Parsons, Mirna Pedalo, Angeliki Sakellariou, Shahed Saleem, Yara Sharif, Matthew Stewart, Yuri Suzuki, Heather Topel, Biky Wan, Santiago Rizo Zambrano

(top) Research and Positioning – Mapping Workshop; (bottom) Danai Ilyadu: *Picturing London*

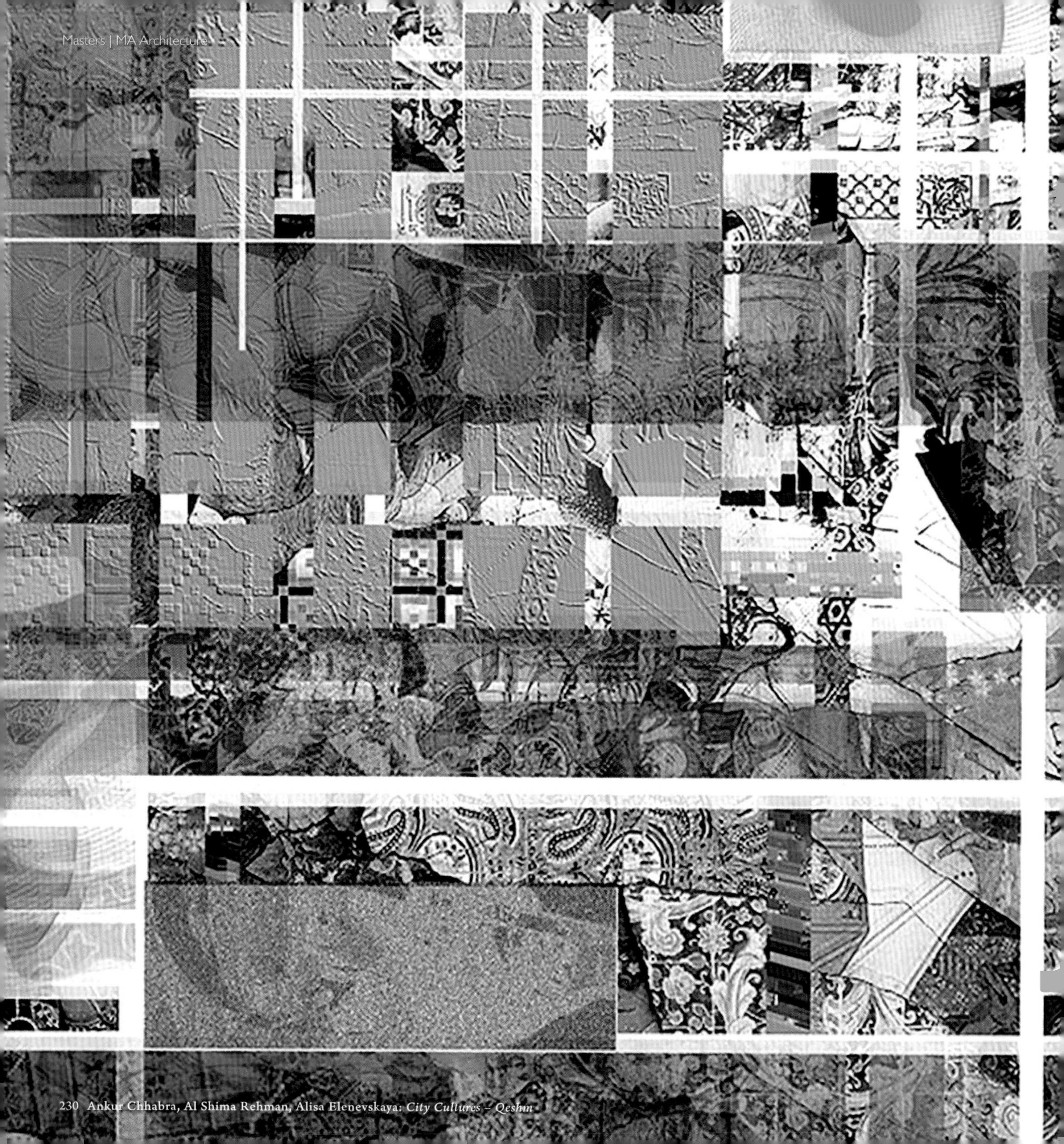

 Ankur Chhabra, Al Shima Rehman, Alisa Elenevskaya: *City Cultures – Qeshm*

Research and Positioning – Making Workshop *(left)* Maria Jose Arenas Escobar, Ankur Chhabra, Linda Ferrari, Freddie Gee; *(top right)* Elmira Afshar, Yaqoob Al Khaja, Alisa Elenevskaya, Jevon Atmabrata; *(bottom right)* Alejandro Gutierrez Fabregat, Danai Ilyadu, Basma Johar, Taraneh Joorabchian

Dusan Decermic (course leader), Lara Rettondini, Richard Difford, Filip Visnjic, Debby Kuypers, Joe King,Claire Richmond

MA Interior Design

Students: Rija Ahmed, Raghad Alkhalifah, Sabrina Barber. Hui Gao, Ella Goodsell, Kerri Mcgonigle, Simrit Panaich, Radhi Soni, Yingying Tian

EMBRACING THE MATERIAL and intellectual complexities and contradictions magnified by the psychological agency inherent in the subject of interiority, our students, like wayfarers, are encouraged to trace their own paths through this ever changing palimpsest-like topography, unearthing traces of history over and through which they weave in active, contemporary practices. Site visits to abandoned buildings and places, devoid of any tangible use or potential future, are seen with fresh eyes and for us become environments full of new promise.

Interiors are elusive by nature, conspiratorial and inviting, dark, brooding, but also strangely alluring. This new territory, for too long ignored by more established disciplines, is rightfully taking it's place of engagement with serious academic study and investigation. Academically young at heart but seasoned in practice, the MA Interior Design programme is poised to deliver new and exciting avenues of creative engagement. As a reflective example bearing these complexities, The Interior modules Retail and Decoding are set up in this context and seen as both antagonists and attractors, offering professional, vocational action, and active intellectual reaction.

Our thesis projects are exemplars of these manifold concerns, embracing ambitious conceptual strategies but also striving for delicate, intricate material renderings. As the static, indulgent 'expert' gaze is being augmented and supplanted by the contemporary democratic idiom of the omnipresent cinematic 'measuring' of time and space, the course is pedagogically engaged through film and animation components of the Case Study and Introduction to Design Computing modules. A matrix of diverse modules is aimed to challenge students to strive for a rich, mature synthesis of these components, a process aimed for successful navigation through the complex, globalised world.

Guest Critics:
Carly Sweeney (Universal Design Studio), Ian Chalk (Ian Chalk Architects), Tomasz Fiszer (MJP Architects), Eva Sopeoglou

Special Thanks:
Claire Richmond (with the generous support of Gensler & Associates) for sharing experience, knowledge and time

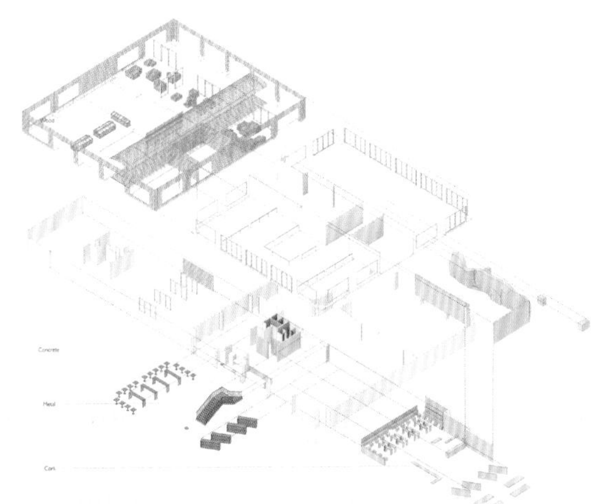
Concrete
Metal
Cork

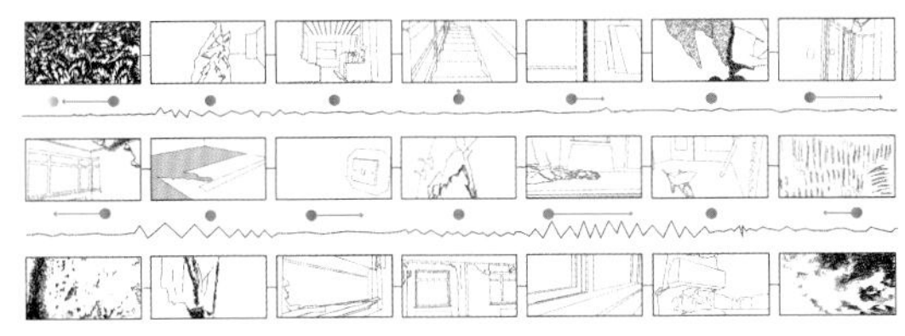

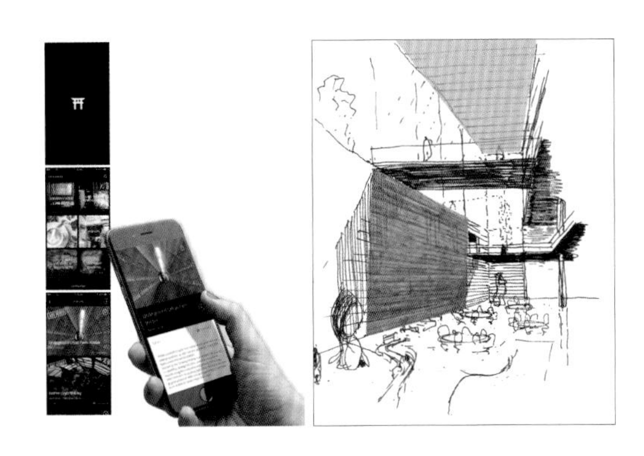

STEM

STEM

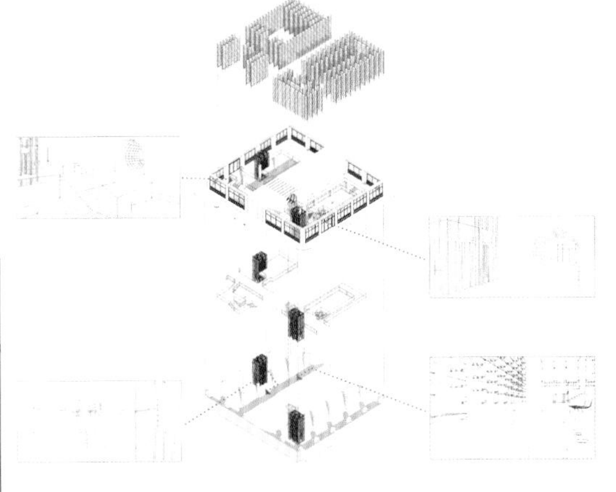

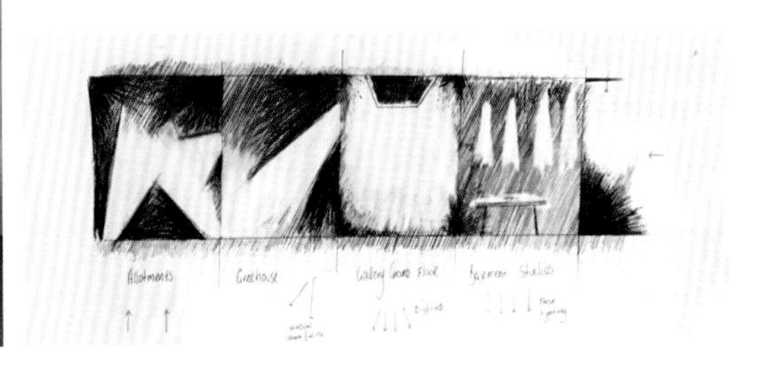
Allotments
Greenhouse
Gallery Ground Floor
Studios

Rosa Schiano-Phan (course leader), Colin Gleeson, Nasser Golzari, Jon Goodbun, Benson Lau, Juan Vallejo, Zhenzhou Weng

MSc Architecture and Environmental Design

Full time students: Hussam Alnahdi, Claudia Danon, Hassan Jafri, Oguz Kablan, Jinhyo Lee, Hadeel Mohamed, Daniela Park, Karan Patel, Deependra Pourel, Sanjog Shrestha, Peng Tan, Bernadette Widjaja, Kristel Zarate-Leon

Part-time students: Cecilia Araujo-Santos, Katrina Urbanik, Urszula Bajcer, Marta Frascoli, Andrzej Kukla, Daniel Owen

THE MSc ARCHITECTURE AND Environmental Design responds to the needs of current and future professionals for a deeper understanding of the principles of environmental design, and their effective application into architectural practice worldwide. The course reacts to recent developments in the discipline, responding to new research and experimentation, addressing the lack of environmental criteria in the creative design process and of comprehensive performance prediction and feedback protocols. Students gain the knowledge and tools to make informed design decisions based on post-occupancy feedback and performance analysis, towards a new paradigm of environmental architecture, which is environmentally and energy conscious, yet sensitive to the contextual and socio-cultural landscape we live in.

The course teaches environmental design methods which relate to the various stages of architectural design, enabling the evaluation of existing buildings and the design of new ones following a combined bioclimatic and building user-focused approach. The core design modules follow an evidence-based approach where the acquisition of specialised software and analytical tools are directly applied to an evaluation and a design project.

The course is interdisciplinary and international providing skills that can be applied to diverse building typologies and global climatic, environmental and contextual issues. The modules focus on the understanding of the principles and methodology of environmental design and on the development of critical thinking to challenge established practices, positively driving change towards a better and sustainable future.

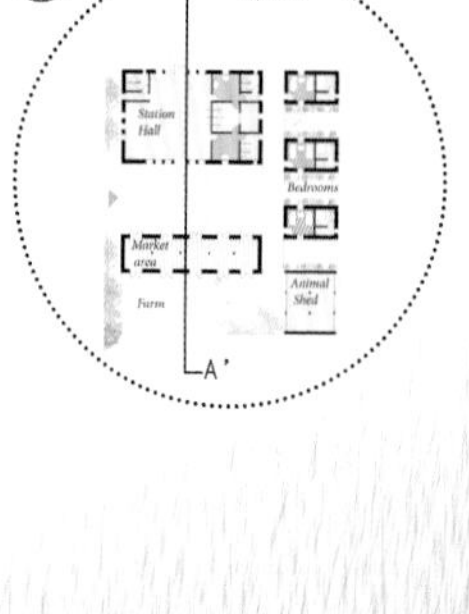

'llustration of Design Proposal 1. T

Guest Critics:
Joana Goncalves (University of Sao Paulo, Brazil), Anna Kerrane (Architype), Luisa Scambia (WSP | Parsons Brinckerhoff), Vera Sarioglu (Arup), Maria-Lida Kou (Arup)

Special Thanks:
Klaus Bode (Chapman+BDSP), Kevin Burchell (PSI), Meytal Ben Dayan (Architype), Camilo Diaz (WSP | Parsons Brinckerhoff), Christian Dimbleby (Architype), Joana Goncalves (University of Sao Paulo, Brazil), Catherine Harrington (Architype), Tony Lloyd-Jones, Phil McIlwain (Westminster Council), Fergus Nicol (Oxford Brookes), Vera Sarioglu (Arup), Maria-Lida Kou (Arup), Zoe Shattock (Waverley Borough Council), Ben Shaw (PSI)

Daniel Buban Ngu: *Sustainable Railway Architecture in Cameroon*

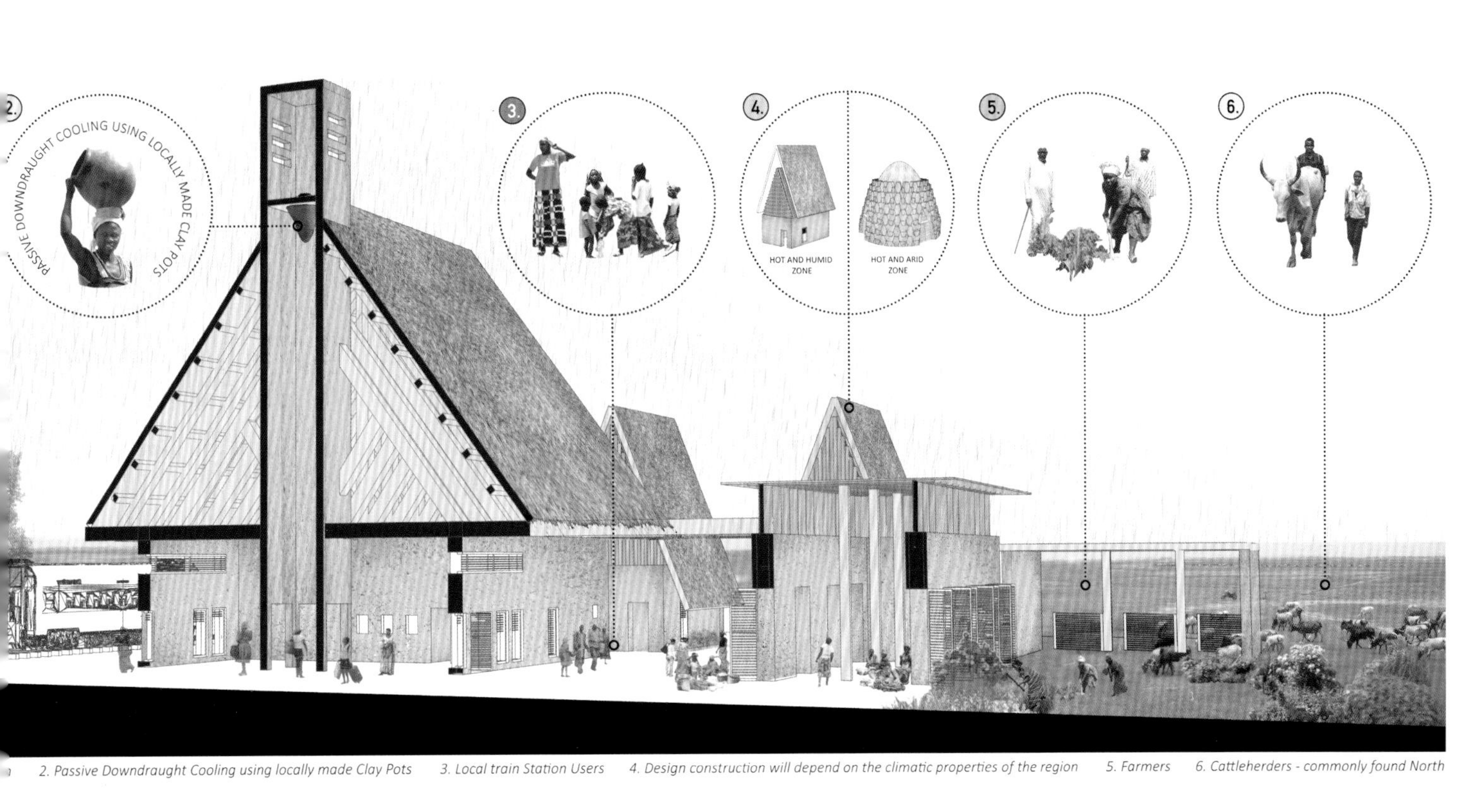

2. Passive Downdraught Cooling using locally made Clay Pots   3. Local train Station Users   4. Design construction will depend on the climatic properties of the region   5. Farmers   6. Cattleherders - commonly found North

THE DEPARTMENT OF ARCHITECTURE fosters a strong and diverse approach to teaching, research and practice. It has an international reputation for excellence in teaching and research, for attracting award-winning staff and students, and for a wide range of scholarly activities. As contributors to the Faculty of Architecture and the Built Environment's submission to the 2014 Research Excellence Framework, our research was placed in the top 50% of the 45 submissions in Architecture, Built Environment and Planning. 20% of our publications and research effort were deemed to be 'world leading' (4*) and 45% 'internationally excellent (3*). The four case studies of our research impact also scored very highly. This significant endorsement of our research capability has provided the foundation for expanding and enhancing our UK and international role since.

Research in the department is organised around five distinct themes, translated into five research groups:

Architectural History and Theory

Environment and Technology

Expanded Territories

Experimental Practice (EXP)

Representation, Fabrication and Computing

These are loose alignments of staff, research students, designers and practicing architects who undertake joint research initiatives and organise events of common interest. For further details, visit our website:

https://www.westminster.ac.uk/architecture-and-cities

The following pages highlight publications and research awards by architecture staff in 2016/17, the bi-weekly research forum and the department's PhD programme. This is followed by details of the four grant funded research projects currently hosted by the department.

Staff Publications and Research Awards 2016/17

Peer Reviewed Journal Articles:

Bremner, L. (2017). 'Observations on the concept of the aquapelago occasioned by researching the Maldives. *Shima* 11(1):17-29.

Bremner, L. (2016). 'Thinking architecture from an Indian Ocean aquapelago.' *Geohumanities* 2(2): 284-310.

Deriu, D. (2016). "'Don't look down!": A short history of rooftopping photography.' *Journal of Architecture* 21 (7):1-29.

Lecaro, M., Lau, B., Rodrigues, L. and Jarman, D. (2017). 'The application of vernacular Australian environmental design principles in Glenn Murcutt's architecture.' *Future Cities and Environment* 3(3):1-18.

Lewi, H. and Peckham, A. (2016). 'Transcribing The Journal of Architecture: research, production and publication 2004–2013.' *Journal of Architecture* 21 (4): 479-489.

Peckham, A. (2016). 'Beyond formalism: the quiescent art of formal analysis in architecture.' *Journal of Architecture* 21 (5):679-689.

Stringer, B. (2017). 'Introduction', 'Villages and Urbanization,' and 'Makutano Junction: A Village Soap Opera for Kenyan TV, Ben Stringer in Conversation with Producer David Campbell.' *Architecture and Culture* 5(1):1-4, 5-20, 99-114.

Watson, V. (2017). 'On the Matter and Intelligence of the Architectural Model: Arthur Schopenhauer's Psychophysiological Theory of Architecture and Konrad Wachsmann's Design of a Space Structure.' *ARENA Journal of Architectural Research*, 2(1).

Editorships of Peer Reviewed Journals:

Lewi, H. and Peckham (eds.). (2016-2018). Six Anthology Issues selected from the last ten years of *The Journal of Architecture*.

McLean, W., Schlimme, H. and Wall, C. (eds). (2017). *Construction History: International Journal of the Construction History Society* 32(1).

Stringer, B. (ed.). (2017). *Architecture and Culture* 5(1): *Villages and Globalization*.

Wall, C. (ed.). (2017). *Oral History Journal* 45(1).

Wall, C. (ed.). (2017). *Construction History Journal* 35(1).

Non Peer Reviewed Journal Articles:

Spencer, D. (2016). 'The Limits of Limits: Schmitt, Aureli, and the Geopolitical Ontology of the Island.' *New Geographies* 8:118-127.

Spencer, D. (2016). 'Out of the Loop: Architecture, Automation and Cognitive Disinvestment.' *Volume* 49.

Spencer, D. (2016). 'The Consistency of Experience: Architecture, Mass Ornament and the Indifferent Environment.' *Praznine* 10.

Edited Books:

Bremner, L. and Bottazzi, R. (eds.). (2016). *Architecture, Energy, Matter.* London: Department of Architecture, University of Westminster.

Joseph-Lester, J, King, S., Bler-Carruthers, A., and Bottazzi, R. (eds.). (2017). *Walking Cities: London.* London: Camberwell Press.

Lau, C. (ed.). (2016). *Dialogical Designs*. London: Department of Architecture, University of Westminster.

Single Authored Books:

Sharif, Y. (2017). *Architecture of Resistance: Cultivating Moments of Possibility within the Palestinian/Israeli Conflict.* London: Routledge.

Spencer, D. (2016). *The Architecture of Neoliberalism: How Architecture Became an Instrument of Control and Compliance*. London: Bloomsbury

Chapters in Books:

Bottazzi, R. (2017). 'Gravesend-Broadness Weather Station.' in Joseph-Lester, J, King, S., Bler-Carruthers, A., and Bottazzi, R. *Walking Cities: London*, 67-80. London: Camberwell Press.

Bremner, L. (2016). 'Thinking architecture with an Indian Ocean archipelago.' in *Disputed Architectures*, 28-31. London: The Bartlett School of Architecture.

Bremner, L. (2016). 'Filter|Funnel.' in D. Malaquais and N. Khouri (eds.) *Afrique - Asie. Arts, espaces, pratiques*, 17-42. France: Presses Universitaires de Rouen et du Havre.

Bremner, L. (2016). 'Muddy Logics.' in M. Przybylski and L. Sheppard (eds.) *Bracket – at extremes – almanac 3*, 199-206. Barcelona: Actar.

Charrington, H. (2016). 'Retailing Aalto in London.' in N. Stritzler-Levine (ed.). *Artek and the Aaltos*, 101–142. New Haven: Yale University Press.

Charrington, H. (2016). 'The Artek Manifesto in Practice' in N. Stritzler-Levine (ed.). *Artek and the Aaltos*, 364–373; 374–379; 380–385; 386–395; 446–453. New Haven: Yale University Press.

Charrington, H. (2016). 'Artek and the Aalto Atelier in Postwar Finland.' in N. Stritzler-Levine (ed.). *Artek and the Aaltos*, 573-604. New Haven: Yale University Press.

Dernie, D. (2017). 'Walking: Material Conditions of the Street.' in Joseph-Lester, J, King, S., Bler-Carruthers, A., and Bottazzi, R. *Walking Cities: London*, 83-101. London: Camberwell Press.

Kamvasinou, K. (2017). 'Short-Term Projects, Long-Term Ambitions: Facets of Transience in Two London Development Sites.' in J. Henneberry (ed.). *Transience and Permanence in Urban Development*, 65-84. NJ: Wiley-Blackwell.

Saleem, S. (2017). 'Building and Becoming: The Shahporan Mosque and the Unfolding of Muslim Visual Identity in London.' in Quash, B., Rosen, A., C. Reddaway (eds.). *Visualising a Sacred City; London, Art and Religion*, 205-217. London: I.B Taurus.

Spencer, D. (2016). 'Less than Enough: A Critique of Aureli.' in T. Stoppani, G. Ponzo, and G. Themistokleous (eds.). *This Thing Called Theory*. London: Routledge.

Wall, C. (2017). 'New notions of value in Modern Architecture.' in H. Neate and R. Craggs, (eds.). *Modern Futures*. London: Unicorn Books.

Williams, J. (2016). 'Site Parade.' in Morrow, R., Harriss, H., Benedict Brown, J., and Soane, J. (eds.). *A Gendered Profession*, 79-85. London: RIBA.

Awards

Deriu, D. (2016 – 2017). Selected Researcher for Architecture and/for Photography, a multidisciplinary project funded by the Andrew W. Mellon Foundation.

Saleem, S.(2016). Shahporan Mosque, 444 Hackney Road E2. Nominated for the Aga Khan Award.

Sharif, Y. and Golzari, N. with the Palestine Regeneration Team (PART). (2016). RIBA president's Award for Research, Cities and Communities Category.

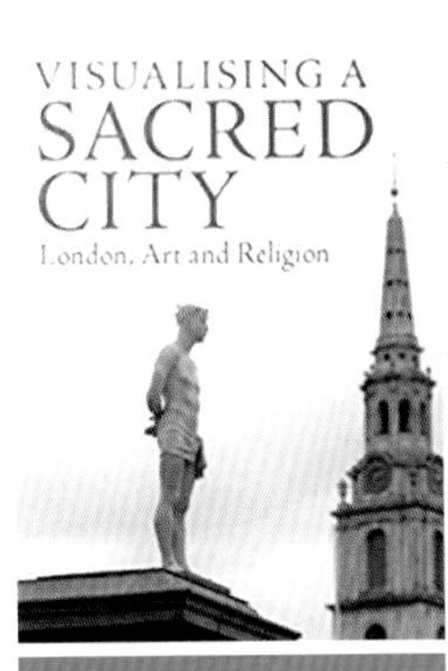

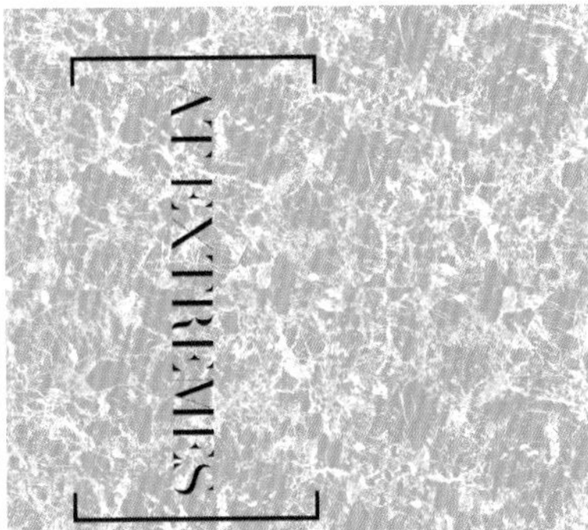

Architectural Research Forum

THE ARCHITECTURE DEPARTMENT holds a bi-weekly research forum. This is an opportunity for staff and visiting fellows to present their work-in-progress to stimulate discussion and critical debate about their research. Seminars are open to all staff and students. During 2016/17, the programme was:

Victoria Watson	Rurality and Minimal Architecture: An Enquiry into the Genealogy of Tate Modern's Bankside Gallery Spaces
Lindsay Bremner, Samir Pandya & Ben Stringer	Panel Discussion on Field Trips
Zhenzhou Weng	An e-Learning Tool for Environmental Design
John Bold	The Politics of Heritage Regeneration in South-East Europe
Alastair Blyth	Measuring the Effectiveness of School Design
Katharine Heron	Practice-based Research in the Context of the ADAPTr Exhibition
Julian Williams	Collaborative Research: Reporting from the Estate.
Joana Goncalves	The Environmental Quality of Brazilian Modernism
Nancy Stevenson & Roberto Bottazzi	Taking a Hike
Camilla Wilkinson	Dazzle
Davide Deriu	The Vertigo Project

WESTMINSTER ARCHITECTURE RESEARCH FORUM 2016 1

WESTMINSTER ARCHITECTURE RESEARCH FORUM 2016 2

WESTMINSTER ARCHITECTURE RESEARCH FORUM 2016 3

WESTMINSTER ARCHITECTURE RESEARCH FORUM 2016 4

WESTMINSTER ARCHITECTURE RESEARCH FORUM 2016 5

WESTMINSTER ARCHITECTURE RESEARCH FORUM 2016 6

WESTMINSTER ARCHITECTURE RESEARCH FORUM 2016/7 7

WESTMINSTER ARCHITECTURE RESEARCH FORUM 2016/7 8

WESTMINSTER ARCHITECTURE RESEARCH FORUM 2016/7 9

WESTMINSTER ARCHITECTURE RESEARCH FORUM 2016/7 10

WESTMINSTER ARCHITECTURE RESEARCH FORUM 2016/7 11

Architectural Research Forum posters

PhD Students

THE DEPARTMENT ACCEPTS candidates who qualify for PhD research in fields in which its staff have expertise. For information of how to apply for a PhD at the University of Westminster, please visit:

www.westminster.ac.uk/courses/research-degrees/phd-study

In 2016/2017, a number of outstanding PhD candidates successfully defended their theses:

Samra Kahn
The Sethi merchants' havelis in Peshawar, 1800-1910: form, identity and status.
Supervisors: John Bold, Davide Deriu

Sarah Milne
Merchants of the City: Situating the London estate of the Drapers' Company, c.1540-1640
Supervisors: John Bold, Lindsay Bremner

John Walter
Alien Sex Club: Educating audiences about continuing rates of HIV transmission using art and design
Supervisors: Linday Bremner, Victoria Watson, Francis White

Noha Alahmadi and Lilit Mnatsakanyan were awarded MPhil degrees.

Current PhD students registered in the Department of Architecture are:

May Aljamea
Cultural Preservation in a Saudi Domestic Environment in the Eastern Province
Supervisors: Lindsay Bremner, Samir Pandya

Harshavardhan Bhat *(Monsoon Assemblages PhD Fellowship)*
On the Skies of Surface life: In Search of Monsoon Air
Supervisors: Lindsay Bremner, David Chandler

Phillip Luehl *(University of Westminster Fellowship)*
Negotiating Informality: Spatial Co-Production as a way to Re-politicise Space in Namibia
Supervisors: Lindsay Bremner, Isis Nunez Ferrera

William McLean *(PhD by Publication)*
A Sociotechnical History of Architecture and Invention
Supervisors: Victoria Watson, Lindsay Bremner

Anthony Powis *(Monsoon Assemblages PhD Fellowship)*
Fluvial City: Reading Chennai through Groundwater
Supervisors: Lindsay Bremner, Beth Cullen

Philippe Saleh
Towards nearly Zero Energy Buildings in Lebanon: bioclimatic design and experimental building strategies for energy demand reduction in new builds.
Supervisors: Rosa Schiano-Phan, Colin Gleeson

Duarte Santos
Hybrid territories, Performative geographies, Fluid cartographies in small islands.
Supervisors: Davide Deriu, Helen Farrell, Lindsay Bremner

Emilia Siandou
Modern architecture in Cyprus as heritage
Supervisors: John Bold, Davide Deriu, Panaiota Pyla

Public Space and the Role of the Architect in London and São Paulo

Principal Investigator: Professor Susannah Hagan
Research Associates: Dann Jessen RIBA, Dr Neal Shasore, Professor Jose Lefèvre
Co Researchers: University of São Paulo: Professor Jose Lefèvre, Professor Monica Carmargo (Brazil)
Project Partners: British Council, Design Council, RIBA, RTPI, 20th Century Society (UK)
Funding bodies: AHRC (UK); FAPESP (Brazil)

THIS THREE-YEAR research project is a collaboration between the Faculty of Architecture and the Built Environment, University of Westminster, and the Faculty of Architecture and Urbanism, University of São Paulo. It takes advantage of the complex and often spectacular legacy of architectural Modernism in both London and São Paulo as a way of reflecting historically on contemporary public spaces in both cities, and on the changing role of the architect in their production.

The research is a response to a growing anxiety about the increasing privatisation of public space, and the demand for greater democratic authorship and ownership of it. This requires a wider and deeper examination of the neglected roles of the designer and design, which are as important to a discussion of the public realm as the debate about what constitutes 'public'. In a contemporary social context of growing demand for greater democratic authorship and ownership of the built environment, in particular its public realm, the role of design needs to be understood by designers and their clients in a far more informed way. If public space is co-constituted, then attention needs to be paid to the space as well as to the public.

Today, there are marked similarities between London and São Paulo: they are both financial capitals, and they both have multicultural populations. They both suffer from a wide divide between rich and poor, and from chronic housing shortages. More importantly for this research, both tend to think about public space defensively, mirroring social segregation with spatial segregation. The emptiness of many public spaces in São Paulo, and its over-surveillance in London, are symptoms of urban dysfunction unanticipated by the optimistic public space agenda of architectural Modernism.

Susannah Hagan: *Centro Cultural São Paulo (CCSP) designed by Eurico Prado Lopes, 1978*

Monsoon Assemblages

Principal Investigator: Professor Lindsay Bremner
Research Associates: Dr Beth Cullen (anthropologist), Christina Geros (architect, landscape architect and urban designer)
PhD: Harshavardhan Bhat (political scientist) and Anthony Powis (architect)
MArch Studio DS18: Aligned with the project 2016-2019

Monsoon Assemblages is funded by the European Research Council under the European Union's Horizon 2020 research and innovation programme (Grant Agreement no. 679873).

European Research Council

European Commission | Horizon 2020 European Union funding for Research & Innovation

MONSOON
[+other] AIRS

20 - 21 APRIL 2017
UNIVERSITY OF WESTMINSTER
Room M416, 35 Marylebone Road, London, NW1 5LS

Monsoon [+ other] Airs is convened by the ERC funded Monsoon Assemblages project to interrogate questions of monsoon + other atmospheres, airscapes, weathers, politics and media.

KEYNOTE LECTURE Thursday 20 April 18.30
SEAN LALLY
ARCHITECT, WEATHERS

SYMPOSIUM Friday 21 April 9.30 - 17.00
ANDREW TURNER
DEPARTMENT OF METEOROLOGY, UNIVERSITY OF READING
NEREA CALVILLO
CENTRE FOR INTERDISCIPLINARY METHODOLOGIES, UNIVERSITY OF WARWICK
VICTORIA WATSON
DEPARTMENT OF ARCHITECTURE, UNIVERSITY OF WESTMINSTER
ANASUYA BASU
THE TELEGRAPH, KOLKATA
RIFAT ISLAM ESHA
DHAKA TRIBUNE
NEHA LALCHANDANI
TIMES OF INDIA, DELHI
HANNAH SWEE
DISASTER RISK REDUCTION, COPENHAGEN, DENMARK
CLEO ROBERTS
PHD CANDIDATE, ART HISTORY, UNIVERSITY OF CAMBRIDGE
ETIENNE TURPIN
RESEARCH SCIENTIST, MIT URBAN RISK LAB
STINE SIMONSEN PURI
DEPARTMENT OF CROSS CUTURAL AND REGIONAL STUDIES, UNIVERSITY OF COPENHAGEN
HARSHAVARDHAN BHAT
PHD CANDIDATE, UNIVERSITY OF WESTMINSTER

EXHIBITION Friday 21 April 9.30 - 18.30
SEAN LALLY, NEREA CALVILLO, VICTORIA WATSON, VISHAL GOWTHAM B, VINUSHA KESHAV, KOUSHIK KRISHNA N, AISHWARYA KV, KEERTHANA MURALIDHARAN, TOM BENSON, CID SCHULER, CALVIN SIN

FREE
Register at https://www.eventbrite.co.uk/e/monsoon-other-airs-tickets-32121557443

Monsoon Assemblages is a research project funded by the European Research Council (ERC) under the European Union's Horizon 2020 research and innovation programme (Grant Agreement No. 679873).

UNIVERSITY OF WESTMINSTER | European Commission | Horizon 2020 European Union funding for Research & Innovation | erc

MONSOON ASSEMBLAGES (MONASS) is a five-year research project funded by the European Research Council undertaking interdisciplinary, design-driven enquiries into relations between changing monsoon climates and urban development in three of South Asia's largest cities: Chennai, Delhi and Dhaka.

The project is being undertaken at a time when extreme weather events converge with neo-liberal urban policies and rapid urban growth to produce fragile futures for urban survival. In this context, it adopts a novel approach, treating the monsoon not as an external threat, but as an organising principle of urban life and urban environments as more-than-human, monsoonal assemblages that operate across multiple scales and through media that are indivisibly natural, social, political and technological. It aims to produce knowledge of and design strategies for these environments and to assess the potential impact of this approach for the cities studied, the spatial design disciplines and the environmental humanities more generally.

In April 2017, MONASS hosted Monsoon [+other] Airs, the first of three annual symposia structured around the monsoon's three material elements: air, water and ground. This was an interdisciplinary symposium that brought together scholars, journalists, designers and artists of monsoon science, air, politics, practices and risks. Sean Lally of Chicago based Weathers Architects was the keynote speaker.

For further information, visit the project's web site:
www.monass.org

(left) Monsoon [+ other] Airs symposium poster; (right) Michele Vianello: *Kilkattalai Ery, Chennai*

ADAPT-r: Practice-based Research

University of Westminster lead: Professor Katharine Heron

The research leading to these results has received funding from the European Union's Seventh Framework Programme FP7/2007-2013.

THE ADAPT-r PROJECT concluded in December 2016 after four years of intense work from the seven international partners including Westminster whose contribution was led by Professor Katharine Heron. In this time over 40 fellows were employed, we engaged in 8 training conferences known as Practice Research Symposia, delivered two research conferences, held a major exhibition in Ambika P3, and completed three key books. All of this is available on the website:

http://adapt-r.eu

Funded by the EU and Marie Curie, the training network expanded the ground-breaking PhD by Practice model developed and established at RMIT. The researchers (Creative Practitioners at varying stages of development of their PhD research) developed new research and exchange their findings across the partnership guided by the partners' Scientific Committee. PhD by Practice assumes creative practitioners have a pre-existing body of mature work.

Participants shared intense public supervisory sessions at twice yearly Practice Research Symposia (PRS). They investigate their own research, within past and current practice, that is transformative of future practice. These generously open events are attended by over 100 practitioners and the work is presented for critique to supervisory panels with peers and external critics. The PhD examination is held in public, and during the course of ADAPT-r, nine candidates satisfactorily completed their defence, eight fellows were Senior researchers with PhD completed.

ADAPT-r Exhibition

ProBE

Prof Linda Clarke (WBS) is co-director of ProBE, Professor of European Industrial Relations in Westminster Business School, and president of the European Institute of Construction Labour Research, based in Brussels.

Colin Gleeson is deputy director of ProBE, Reader in fABE and chartered building services engineer with a doctorate in energy and buildings.

Christine Wall is co-director of ProBE, and Reader in Architectural and Construction History, fABE.

Research Fellow: Dr Melahat Sahin-Dikmen

PhD student: Denise Bowes

Resident visitors: PhD student Michael Mulvey (Maynooth University)

Visiting Scholars: Dr Valerie Francis (University of Melbourne), Dr Richard Clark (Birkbeck) and Prof Kazuhiko Asami (Senshu University, Japan)

THE CENTRE FOR Research into the Production of the Built Environment (ProBE) is a cross-faculty centre spanning fABE and WBS. It is committed to a multi-disciplinary approach to investigating the planning, production, and social processes creating the structures and spaces that constitute our urban and rural built environments. The Centre consists of three joint Directors: Prof. Linda Clarke (WBS) and Readers, Christine Wall and Colin Gleeson (fABE) with Research Fellow Dr Melahat Sahin-Dikmen, full-time PhD students, Visiting Scholars and an external Advisory Board.

Our research spans contemporary issues such as the European Commission funded project Inclusive Vocational Education and Training for Low Energy Construction *(€50,000)*. Prof Linda Clarke, Dr Colin Gleeson and Dr Melahat Sahin-Dikmen are external experts to 10 country partners. Clarke and Gleeson are also Co-Applicants on a Canadian Social Sciences and Humanities Research Council Partnership Grant *($2,547,130.00)* which funds the international project Adapting Canadian Work and Workplaces to Respond to Climate Change: Canada in International Perspective (ACW) including the University of Westminster projects:

> Green Transitions in the US and Europe: breadth, depth and worker agency, with Fred Steward (PSI)
>
> Green Transitions in the Built Environment

The Centre also has a strong and active profile for research into architectural and construction history and has recently run two University of Westminster Strategic Research Funded Projects. Architecture and Building Labour: using oral and visual evidence to enrich policy and practice in the built environment *(£23,750, 2016)*, with PI Dr Wall, and Co-Applicant Prof Clarke, catalogued and deposited the archive of the *Constructing Post-War Britain* oral history project at the Bishopsgate Library, produced a portable exhibition, and organised a symposium on *Architecture and Building Labour*. The current project Housing and Labour: a pilot oral history of post-war council house building in England and Scotland *(£23,750)*, with PI Dr Wall, Co-Applicant Prof Clarke and Research Fellow, Dr Melahat Sahin-Dikmen, prepares the groundwork for a major exploration of the role of local authority builders in post-war social house building. The Faculty also funded Dr Wall for Housing and Urban Change in London Fields: from gentlemen traders to feminist activists, a project using oral histories of former squatters and visual archive documents, to provide new insights into the origins of feminist architecture in London and wider processes of urban change.

© Hackney Archives: *Former Squatted Homes Prior to Demolition, Hackney c.1989* [Ref.P08330]

Ambika P3

AMBIKA P3 PROVIDES a platform for research. It is a laboratory to invent new work and publicly disseminate the outcome. Multi-disciplinary and inter-disciplinary research can flourish here with external partners.

In late 2016 the ADAPT-r exhibition was presented as one of the outcomes of a €4 million grant awarded to a partnership of seven European Universities, accompanied by the eighth Practice Research Symposium also held at Westminster.

This explored the research processes of working artists, architects and designers from digital designers to landscape architects, brand designers to design activists, painters to performance artists, and many architects. 35 practitioners exhibited work in progress and four individuals were examined for their PhD within the exhibition context. A series of public events ran throughout the exhibition – notably a screening of *Something Rich and Strange*, the film made about the life and times of Iannis Xenakis with live performances.

In March/April 2017, an exhibition of six new commissions was enabled through the Casebooks Project at the University of Cambridge, under the directorship of Dr Lauren Kassell, and funded by the Wellcome Trust. International contemporary artists were commissioned to make new works engaged with the Casebooks Project and their research into the manuscripts of two seventeenth-century English astrologer-physicians: Simon Forman and his protégé Richard Napier. The manuscripts themselves (housed at the Bodleian Library, Oxford), document 80,000 medical consultations, and are testament to the preoccupations of patients with questions of health, disease, fertility, stability and their place within wider natural and supernatural schemes.

The six artists – Jasmina Cibic, Federico Díaz, Lynn Hershman Leeson, Rémy Markowitsch, Lindsay Seers and Tunga – each made new works spanning sculpture, video and audio installation, live performance, robotics and artificial intelligence.

Sign up for our newsletter, Facebook or look at our website:

www.p3exhibitions.com

Professor Katharine Heron
Director

(top) CASEBOOKS Exhibition
(clockwise from top left): Tunga: *Eu, Você e a Lua*; Lindsay Seers: *Mental Metal*; *Main exhibition space showing from foreground*: Federico Díaz: *BIG LIGHT (Space of Augmented Suggestion)*, Rémy Markowitsch: *Casebook Calf*, & Tunga: *Eu, Você e a Lua*; *Casebooks Exhibition book*; Jasmina Cibic: *Unforseen Forseens*

(bottom) Adapt-r Exhibition
(left) Adapt-r Exhibition Space;
(right) Leon van Schaik & Lady Frances Sorrell

CASEBOOKS
exhibition at Ambika P3

adapt-r
An exhibition about research processes
Methods
Public Behaviours
adapt-r

Staff

Wilfred Achille
Yota Adilenidou
Alessandro Ayuso
Peter Barber
Scott Batty
Alastair Blyth
Stefania Boccaletti
John Bold
Shumi Bose
Roberto Bottazzi
Anthony Boulanger
Eva Branscombe
Lindsay Bremner
Stephen Brookhouse
Terence Brown
Toby Burgess
Clare Carter
Harry Charrington
Matt Cousins
Paul Crosby
Ruth Cuenca
Beth Cullen
Claire Dale-Lace
Miriam Dall'Igna
Rita Darch
Corinna Dean
Darren Deane
Dusan Decermic
Davide Deriu
Richard Difford
Chris Dite
Jeg Dudley
Julia Dwyer
John Edwards
Anthony Engi Meacock
Elantha Evans
Stephanie Fischer
Jonathan Fisher
Theeba Franklin
Isabel Frost
François Girardin
Colin Gleeson
Nasser Golzari
Jon Goodbun
Sean Griffiths
Eric Guibert
Michael Guy
Mohamad Hafeda
Susannah Hagan
Tabatha Harris Mills
Stephen Harty
Matt Haycocks
Catherine Hennessy
Katharine Heron
Andrzej Hewanicki
Adam Holloway
Edward Ihejirika
Bruce Irwin
Platon Issaias
Andrei Jipa
Alan Johnson
Kate Jordan
Maja Jovic
Gabriel Kakanos
Krystallia Kamvasinou
Joe King

Maria Kramer
Diony Kypraiou
Debby Kuypers
Gillian Lambert
Benson Lau
Constance Lau
Dirk Lellau
Chris Leung
Tony Lopez Winkler
Alison Low
Gwyn Lloyd Jones
Michael MacNamara
Jane Madsen
Arthur Mamou-Mani
Andrei Martin
Will McLean
Alison McLellan
Clare Melhuish
Sarah Milne
Richa Mukhia
Natalie Newey
John O'Shea

Samir Pandya
Harry Paticas
Amanda Pawliszyn
Andrew Peckham
Mirna Pedalo
Ruby Ray Penny
Emma Perkin
Callum Perry
Catherine Phillips
Sue Phillips
Stuart Piercy
Juan Piñol
Alicia Pivaro
David Porter
Anthony Powis
Virginia Rammou
Kester Rattenbury
Ruby Ray Penny
Tom Raymont
Lara Rettondini
Paul Richens
Michael Rose

Duarte Santo
Shahed Saleem
Rosa Schiano-Phan
David Scott
Yara Sharif
Neal Shasore
Gabby Shawcross
Gordon Shrigley
Jeanne Sillett
Pete Silver
Giles Smith
Ro Spankie
Afolabi Spence
Douglas Spencer
Kate Squire
Manos Stellakis
Joanne Stevens
Rachel Stevenson
Matthew Stewart
Bernard Stilwell
Ben Stringer
Allan Sylvester

Jane Tankard
Juan Vallejo
Giulio Verdini
Filip Visnjic
Christine Wall
Elly Ward
Richard Warwick
Richard Watson
Victoria Watson
Zhenzhou Weng
Andrew Whiting
Camilla Wilkinson
Elizabeth Wilks
Julian Williams
Nick Wood
Andrew Yau
John Zhang
Fiona Zisch

Practice Links 2017

Anne Thorne Architects
aLL Design
Arboreal Architecture
Architype
Arup
Assemble
AY Architects
BGS Architects
Bradley Van Der Straeten Architects
Chapman+BDSP
Coffey Architects
Collective Works
Corbett & Tasker
Curl La Tourelle Head Architects
Dan Marks Studio
David Chipperfield Architects
Darling Associates
DCUK
de Rijke Marsh Morgan Architects
DSDHA Architects
Duggan Morris Architects
Edward Williams Architects
Eric Parry Architects
Exploration Architecture
FACtotum
Fletcher Priest Architects
Gensler & Associates
Green Infrastructure
Grimshaw Architects
Haptic Architects
Hawkins\Brown
Hayhurst & Co
Hopkins Architects
HTA
Hunters
Ian Chalk Architects
Jason Bruges Studio
Karakusevic Carson Architects
Lama Studio
Leslie Jones Architects
Lobby
Loyn & Co Architects
Mae Architects
MATT Architecture
McCarthy Architects
MJP Architects
Mobile Studio
Modern Architect
MRA Architects
NG Architects
nimtim architects
OPEN Architecture
Perkins + Will
Piercy&Co
Platform 5 Architects
Platforms
PLP Architecture
Pritchard Themis
Project Orange
RALA
Ruimte Design
Sam Jacob Studio
Simon Bowden Architecture
SimpsonHaugh and Partners
Square Feet Architects
Smout Allen
SNAS Design & Development
Something and Son
Spaced Out Architecture
SPPARC Architects
Studio Memo
StructureMode
Studio Hardie
Studio Gkoudkoudi
TAFH
The Klassnik Corporation
Thomas Heatherwick Studio
Tim Ronalds Architects
Universal Design Studio
Urbanus
Veretec
VOLA
Wandle HA
Wayward Architects
Weston Williamson
Wilkinson Eyre Architects
Wood Bagot London
WSP | Parsons Brinckerhoff
Zaha Hadid Architects

We wish to thank the following organisations for their support: